Molecular Insights into the Living Process

MOLECULAR INSIGHTS
INTO THE
LIVING PROCESS

BY

DAVID E. GREEN

INSTITUTE FOR ENZYME RESEARCH
UNIVERSITY OF WISCONSIN
MADISON, WISCONSIN

ROBERT F. GOLDBERGER

NIAMD
NATIONAL INSTITUTES OF HEALTH
BETHESDA, MARYLAND

1966

Academic Press   New York · London

ACADEMIC PRESS INC.
111 Fifth Avenue, New York, New York 10003

United Kingdom Edition published by
ACADEMIC PRESS INC. (LONDON) LTD.
Berkeley Square House, London W.1

LIBRARY OF CONGRESS CATALOG CARD NUMBER: 66–19130

PRINTED IN THE UNITED STATES OF AMERICA

To Doris Green and Marianne Goldberger,
whose encouragement and good-natured forbearance
provided a happy setting for the writing of this book.

Preface

"Molecular Insights into the Living Process" is the product of a long gestation period. Our original intent was to present a unified picture of biochemistry, written in simple language and stripped of unnecessary detail, to be read, hopefully, with profit by the uninitiated and expert alike. This turned out to be too vague and too general a frame of reference. During the several years of writing and rewriting, the thought slowly took shape that since biochemistry is an expression of a set of universal principles that apply to all living systems, a unified picture of the subject could best be presented by concentrating on these principles and using them as the basis of the book. It is neither a conventional textbook nor a collection of essays. The treatment of biochemistry is intended to be an organic whole, leading, we hope, to an appreciation of the ideas and principles which underlie and unify our knowledge of the chemistry of living processes. Some knowledge of the rudiments of chemistry and biology has been assumed for the reader but a conscientious effort has been made to provide sufficient background information to enable the nonexpert to follow the arguments. The book is aimed not only at the science student and the science teacher but also at the biologist, chemist, and medical practitioner who are interested in the basic ideas of biochemistry. On the contemporary scene, in which extreme specialization is the order of the day, there is need to achieve the overall view. It is toward this objective that the book is aimed.

"Molecular Insights into the Living Process" has been written in narrative style and includes a minimum of detail, so that the reader who is not an expert may flavor some of the fascination and excitement of biochemical developments without having to wade through a mass of minutiae and scientific jargon. We have not been reluctant to express *our* preferences of interpretation and *our* views of the meaning and significance of data—this with full awareness that not all opinions have been presented in the development of the subject matter of the book. The necessities of keeping the book to reasonable size have made it impossible to provide more than token documentation of all the relevant papers or to enumerate all those who have contributed to our knowledge. Wherever possible, review articles as well as books in which the full documentation can be found have been cited in the reference lists at the end of the chapters.

We are greatly indebted to Dr. Christian B. Anfinsen, Dr. Victor Auerbach, Dr. Myron Bender, Dr. Mary Anne Berberich, Dr. Robert Bock, Dr. Oscar Hechter, Dr. Frank Huennekens, Dr. Solomon Kadis, Dr. Irving Klotz, Dr. Emanuel Margoliash, Dr. Larry Matthews, Mrs. Rowena Matthews, Dr. John Penniston, Mrs. Joyce Penniston, Dr. Jack Strominger, and Dr. Robert D. Wells for their helpful criticisms of part or all of the manuscript. Our special thanks are due Dr. David Rammler for his help with several chapters, Dr. Charles Epstein for his collaboration on Chapter XIII, Dr. E. Frank Korman for his assistance in systematizing the chemical formulations throughout the book and for his collaboration on Chapters II and VIII, Dr. Harold Baum for his wise counsel about the details and design of the book and for his collaboration on Chapters III and V, and Dr. Mary Buell for her tireless efforts in reading and rereading the manuscript with the astute eye of scientist and editor. Mrs. Sonia Kingan took the brunt of the grueling task of typing and retyping the many versions of each chapter.

DAVID E. GREEN
November, 1966   ROBERT F. GOLDBERGER

Table of Contents

CHAPTER 1 ———————————————

The Biochemical
Approach to the Study of Life

Throughout recorded history thoughtful individuals have sought to understand the nature of life. For much of the time, this quest took the form of speculation about the laws which govern the living process. The overwhelming disparity between the living and nonliving worlds convinced the great thinkers of the past that entirely different concepts applied to these two states of nature. Living processes were considered to be endowed with mystical properties; therefore, at the same time when the principles of physics and chemistry were being systematically probed, the realm of the living world remained inviolate. It was as if a fog had enshrouded one set of phenomena, whereas the sky was the limit for the other.

What finally dispelled the fog? What started the same fearless approach to the study of life processes that had been taken several centuries earlier in the study of physics and chemistry? The growth of chemistry and particularly of organic chemistry (a chemistry highly relevant to, and at one time believed to be peculiar to, living systems) was a necessary preliminary.* Without an understanding of atoms and molecules, and their myriad configurations, there was no possibility even of beginning to comprehend the operational principles of the living world.

---

* The growth of organic chemistry coincided with the rise of the humanist movement and with the general atmosphere of skepticism engendered by this movement. A remark of Voltaire in his "Ignorant Philosopher" epitomizes the healthy skepticism of the humanist movement: "It would be very singular that all nature, all the planets, should obey eternal laws, and that there should be a little animal, five feet high, who, in contempt of these laws could act as he pleased, solely according to his caprice."

The lifting of the intellectual fog began in 1828, when Friedrich Wöhler announced the first synthesis of an organic compound known to be formed by living organisms—urea. Seventy years later Edward Büchner demonstrated that enzymes (the catalysts of the cell), after extraction from yeast, can digest starch as efficiently as can living yeast cells. These demonstrations were among the revolutionary events that led to the beginnings of biochemistry—a science which has matured only in the last two generations.

The impact of discoveries such as those of Wöhler and Büchner was immediate and profound. Since urea, a compound produced by living organisms, could be synthesized in the laboratory, it was thought by extension that all the materials present in the living system should be capable of description and synthesis. If an important function of *living* yeast cells (namely, the capacity to digest sucrose) could be retained in a cell-free *extract*, it should be possible by extension to study all other functions of living organisms independent of the whole cell.

Fittingly, the line which separated the living from the nonliving —the very line which had been so clear in the past as to constitute a barrier to fruitful research—has become somewhat obscured by recent developments in biochemistry. The contemporary investigator is hard put to say whether or not a crystallized virus is a "living" organism, and whether or not a strand of nucleic acid reproducing itself in a test tube is "alive."

The creed of the biochemist today is that all phenomena which characterize life processes can be described in chemical and physical terms and that the principles of chemistry and physics which apply to the inanimate world are equally valid for the world of life. By whatever devices the chemical systems found in living organisms were evolved, a truly remarkable chemistry has emerged. To discover how Nature, while obeying physical and chemical principles exclusively, has been able to evolve such perfection will present a challenge to the scientist for many decades to come.

The unit of life is the cell. This entity contains the basic equipment for the maintenance and continuity of life. When a cell is damaged and the damage cannot be corrected, it is only a matter of time before all activity will come to a halt and disintegration of the working parts will ensue. Cells vary widely in size, in shape, and in range of activities (cf. Figure 1.1). We will not be concerned with the bewildering variation of cellular form and function but with the minimum of constituents which all cells must have; these constitute the stark essentials without which no cell can survive. We shall invoke a "minimal" cell in which this minimum of

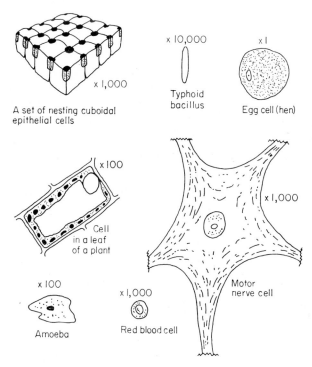

Fig. 1.1. Shapes and relative sizes of cells from animal, plant, and microbial organisms. Diagrammatic.

essential equipment is contained. No known cell fits this description precisely, although some microorganisms may approach it. There are living units (the viruses and the rickettsiae) which are smaller than the minimal cell, but these are not complete cells; they can flourish only by parasitizing cells.

We may say with confidence that the following minimal equipment (cf. Figure 1.2) is common to all cells: (1) a system of membranes which encloses the cell, compartmentalizes the interior, controls the chemical economy, and packages the key catalysts of the cell; (2) an apparatus for reproducing exact copies of the cell and for replicating key parts; (3) an apparatus for powering the activities of the cell through coupled oxidations. All of biochemistry centers around these three key systems of the cell and around the principles underlying the operation of these systems.

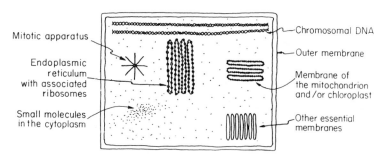

Fig. 1.2. The parts of a hypothetical, minimal cell. It is assumed in this interpretive drawing that essentially all macromolecules are localized in membrane structures.

Although the *categories* of equipment required by all cells can be specified fairly completely, the exact *form* and *location* of this equipment within the cell are more difficult to define. The delineation of the ultrastructure of the cell is still far from complete. Hence, there is considerable uncertainty about the correlation of the ultrastructure with the functional role of structured elements in the cell. The nature of some of these uncertainties needs spelling out.

The systems concerned with reproduction of exact copies of an entire cell or of key parts are basically identical in all cells; however, where these are found in the cell, in which form, and associated with which membrane are highly variable factors. Thus, at present we have insufficient knowledge about the structure of cells to seek out the principles which underlie the form and location of the replicating systems of all cells. At the gross level of cell structure it is virtually impossible to find the principles, but at the molecular level the search is more promising and rewarding. In time it should be possible to define with great precision which structural features of the replicating system are common to all cells.

An elaborate network of membranes is found in all cells. At present we do not know which of the membranes are common to all cells and which are performing functions essential to all cells. The essential functions which all cells must carry on are well known, but in which membranes these functions are exercised is still a largely undefined area of knowledge. The art of relating cellular function to the particular membranes visualized by microscopy is not yet highly developed.

In respect to a basic function, such as replication, there are unvarying features [nucleic acids, ribosomes, and transfer- and messenger-RNA (ribonucleic acid)] and optional features. It is the optional features that give an unavoidable fuzziness to the concept of the minimal cell. This is particularly true for the mechanism by which the minimal cell can derive utilizable energy by oxidative reactions. There are, in fact, three different devices known to be present. All three devices involve the coupling of oxidation to the synthesis of adenosine-5-triphosphate (ATP). The minimal cell could contain any one of these three, or all three. One could make a case for singling out one of the three as probably the first to have been elaborated and the other two as later evolutionary developments. However, this simplification will not add much to the concept of the minimal cell. We shall have to think in terms of several alternative forms of minimal cell. The minimal cell that lives under anaerobic conditions has an energy-transducing system known as the glycolytic system of enzymes (a system probably housed in the outer membrane). All aerobic cells contain a second energy-transducing system known as the mitochondrion. The minimal cell that lives under aerobic conditions thus has two energy-transducing systems—the glycolytic system and the mitochondrion. Cells of the plant kingdom contain yet another device, namely, the chloroplast, which is an energy-transducing system activated by radiant energy. Thus, minimal cells that require light for growth and maintenance have three modalities for energy transduction—the glycolytic system, the mitochondrion, and the chloroplast.

The hypothetical minimal cell (cf. Figure 1.2) carries out the basic activities common to all cells, but these activities are only a small fraction of the total range of activities observed when one examines cells of many different types. Cells may be specialized for functions such as contractility, sensitivity to light, and secretory activity. In the same way, there is a chemistry common to all cells and, in addition, a chemistry peculiar to the individual cell. However, all these additional activities are basically variations on themes recognizable in the systems of the minimal cell.

Some cells may be distinguished by the presence of special molecules that are the instruments of function; for example, hemoglobin in red blood corpuscles for transport of oxygen, rhodopsin in the cells of the retina for light sensitivity, and actomyosin in muscle cells for contraction. Here again, despite the diversity of special molecules, we can trace a connection between the processes and the range of molecules in specialized cells, and those in the minimal cell. It is quite remarkable how few principles have been exploited by Nature for the development of the fantastic variety among living organisms. Indeed, the *magnum opus* of the evolutionary process might be named "Theme and Variations."

There are microorganisms, such as the pleuropneumonia-like organism, that have more than superficial resemblance to the minimal cell. These are exceedingly small in size (at the very limit of resolution of a light microscope), are highly compact in their internal structure, and are characterized by severe limitation in their range of chemical potentialities. One would suspect that such cells contain little more than the basic essentials if only because there would be no room in a cell of such small size for anything but essential equipment (cf. Figure 1.3). The microorganisms that come closest to the description of a minimal cell are not necessarily primitive. On the contrary, the simplicity of such microorganisms makes one wonder whether they should not be considered among the highest forms of life, since they do essentially what any other cell can do, but with a minimum of machinery.

The professed aim of this book is to introduce the reader to some of the molecular features of the living process. There is only one proper way to penetrate the domain of molecular events and that is through the portals of the cell. As we have come to appreciate,

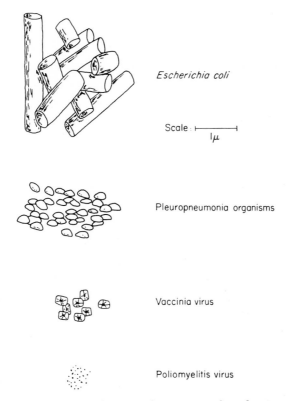

Escherichia coli

Scale: ⊢————⊣
1μ

Pleuropneumonia organisms

Vaccinia virus

Poliomyelitis virus

Fig. 1.3. Hierarchy of size in the transition from bacteria to viruses.

the cell is more than a container for the "vital" machinery. The cell is, more correctly, an expression of a universal set of mechanistic principles and of a unique molecular architecture and structural pattern. There may be alternative forms of life on other planets, based on a unit other than the cell. However, the only unit of life we have knowledge of, and evidence for, is the cell, and it is the cell which must be our text and our initial point of reference.

Suggested Reading

Books

"Classics in Biology," Philosophical Library Inc., New York, 1960.

Conant, J. B., "On Understanding Science," Yale University Press, New Haven, Connecticut, 1947.

Dampier, Sir William Cecil, "History of Science," Cambridge University Press, London and New York, The Macmillan Co., New York, 1943: see Chapter I.

Fraenkel-Conrat, H., "Design and Function at the Threshold of Life: The Viruses," Academic Press, New York, 1962.

Gabriel, M. L. and Fogel, S., eds., "Great Experiments in Biology," Prentice Hall, Englewood Cliffs, New Jersey, 1955.

Ihde, A. J., "Development of Modern Chemistry," Harper, New York, 1964.

Marsland, D., "Principles of Modern Biology," 4th Ed., Holt, Rinehart, and Winston, New York, 1964.

Stanley, W. M. and Valens, E. G., "Viruses and the Nature of Life," E. P. Dutton, New York, 1961.

Special Articles

Klug, A. and Caspar, D. L. D., *Advan. Virus Res.* **7**, 225 (1960): on the structure of small viruses.

Morowitz, H. J., and Tourtelolte, M. E., *Sci. Am.* **206**, 117 (1962): on the minimal cell.

Morowitz, H. J., Tourtellote, M. E., Guild, W. R., Castro, E., Woese, C., and Clevenden, R. C., *J. Mol. Biol.* **4**, 93 (1962): on avian pleuropneumonia-like organism.

Pirie, N. W., *in* "Perspectives in Biochemistry" (J. Needham and D. E. Green, eds.), Cambridge University Press, London and New York, 1937: on living versus non-living systems.

Robinow, C. F., *in* "The Cell" (J. Brachet and A. E. Mirsky, eds.), Vol. 4, Academic Press, New York, 1960: on the organization of the bacterial cell.

CHAPTER 2 ———————————————

Atoms and Molecules of the Cell

There are literally billions of atoms and molecules in even the smallest cell. Our particular concern in this chapter is with the following basic questions: (1) Which atoms are found in living cells? (2) Which molecules are formed from these atoms, and in what quantities are these present? (3) Which molecules are common to all cells? (4) Which functions are served by which molecules? (5) What are the principles that underlie the "selection" of molecules and the "fitting" of particular molecules to special tasks?

The Elements or Atoms of Cells

Of the hundred odd chemical elments, only six have been selected by Nature for building up the vast majority of the molecules of living systems: carbon (C), hydrogen (H), nitrogen (N), oxygen (O), phosphorus (P), and sulfur (S). In addition to this sextet of most-used elements, twelve others are known to be essential for life: calcium (Ca), chlorine (Cl), cobalt (Co), copper (Cu), iodine (I), iron (Fe), magnesium (Mg), manganese (Mn), molybdenum (Mo), potassium (K), sodium (Na), and zinc (Zn). A few varieties of cells require boron (B), vanadium (V), or silicon (Si). The essentiality of fluorine (F) is still a moot question. Figure 2.1 shows the periodic table of elements, with the atoms commonly found in living systems clearly designated in boldface. In general, the atoms of small atomic number have been preferred by Nature, but there are notable exceptions. Some of the smallest atoms (beryllium, lithium, and fluorine) are conspicuously absent from most living systems other than as contaminants. None of the no-

9

ble gases, however small in atomic number, has found a place in the biochemical hierarchy of atoms. Whatever might have been the nature of the selective process that determined which atoms would be used, availability could not have been the sole determinant. Bromine and fluorine are as abundant in Nature as is iodine, yet only iodine was selected. Lithium and beryllium are admittedly less abundant than sodium, potassium, and magnesium, but living sys-

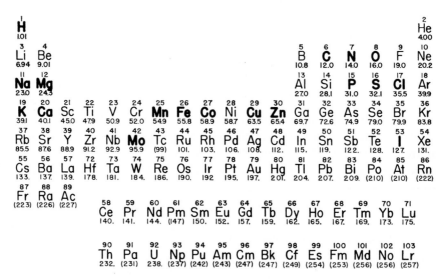

Fig. 2.1. The periodic table of the elements, with the atoms commonly found in living systems set in boldface.

tems often require elements (such as cobalt and molybdenum) that are generally present in relatively low concentrations in the ocean or in the soil. Suitability of the atoms as well as availability would appear to be the principal determinants in the process of selection. The chemical inertness of the noble gases is probably as relevant a consideration for their exclusion as their rarity. In the same way, it is probable that lithium and beryllium were excluded because some of their chemical properties were not ideally suited for the delicately balanced systems of the cell. The very large atoms of the periodic table pose almost insuperable problems connected with insolubility in aqueous systems at physiological pH, and this factor undoubtedly has been crucial in the selective process.

It is of interest that the sextet of most-used atoms includes the smallest atoms that, to achieve a stable configuration, must gain, respectively, one electron (H), two electrons (O), three electrons (N), four electrons (C), five electrons (P), and six electrons (S).* The properties of this set of atoms are sufficiently comprehensive to permit the building of most of the molecules required by the cell. Only occasionally is it necessary to draw upon another atom for some unique requirement in molecule building.

The smallest atoms make the tightest and most stable bonds when they unite with other atoms by sharing a pair of electrons (one electron from each atom). Moreover, if a small atom "desires" to gain more than one electron by sharing (in the interest of greater stability), it may do this in one of several ways. Either it may share a pair of electrons with each of several atoms, as oxygen shares a pair of electrons with each of two hydrogen atoms to form water, or it may share more than one pair of electrons with another single atom. Bonds of this latter type are called multiple bonds: double bonds when four electrons are shared, and triple bonds when six electrons are shared. Such multiple bonds are very important in the molecules of the living cell; the smaller atoms readily form such bonds.

Central Position of the Carbon Atom

Apart from the molecules of water, the vast majority of the molecules of living systems can be described as edifices constructed with carbon atoms as the skeletal building stones. The other atoms are fitted onto the carbon skeletons of the various molecules. A significant feature of the carbon atom, and the one which is particularly important in the chemistry of living systems, is the property of sharing one or more electrons with another carbon atom. By virtue of this mutual sharing of electrons, carbon atoms can link with one another to form extended chains of any required size and of myriad structural patterns. The tetravalency of the carbon

---

* The atoms in this set may have more than one valency state. We are concerned here with the most stable configuration of the atom.

atom has a very profound significance. Three of the valences can be used to build a three dimensional network, and one valency is still available for insertion of some functional group which can serve as the modulator or determinant of chemical properties.

Atoms such as silicon (Si) have the same tendency as carbon atoms to combine with one another. However, the range and variety of molecules that can be built with silicon atoms are severely limited in comparison with the range and variety of carbon-containing molecules. This limitation is an expression of the chemistry of the silicon atom, particularly the reactivity. The inability of silicon to form multiple bonds with other atoms is, perhaps, the most crucial limitation to its usefulness in the building of molecules.

Central Position of the Water Molecule

Well over 90% of the total mass of a cell is made of one molecular species—water. However, the importance of water is not exclusively a quantitative one. The chemistry of the cell is based on water as the solvent, and the properties of the molecules within the cell would be entirely different in any other solvent. We could imagine a living system based on other solvent systems such as ethanol, but a whole new chemistry would have to be explored, and new principles of molecule-building would have to be developed to perfect a living system based on these solvents. L. J. Henderson, in one of the classics of physiology, has pointed out how ideally suited are the physical properties of the water molecule for the needs of living systems, but this may be putting the cart before the horse. The living system was designed, so to speak, around water as the solvent. The properties of the water molecule were an intrinsic part of the program fed into the evolutionary computer, and it is, therefore, not surprising that the end result mirrors these properties so well.

Perhaps the most significant property of the water molecule is its dipolar character. Each molecule has a region of positive and negative charge which may be represented by the formulation

This dipolar character underlies the tendency of water molecules to "stick" to one another.* The key molecules of living cells are charged species when dissolved in water. It follows then that the dipolar character of water, the solvent of living systems, has dictated a chemistry of dipolar solute molecules. Had the solvent of living systems been a hydrocarbon, a set of solute molecules with radically different chemical properties would have had to be developed.

The properties of the carbon atom and of the water molecule are the most basic part of the design of living systems. The whole of evolutionary development has been dictated and modulated by the properties of this one atom and this one molecule.

Aqueous and Nonaqueous Phases of the Cell

If all parts of the cell were soluble in water, the cell would soon fall apart (dissolve) and cease to be a structured unit. The structures which make up the skeleton of the cell, the walls of the chambers, and the membrane systems, are completely insoluble in water, as they must be to achieve permanence in an aqueous environment. Actually, the membrane systems of the cell and many of the individual molecules (to be described in later chapters) are two-phase systems. One phase is directed toward the aqueous solvent; although intrinsically insoluble, it can interact with molecules or ions in the solvent. The other phase, which is buried in the interior (away from the aqueous solvent), can interact with or dissolve molecules that are insoluble in water. The two-phase character of cellular systems and macromolecules (aqueous and nonaqueous) makes possible not only the permanence of structure referred to above, but also an alternative to water as a medium in which selected chemical reactions can take place. This is important because there are many essential chemical reactions which do not proceed in an aqeous environment. For these particular chemical reactions, the cell has provided localized regions, "microchambers," from which water is excluded.

* Molecules of water are linked to one another by a bond between a hydrogen of one molecule and an oxygen of another molecule. This is known as a hydrogen bond. In ice, each water molecule is attached to four other water molecules by hydrogen bonding in a tetrahedral arrangement.

Number, Size, and Functions of the Molecules of the Cell

The living cell may contain many copies (billions in fact) of certain molecules and only few copies of other molecules. Molecules that provide "fuel" would be in the first category; chromosomal DNA (deoxyribonucleic acid) would be in the second category. The more general the biological purpose, the larger the number of molecules; the more specialized the purpose, the fewer the number. In the context of this discussion, specialized purposes are cellular tasks that are quantitatively very limited in magnitude, although not necessarily in importance.

The molecules of the cell cover a size range from a molecular weight of 18 for water to one of several billions.* There are three broad categories into which the molecules or atoms of the cell may be classified: (1) the simple ions of atoms (such as chloride, sodium, and magnesium) and the complex, or multiatomic, ions (such as phosphate, sulfate, and carbonate), (2) the small organic molecules, which include carbon-containing molecules with molecular weight of 1000 or less, (3) the large organic molecules, or macromolecules, which include carbon-containing molecules with a molecular weight above 1000. The first category is limited in number—certainly no more than one hundred such species of molecules or ions are of physiological importance. The second and third categories number in the thousands. Not every cell contains the same number of small molecules and macromolecules; there is enormous variation from one cell type to another. The magnitude of the problem of defining what goes on in a cell can be expressed in terms of the question: What function is fulfilled by each of the several thousand small molecules and macromolecules as well as by each of the ions that are present in a typical living cell?

In terms of *broad* purpose or use, relatively few functional categories are needed to encompass essentially all the molecules of the cell. A molecule (or ion) can serve as a fuel, as a building stone for other molecules or macromolecules, as a macromolecule, or as a contributor to the ionic environment. Molecules which serve as fuels, or as building blocks for macromolecules, are constantly

---

* The DNA of *Escherichia coli* has been shown to be a single molecule with a molecular weight of 3×10^9.

being used up. If the molecule is a fuel, it is converted to products such as carbon dioxide and ammonia, which are excreted. The macromolecules have a higher degree of permanence in the cell than the smaller molecules. Some last for the lifetime of the cell, whereas others are more rapidly destroyed and must be replenished by newly formed macromolecules. The inorganic ions of the cell (other than those which fulfill the role of building blocks) are with a few exceptions not used up, but are impermanent in the sense that there is a continuous ebb and flow of these ions between the areas inside and outside the cell.

An additional functional category is needed to encompass a small group of special molecules that move in and out of the cell, or in and out of the membrane systems of the cell. These molecules are concerned with the shuttling of packets of energy from one place to another. In the course of this shuttle service they undergo a cycle of simple transformations, and it is this cyclic behavior that distinguishes them from the ions that contribute only passively to the ionic environment.

Categories of Molecules Involved in Cellular Processes

The interior of a cell is a miniature factory where the fuel molecules are burned to provide energy (oxidation), where the building-block molecules are fitted together to make the macromolecules and the structures constituting the biochemical machinery (anabolism or biosynthesis), and where the molecules of the biochemical machinery carry out the many tasks required for the activity of the cell (catalysis). There are ions that control and regulate these processes as well as molecules elaborated by the control centers that direct and modulate the chemical activities of the cell (regulators). This is the basic, but by no means complete, classification of the multiplicity of molecular events that occur continuously within a living cell.

Properties of Biological Molecules

In living systems the various molecules serve many purposes which, in turn, require a set of special properties in the molecule.

For example, the molecules that are in the building blocks of bone have to impart hardness and tensile strength, and the molecules that make up the tissue of the lens of the eye have to form ordered arrays transparent to light. The many different properties of various molecules are expressions of their unique configurations. There are literally thousands of specific chemical tasks imposed on the catalysts of the cell, and each such task calls for a specific macromolecule with a unique arrangement of atoms. The membrane systems of the cell, which house the most intricate and basic biochemical machinery, are composites of hundreds of highly specialized macromolecules, each with specific features of design, whether for a structural purpose or for some catalytic task.

The physical and chemical properties of any organic molecule result from (1) the carbon skeleton (the number and arrangement of carbon atoms); (2) the nature and position of the atoms attached to the carbon chain; (3)* the nature of the functional groups (carboxyl, hydroxyl, amino, sulfhydryl, ether, ester, etc.); (4) the nature of the bonds between the various atoms of the molecule; and (5) the three-dimensional arrangements of the atoms in the molecule.

Let us briefly consider each of these factors in turn. Hexane and cyclohexane are both made up of six carbon atoms with attached hydrogen atoms, but the arrangements of the carbon atoms in the skeletons are different. These two compounds differ signifi-

$$CH_3 \cdot CH_2 \cdot CH_2 \cdot CH_2 \cdot CH_2 \cdot CH_3$$

Hexane

Cyclohexane

cantly in boiling point, melting point, and density, and these differences are primarily expressions of the arrangement of the carbon atoms in the molecule (ring form versus straight chain).

Benezene and hexafluorobenzene have identical ring forms and numbers of carbon atoms, but differ in the nature of the atom linked to the carbon skeleton. These two compounds have greatly

---

* There is intentional overlap in categories (2) and (3).

differing melting points, densities, and solubilities in water, referable primarily to the replacement of hydrogen atoms by atoms of fluorine.

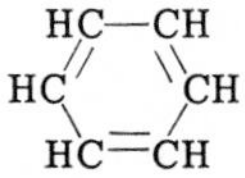

Benzene

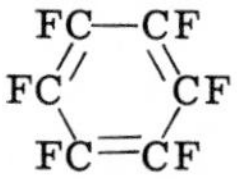

Hexafluorobenzene

Even greater differences, not only in physical properties but particularly in chemical properties, result when certain hydrogen atoms of cyclohexane are replaced by hydroxyl groups. Hexahy

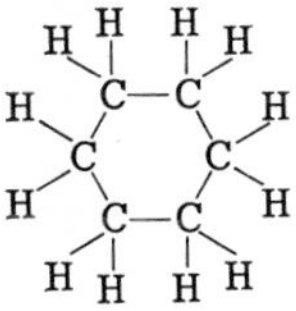

Cyclohexane

Hexahydroxycyclohexane

droxycyclohexane is very soluble in water, whereas cyclohexane is not; the melting points and boiling points of the two compounds are profoundly different, as are the densities, and in terms of chemical reactivity, hexahydroxycyclohexane is as different from cyclohexane as day is from night. All these differences stem from the replacement of one hydrogen atom at each carbon atom by a hydroxyl group.

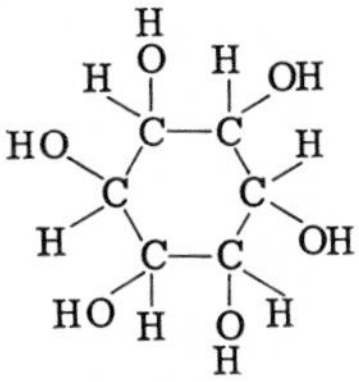

As another example, cyclohexane and benzene both have ring systems composed of six carbon atoms but with different sets of bonds between the carbon atoms. Benzene, but not cyclohexane, is significantly soluble in water. Benzene is 200 times more toxic to

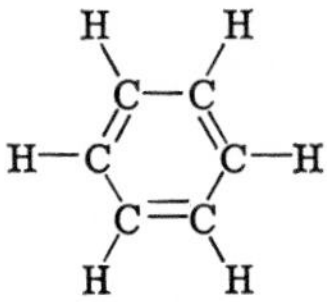

Benzene

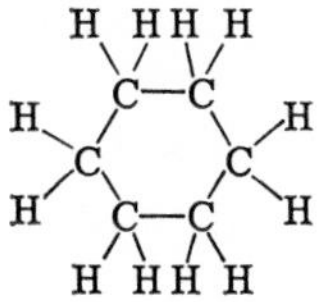

Cyclohexane

mice than cyclohexane and is vastly more reactive chemically. Substitution of single bonds between the carbon atoms by double bonds (which leads to the elimination of six hydrogen atoms) has a profound influence on the physical and chemical properties of a given molecule.

The formulation shown above for benzene and cyclohexane fails to show up a feature which has a great influence on the properties of a molecule. By virtue of the alternating (resonating) double bonds, benzene is constrained to exist with all six atoms in the same plane. However, cyclohexane has no such spatial constraints. The ring can buckle in several ways and assume various nonplanar conformations, for example, the boat and chair forms of cyclohexane. Whether a molecule is planar or nonplanar, and if nonplanar whether in one or another conformation, has a profound effect on its chemical properties. In molecules of biological interest the configurational and conformational aspects are of considerable importance. In the succeeding chapters we shall be dealing with many examples of the relation between three-dimensional shapes and the properties of biologically important molecules.

In principle, a molecule of any desired set of properties could be constructed by selection of the right carbon skeleton and the appropriate set of atoms, functional groups, and bonds. Conceivably, a program could be devised which would allow a computer to predict the structure of a molecule needed to possess a given set of required properties.

Fitness of Molecules for the Tasks of the Cell

The molecules of the cell perform a variety of functions, and we shall now address ourselves to the factors that determine the performance of these tasks. One of the key catalysts of the cell is a molecule known as coenzyme A. The important functional group in this molecule—the key to the catalytic process—is a sulfhydryl (thiol) group. In this particular instance the evidence is clear that any of a large number of compounds with a sulfhydryl group can mimic all the chemical reactions of the thiol group of coenzyme A, yet none of them has biological activity. The uniqueness of coenzyme A lies not alone in its own special chemistry but in its perfect fit into other macromolecules (enzymes) which guide and direct the catalysis. Other molecules bearing sulfhydryl groups fail to fit this macromolecule and are thus inactive no matter how closely they resemble coenzyme A chemically. This important principle of fitting into a specific macromolecule may well underlie the stringent requirements for the biological activity of many small molecules. In terms of this requirement, then, the relative suitability of small molecules for particular tasks involves the question of how well they fit into the catalytic machinery of the cell. Admittedly, it is not the fitting *per se* that makes the small molecule active; the right chemical properties are also required. However, it is the fitting process that excludes other small molecules of equivalent catalytic potentiality. It is, therefore, very often useless to ponder why a certain small molecule—let us say adrenaline—is the active principle (in specified circumstances) and not some other molecule with similar chemical properties. The answer has to be found not in adrenaline itself but in the fit of adrenaline into the macromolecular system that governs its behavior.

Factors in the Selection of Molecules for Biological Tasks

It is useful to ask why D-glucose is the sugar of choice for entry into the cellular combustion chamber; why fatty acids and not fatty alcohols were selected as the particular form of an important biological fuel; why acetic acid and not formic acid or ethyl alcohol serves as the starting point for synthesis of long chain fatty acids; why, in fact, any one of a large number of molecules is preferred for a particular task of the cell. Much can be learned by assessing the various considerations that undoubtedly influenced the final selection of molecules.*

* Throughout this discussion we have referred to the idea that certain molecules were "chosen" by Nature for particular tasks. This terminology is obviously colloquial since actual selection occurring throughout the evolutionary process does not operate at the level of molecules at all, but rather at the level of populations of organisms. One may speak of the selection of certain molecules only in the sense that these molecules may confer attributes on organisms which lead to increased ability to survive and procreate.

Perhaps the special virtue of D-glucose is that it is a sugar molecule, and this fact has three consequences: first, that a substantial amount of utilizable energy is locked in the molecule; second, that it is readily susceptible to oxidative attack; and third, that it is eminently water-soluble. The cell may have "recognized" the value of sugar as a fuel long before the particular sugar, D-glucose, was finally selected. Some case could be made for the thesis that the six-carbon sugar has advantages of stability not shared by the sugars of smaller chain lengths, and advantages of reactivity not shared by the sugars of longer chain length. Furthermore, a strong case could be made for the chemical uniqueness of D-glucose as compared to other sugars containing six carbon atoms. However, these purely chemical considerations have to be balanced against the necessities of the catalytic problem involved in tapping the chemical energy of glucose. Unless this energy can be tapped, none of the other chemical virtues of glucose would be of any significance. The problem then narrows to the suitability of D-glucose as the starting point for an oxidative attack by some enzymic system of the cell. If D-glucose offered kinetic advantages to the enzymic system not shared by other sugars, *these* advantages would then be the overriding consideration in the selective process. Was the enzymic system built around D-glucose because D-glucose was already available, or was the sugar-attacking system in its earliest form capable of attacking sugars other than D-glucose? We have no way of knowing, but at least two features of the selective process can be specified: (1) the intrinsic virtue of a sugar molecule as a stable fuel, and specifically the virtue of a sugar with six carbon atoms and a 1:5 pyranose ring compared to other sugars; (2) the extrinsic relation of D-glucose to the metabolic machinery which carries out the oxidative release of utilizable energy. It is possible that the necessities of the machinery* decided whether glucose should be D- or L- (see formulas below), whether the ring system should be six- or five-membered, and whether the orientation of the first carbon atom in D-glucose should be α or β.

* The bias of machinery for D- or L-glucose could have been a random event in the evolution of catalysts, but once the bias became introduced by chance, the consequences extended to all other catalysts and molecules.

α-D-Glucose   α-L-Glucose

Yet another consideration has to be introduced into this discussion of the selective process. In the breakdown of glucose not only is utilizable energy released and conserved, but also several small molecules of great value for synthetic and other purposes are formed as intermediates in the process. Could the nature of the small molecules derivable by the oxidative attack on the sugar be a determinant of the selective process? This consideration clearly must have influenced the final decision because the process by which D-glucose is oxidatively degraded is the principal source of supply for a set of small molecules (lactic acid, acetaldehyde, pyruvic acid, α-glycerophosphoric acid) which fulfill key metabolic roles in the economy of cells. Thus, to the necessity of milking the energy of glucose had to be added the necessity of combining the energy-releasing process with the production of intermediates, or end products, useful for other cellular purposes.

Each of the advantageous features of D-glucose mentioned above could be explored in far greater detail. The fullest elucidation of these features would require an analysis of the properties of the molecule resulting from the atoms of which it is made, and the properties resulting from the interactions among these atoms. Such an analysis would be far too lengthy and detailed to be presented here. However, we shall discuss in some detail one of the biologically important features of D-glucose, namely, its stability, as an illustration of the depth of understanding which is possible. We shall attempt to explain why this compound is the most stable six-carbon sugar as a consequence of the three-dimensional relationships of the atoms which go to make up the molecule. First, however, we will discuss a simpler molecule in order to illustrate the structural basis of chemical stability among compounds generally related to glucose.

Cyclohexane is a very stable six-membered carbon ring. This cyclic molecule bears certain close relationships to glucose. A study of these relationships will help us to understand the stability of glucose. The structural formula of cyclohexane is usually written:

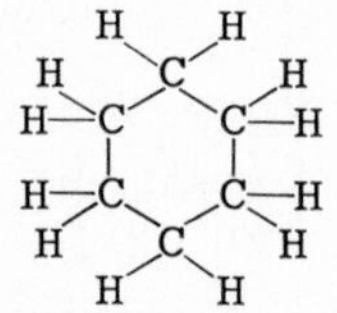

```
          H    H
           \  /
        H   C   H
         \ / \ /
     H—C       C—H
        |       |
     H—C       C—H
         / \ / \
        H   C   H
           / \
          H    H
```

This written form, while useful for showing the cyclic nature of the molecule and the bonding of the atoms, is, however, quite misleading since it obscures the three-dimensionality of the molecule. One might assume, on the basis of this formula, that all six carbon atoms lie on the same plane, as illustrated below:

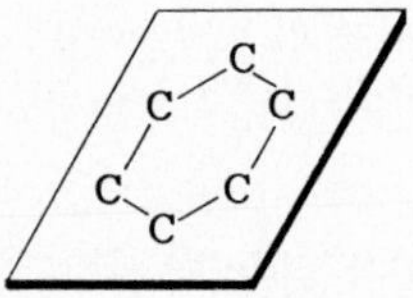

```
           C
         /   \
       C       C
       |       |
       C       C
         \   /
           C
```

Indeed, many early chemists thought that all cyclic organic compounds were "flat." However, it is now realized that cyclohexane is not flat, but rather "puckered." This puckering is due to the fact that the carbon atoms in cyclohexane are tetrahedral. This simply means that the four atoms bonded to any individual carbon atom occupy the apices of a regular tetrahedron. A regular tetrahedron is a pyramid-shaped three-dimensional figure, not unlike the pyramids of Egypt. The Egyptian pyramids stand on a square base and have four equilateral triangular faces, whereas the regular tetrahedron can be thought of as standing on an equilateral triangular base with three equilateral triangular faces.

The six carbon atoms of the cyclohexane molecule can be closed into a ring and can retain their tetrahedral character, *only* by a puckering of the ring, as shown in Figure 2.2. We see that the carbon atoms, represented by the shaded balls, do not all lie on a single plane.

Thus far we have been concerned with the carbon atoms of the cyclohexane ring, but the hydrogen atoms are of equally great interest to us. Examination of Figure 2.2 shows that there are two different types of hydrogen atoms in the molecule as far as spacial orientation within the molecule is concerned. There are six hydrogen atoms which form an equatorial belt girdling the six-membered carbon ring, and all lie more or less in the same "average" plane of the ring. These hydrogen atoms are called *equatorial*.

Fig. 2.2. The puckered ring form of cyclohexane. After Figure 9.9 *in* "Organic Chemistry" by D. J. Cram and G. S. Hammond. McGraw-Hill Book Company, New York, 1964.

Also, there are six hydrogen atoms which are bonded parallel to an axis perpendicular to the average plane of the ring and which are called *axial*. These relationships are illustrated in Figure 2.3 A and B.

In addition to the difference in the spacial orientation of the axial position compared with the equatorial position, there is a marked difference in the stability of the two orientations. The axial

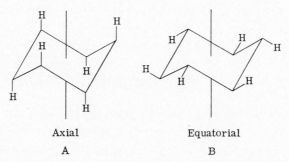

Fig. 2.3. Axial and equatorial hydrogen atoms of cyclohexane.

hydrogens in cyclohexane are more crowded than the equatorial
hydrogens because the distance between axial hydrogen atoms is
considerably less than the distance between equatorial hydrogen
atoms. The axial hydrogens, therefore, have a greater tendency to
"bump" and to repel each other than do the equatorial hydrogen
atoms. These effects are particularly evident in molecules where
the axial groups are large. In general, the equatorial position is
more favorable than the axial position, especially for large bulky
groups.

With this discussion of cyclohexane as background, we are now
in a position to consider the glucose molecule. Like cyclohexane,
glucose can exist as a cyclic six-membered ring compound, as
shown in Figure 2.4.

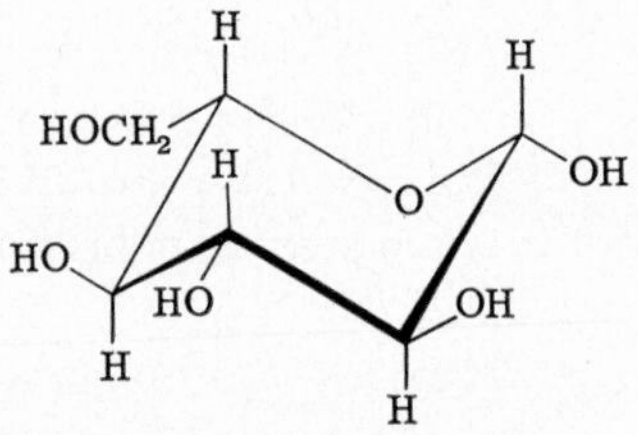

Fig. 2.4. Three-dimensional formulation of D-glucose.

This ring contains an oxygen atom as one of its members, but
the general shape of the glucose ring does not differ greatly from
that of the cyclohexane ring. Like the cyclohexane ring, the glucose ring is puckered, and has both axial and equatorial groups
bonded to the carbon atoms of the ring. The unique structural feature of glucose can now be fully appreciated. In glucose, *all the
large bulky groups are equatorial. No other six carbon sugar has
this spacial feature.* All other six carbon sugars have at least one
large group axial. This means that glucose is the most stable six-
carbon sugar possible.

From the standpoint of energy content, the fuel *par excellence*
(which outranks even D-glucose) is the long-chain fatty acid. The
fatty acid is capable of liberating more than twice as much energy per carbon atom as is glucose. However, glucose is very soluble

in water, whereas long-chain fatty acids (or their salts) are only sparingly soluble; thus, glucose has the advantage of greater availability in an aqueous medium. Fatty acids are, indeed, used as fuels in the animal body, but usually as an auxiliary source of energy. The fatty acids preferred as fuels by Nature have sixteen or eighteen carbon atoms. Why this particular number? Fatty acids with more than eighteen carbon atoms are so nearly insoluble in water that it is impossible to use them in an aqueous medium. Fatty acids with less than sixteen or eighteen carbon atoms are *too* soluble. At high concentrations they rapidly disrupt the delicate membranes of the cell. Thus, the exact length of the fatty acids that are selected for use as a source of energy is a compromise between the potentially dangerous, more soluble acids and the unmanageable, less soluble acids.

Nevertheless, one may ask why fatty acids are utilized, and not fatty alcohols, or fatty amines? Two chemical advantages of fatty acids over fatty alcohols or fatty amines are decisive: these are their greater solubility in water and higher reactivity, particularly after thioester formation.

Acetic acid is Nature's choice for building larger molecules. The arithmetic for the synthesis of long chain fatty acids takes the form of the series $2 + 2 + 2 \ldots$ rather than $1 + 1 + 1 \ldots$ or $3 + 3 + 3. \ldots$ The numbers refer to the number of carbon atoms in the fatty acid. Formic acid, the one-carbon atom acid, can be disqualified on each of several important chemical grounds. An essential metabolic feature of a fatty acid is the terminal methyl group, and this is missing in formic acid. Thus, it would be difficult to build up larger saturated molecules by successive condensation of units of formic acid. The three-carbon acid is too unreactive chemically for purposes of condensation. The two-carbon molecule of choice could be an acid (CH_3COOH), an alcohol (CH_3CH_2OH), or an aldehyde (CH_3CHO). Why was the acid selected as the starting point for synthesis? The alcohol is too unreactive and the aldehyde, although reactive, is somewhat unstable. We may conclude that chemical considerations were paramount in the selection of acetic acid as the starting point for synthesis of larger molecules. No other compound comes close to acetic acid in respect to properties excellently suited for building molecules by condensation reactions. Nature has devised the tactic of combining this two-carbon acid with coenzyme A (abbreviated CoA), and the product is a highly reactive ester referred to as

$$
\begin{array}{c}
\text{H} \\
| \\
\text{H—C—C} \\
| \quad \diagdown \\
\text{H} \quad \text{S} \sim \text{CoA}
\end{array}
\quad
\begin{array}{c}
\diagup \text{O} \\
\\
\end{array}
$$

acetyl coenzyme A. The bond between the carboxyl carbon atom of acetic acid and the sulfur atom of CoA has relatively high reactivity as indicated by the symbol $(\sim)$.* The CoA ester of acetic acid is as reactive as acetaldehyde, but this reactivity is more readily controlled in the cell than is that of acetaldehyde.

The notion of the fit of molecules to the cellular machinery is one which has turned up again and again in our examination of biologically important molecules. In order to give more precision to this concept let us consider the problem of the storage form of chemical energy in the cell. There is one compound universally selected by Nature for this role. The compound is the triphosphate of the nucleoside adenosine, usually referred to by the abbreviation ATP. In the chain of three phosphate groups attached to adenosine, the two P—O—P bonds in the chain have relatively high reactivity (like that in acetyl-CoA discussed above). Why was ATP fastened upon as the storage form of chemical energy? The P—O—P bonds in ATP (the actual repositories of the energy) are essentially the same as the corresponding bonds in the triphosphates of other naturally occurring molecules resembling, and chemically related to, adenosine. Obviously, the energy content of the P—O—P bonds in ATP could not have been the sole determinant in the selective process because the P—O—P in any of a large number of polyphosphate compounds is essentially the same.

There are three equally important aspects of the storage of chemical energy in cells: (1) the problem of the formation of the bonds; (2) the problem of the storage of the energy of the bonds; and (3) the problem of the transduction of the energy into other

---

* The concept of a high energy bond implicit in the symbol $(\sim)$ will be developed at length in Chapter 6.

forms useful to the cell. Systems had to be designed not only to tap the chemical energy of ATP but also to convert this energy into other forms. The original selection of ATP may have been a happenstance (in the sense that similar molecules could have done as well), but once the choice was made, the auxiliary systems designed for ATP could not operate with other triphosphates. It is as if any of several sizes of electrical plugs might have been chosen initially, but once machines were designed for one particular size of plug, then variation of size was no longer permissible.

The P—O—P bonds of ATP represent a convenient packet of chemical energy in the sense that it is sufficient to drive all the chemical reactions for which it is required while not being so large that its power is wasted. Another important prerequisite that a molecule must meet as a satisfactory energy store is stability. There are many compounds with "energy-rich" bonds which are highly unstable in water at body temperature. Such compounds would not be very useful. The P—O—P bonds of ATP are remarkably stable under physiological conditions; thus, ATP poses no difficulties of storage.

Universality of Some Molecules of the Cell

Certain molecules are invariably present and serve in the same capacities in the cells of all living organisms. ATP is almost always the molecular instrument for energy conservation and storage. D-Glucose is almost always the particular sugar that serves as one of the fuels in the reactions leading to the release of utilizable energy. Certain purines and pyrimidines are always essential building blocks for nucleic acids. A set of some twenty organic molecules with unique catalytic capacities is universally present in all forms of life. It would lead us too far astray at this point to specify all the molecules in the list of universals, but it is sufficient to say that a significant proportion of the total number of molecules in any cell is common to all cells. What is the basis of this universality? It stems from the fact that the most fundamental systems of the cell (the systems of the minimal cell) are common to all cells, and interact with, and are made up of chemically identical molecules. The evolutionary process which led to the perfection of these universal systems of the cell preceded the differentiation of species; thus, the biochemical machines and the entire panoply of special molecules became the heritage of all living forms. Since the molecules are designed for the machines, and the machines for the molecules, the area of permissible variation was reduced to negligible proportions. D-Glucose could not have been replaced by any other sugar without necessitating major changes in the large numbers of interlocking parts that constitute the machine concerned with the glycolysis of D-glucose. The inviolability of the universal molecules is a consequence of this multifaceted fitting together of parts in highly complex machines. One cannot easily change from AC to DC current when all the equipment is wired for AC, or change from 110 to 220 volts after all electrical equipment has been constructed for 110 volts.* Once the "definitive" forms of the basic systems of the cell were achieved, the molecular pattern of these systems became fixed; thus, the molecules that participate in these systems have become the invariant features of all cells.

Suggested Reading

Books

Fieser, L. F., and Fieser, M., "Organic Chemistry," 3rd ed., D. C. Heath and Co., Boston, Massachusetts, 1956.

Heilbrunn, L. V., "The Dynamics of Living Protoplasm," Academic Press, New York, 1956.

Henderson, L. J., "Fitness of the Environment," The Macmillan Co., New York, 1913; Reprint Edition: Beacon Press, Boston, Massachusetts, 1958.

Höber, R., "Physical Chemistry of Cells and Tissues," Blakiston, Philadelphia, Pennsylvania, 1946.

Karlson, P., "Introduction to Modern Biochemistry," 2nd ed., Academic Press, New York, 1965.

Loewy, A. G., and Siekevitz, P., "Cell Structure and Function," Holt, Rinehart, and Winston, New York, 1963.

Pauling, L., "The Nature of the Chemical Bond," 3rd ed., Cornell University Press, Ithaca, New York, 1960.

* The analogy is a loose one, its validity resting on the assumption that the changeover is not only difficult but impossible. Actually, one could use a rectifier to convert AC to DC current or a resistance to get the correct line voltage.

Stanier, R. Y., Doudoroff, M., and Adelberger, E. A., "The Microbial World," Prentice-Hall, Englewood Cliffs, New Jersey, 1963.

White, A., Handler, P., and Smith, E. L., "Principles of Biochemistry," Mc-Graw-Hill Book Co., New York, 1964.

Special Articles

Bernal, J. D., and Fowler, R. H., *J. Chem. Phys.* 1, 515 (1933): theories relating to water.

Bernal, J. D., Calvin, M., Gaffron, H., McElroy, W. D., and Seliger, H. H., Rich, A., and Wald, G., in "Horizons in Biochemistry" (M. Kasha and B. Pullman, eds.), Academic Press, New York, 1962: chapters on biochemical evolution.

Edsall, J. T., and Wyman, J., "Biophysical Chemistry," Vol. I, Academic Press, New York, 1958: see Chapter 1 on biochemistry and geochemistry, and Chapter 2 on water and its biological significance.

CHAPTER 3 ————————————————

Macromolecules

There are two modes of building molecules. The first we have already discussed—arranging atoms in various combinations. This mode of building, with atoms as the building blocks, results in relatively small molecules. The second mode involves the use of preformed molecules as building blocks and results in molecules of giant size which are called macromolecules. These are made up of hundreds or thousands of smaller molecules, chemically bonded together to form a distinctive whole. As we shall discuss later, the cell has exploited the remarkable properties inherent in macromolecules. There are many varieties of biological macromolecules; some of the most fundamental properties of living systems are determined by specific macromolecules. In this chapter we shall consider a few examples of each of the main categories of cellular macromolecules with emphasis on some of the important chemical principles that underlie their structure.

Polysaccharides

Polysaccharides are macromolecules built up from a large number of identical, characteristic, repeating units which may be a simple sugar, such as glucose or fructose, or a more complex sugar, such as hyalbiuronic acid (which is built up of two linked simple sugars, D-glucuronic acid and N-acetyl-D-glucosamine). The properties of any polysaccharide are expressions of (1) the nature and number of repeating units and (2) the way in which these repeating units are strung together to form the macromolecule. These variations in the way polysaccharides are constructed have been the basis of much experimentation by Nature and have lead to the development of a large number of different polysaccharides of biological importance. We shall consider starch, glycogen, and cellulose—three polysaccharides, all of which are built up from an identical subunit, D-glucose. There are a number of profound differences in the properties of these three polysaccharides which result from the way in which the repeating units are linked one to another.

Starch and glycogen are the storage forms for glucose in plants and animals, respectively; cellulose is the material which makes up the tough cell walls found in the plant kingdom. Whether the bonds joining the repeating units are of the α- or β-variety is the principal determinant of the differences in properties between starch and glycogen on the one hand and cellulose on the other. The frequency of branch points (an alternative way of joining repeating units) determines the difference in properties between starch and glycogen.

α- AND β-ORIENTATION

The orientation of the polysaccharide subunits plays a paramount role in the determination of the physical properties of starch, glycogen, and cellulose. The aldehydic group of D-glucose readily interacts with the hydroxyl group on the fifth carbon atom and thereby forms a six-membered ring structure (cf. Figure 3.1). The reaction leads to an oxygen bridge between the first and fifth carbon atom in the molecule and to asymmetry of carbon atom 1 (C-1). The —OH group of C-1 will be oriented either below or above the plane of the six-membered pyranose* ring. These two orientations of the —OH group are designated as α and β, respectively (cf. Figure 3.1). In solutions of glucose, the α- and β-forms can achieve equilibrium with one another and with small amounts of the free aldehydic form. However, when two glucose molecules are covalently linked together by a bond that involves the —OH group on the first carbon atom of one of the two glucose molecules, freedom of rotation about this carbon atom is lost; this hydroxyl group is then fixed in either the α- or β orientation. Which orientation it will be is determined by the nature of the catalytic influences operative during the interaction of the two

* Pyranose is a six-membered ring containing five carbon atoms and one atom of oxygen.

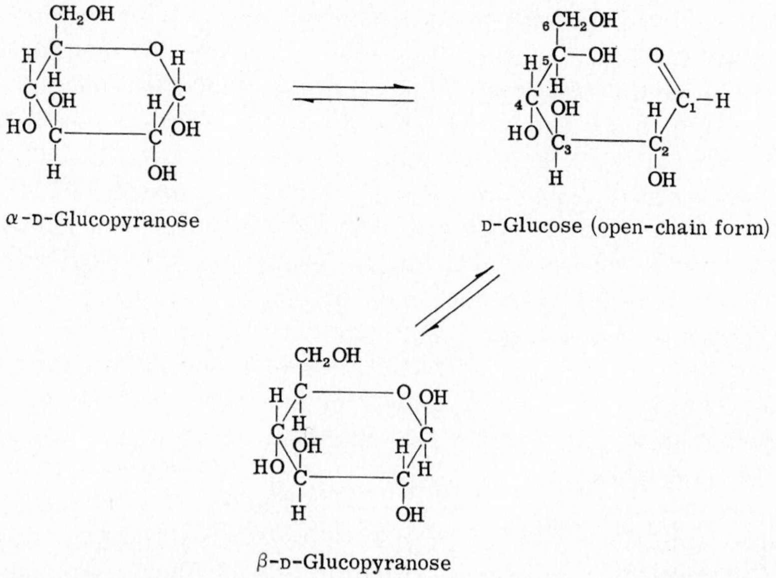

α-D-Glucopyranose

D-Glucose (open-chain form)

β-D-Glucopyranose

Fig. 3.1. Equilibrium between the open chain aldehydic form of D-glucose and the α- and β-D-glucopyranose forms.

glucose molecules. In starch and glycogen this orientation is α; in cellulose it is β.

α-Orientation and Helix Formation

Chains of glucose molecules linked to one another by 1:4 links, with α-orientation at C-1, tend to assume a helical* arrangement, whereas similarly linked chains, with β-orientation at C-1, extend in a nearly linear fashion. The helical arrangement of the glucose chains makes it difficult for two such chains to line up together. Indeed, little tendency for adhesion of such chains is noted.

β-Orientation and Adhesion of Chains

Linear glucose chains with β-orientation at C-1 present a uniform distribution of hydroxyl groups to the outside—that is, to the solvent. The result is that two cellulose chains coming together have large numbers of possible points of contact along their entire

---

* A helix is a coil like the thread of a screw.

length. Moreover, once contact has been made at one such point along the length of a pair of cellulose molecules, the local concentration of hydroxyl groups on the adjacent chains can compete effectively with the hydroxyl groups of the aqueous solvent, and the two chains will, so to speak, zip together. This process will continue until an insoluble, fibrous matrix "crystallizes" out, ideally suited for its role as an inert, rigid cell-wall structure. Thus, the two possible orientations about C-1 in the subunits of a polysaccharide can profoundly influence the physical properties of the polysaccharide.

In summary, the geometry of 1 : 4-linked chains with α-orientation leads to a helical arrangement, whereas the geometry of 1 : 4-linked chains with β-orientation leads to a linear arrangement. In turn, a helical arrangement of glucose chains predisposes against adhesion of chains, whereas a linear arrangement facilitates interchain adhesion.

BRANCHING OF CHAINS

The glucose units in cellulose are joined, head to tail, by 1 : 4 β-glycosidic links—that is, the bonds are formed between the hydroxyl group on C-1 (in β-orientation) of one glucose molecule and the hydroxyl group on C-4 of the next molecule in the chain. In glycogen and starch a head to tail 1 : 4 link is also found, albeit in α-linkage, but there is an additional link between certain glucose molecules (a 1 : 6 link) that plays a key role in the determination of the difference in properties of these two polysaccharides, even though no more than one in six of the glucose units in any chain is involved in such a link (cf. Figure 3.2). To visualize the 1 : 6 link, imagine two different chains of α, 1 : 4-linked glucose units which may be represented as where G* represents a glucose unit whose C—1 is not yet involved in a glycosidic bond. In the presence of a "branching" enzyme, the "free reducing group"

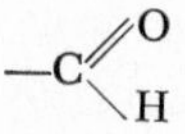

$$-C \overset{\displaystyle O}{\underset{\displaystyle H}{\diagdown}}$$

on one such unit can react with the free hydroxyl group on C—6 of the circled glucose unit in the other chain to form a 1 : 6 gly-

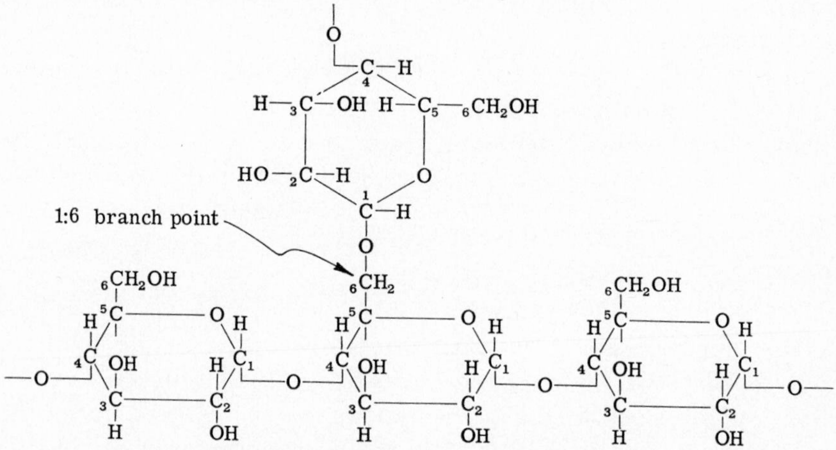

Fig. 3.2. Structures at a branch point in the glycogen or starch molecule.

cosidic bond, and the two chains are thereby joined (cf. Figure 3.2). The circled glucose has now become a branch point and is involved in glycosidic bonds with three different glucose residues through carbon atoms 1, 4, and 6, respectively. By virtue of such branch points a single molecule of glycogen (or amylopectin, the nearest equivalent to glycogen found in the mixture of molecules that make up starch) can be "grown," by the addition of many more molecules of glucose, into a vast, three-dimensional, bushlike structure with a molecular weight of several million (cf. Figure 3.3).

DISTANCE BETWEEN BRANCH POINTS

In glycogen the average distance between branch points is about six glucose units, whereas in amylopectin the average distance is about twelve glucose units. Amylose (another form of starch) has no branch points at all. As noted above, the intervals of the chain between branch points have a helical arrangement. Thus, the size of the helix in the segments between branch points is determined by the frequency of branching. Each helix has a large number of its polar hydroxyl groups directed toward the outside—that is,

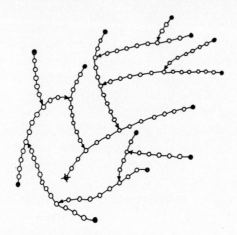

○	Glucose unit
●	Glucose unit with OH at C–4 not included in glycosidic link (free nonreducing group)
✗	Glucose unit with OH at C–1 not included in glycosidic link (free reducing group)
—	α,1:4 glycosidic bond
↑	α,1:6 glycosidic bond (arrowhead at C–6)
⟪	Glucose unit at branch point with glycosidic links at C–1, C–4 and C–6

Fig. 3.3. Diagrammatic representation of the structure of a glycogen molecule.

into the solvent—and relatively few directed toward the interior. The low concentration of polar groups, and the high concentration of hydrogen residues in the interior, gives this region of the helix chemical properties not unlike those of a nonpolar organic solvent.

RELATION OF GLYCOGEN STRUCTURE TO FUNCTION

The structure of glycogen is not just a piece of fanciful design by Nature: it is uniquely suited for the role of glycogen as a storehouse for glucose in the animal organism. The storage of thousands of glucose molecules in one macromolecule accomplishes three related purposes. First, being a large molecule, glycogen cannot diffuse across the cell membrane and is thus a stable source of glucose. Second, the storage of many glucose units in a single macromolecule forestalls the osmotic problem which a high concentration of free glucose molecules would entail for the cell. Finally, the localization of glucose units within a macromolecule simplifies enormously the logistics, both of commandeering glucose when the concentration of free glucose is low and of storing glucose when the concentration of free glucose is high. There are sets of enzymes which catalyze the detachment of glucose units from glycogen and the addition of free glucose units to glycogen. Both sets of enzymes work at the many end groups of the glycogen chains in which the reducing group of the terminal glucose unit is tied up (cf. Figure 3.3); these enzymes either make or break α, 1 : 4 glycosidic bonds.

By virtue of the branched structure, the outer surface of the glycogen molecule presents a high concentration of substrate to the enzymes that regulate glycogen synthesis and breakdown, although in molar terms glycogen is present in very low concentration in the cell. The lower degree of branching in starch is no disadvantage to plant cells, since plants have a much lower metabolic rate than animals. Both starch and glycogen are in constant state of flux as far as size is concerned. In times of glucose deficiency the macromolecule will be pared down to the nub; in times of glucose excess the macromolecule will be enlarged.

Functions of Polysaccharides

Many different polysaccharides are found in nature, serving many functions. The blood group substances, for example, have an important role in certain immune reactions, whereas chitin, and the matrix material of connective tissues, have structural importance. These polysaccharides differ in respect to type and to configuration of the repeating sugars. They also differ in respect to the position and orientation of the bonds which link one sugar to another. As we have seen, the properties of polysaccharides are determined by all these parameters, and Nature has taken advantage of the different parameters to match particular macromolecules with appropriate and specific roles in the structure and functions of the cell.

Proteins

AMINO ACIDS AND THE PEPTIDE BOND

The principal workhorses of a cell are the proteins. The repeating units from which all proteins are made are the amino acids. There are twenty commonly occurring amino acids, and all or nearly all of them are present in every protein. Each of the amino acids contains the same two functional groups, an amino group ($-NH_2$) and a carboxyl group ($-COOH$), both attached to the same carbon atom; however, the remainder of each amino acid—that is, the side chain—is unique and distinguishes each amino acid from the others (see Figure 3.4). The simplest amino acid, glycine, has the form NH_2-CH_2-COOH and all other amino acids except proline have the form

$$NH_2-CH-COOH$$
$$|$$
$$R$$

where the side chain, R, represents the group of atoms with a characteristic structure for each amino acid.

When two amino acids are brought together under appropriate conditions, the amino group of one interacts with the carboxyl group of the second to form an acid amide grouping known as the *peptide bond*. If we represent the first amino acid as

$$NH_2-CH-COOH$$
$$|$$
$$R$$

and the second as

$$NH_2-CH-COOH$$
$$|$$
$$\overline{R}$$

the formation of the peptide bond may be represented by the formulation below, where $\overline{R}$ represents a side chain other than R. Thus, a

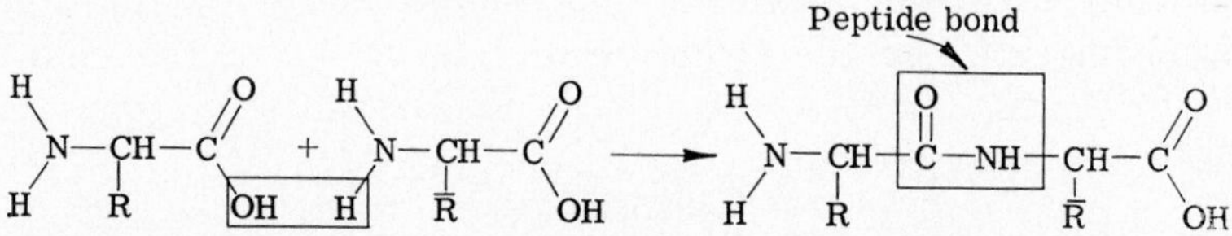

Peptide bond

dipeptide is formed. By condensation of this product with a third amino acid, a *tripeptide* can be formed, and in this way long chains

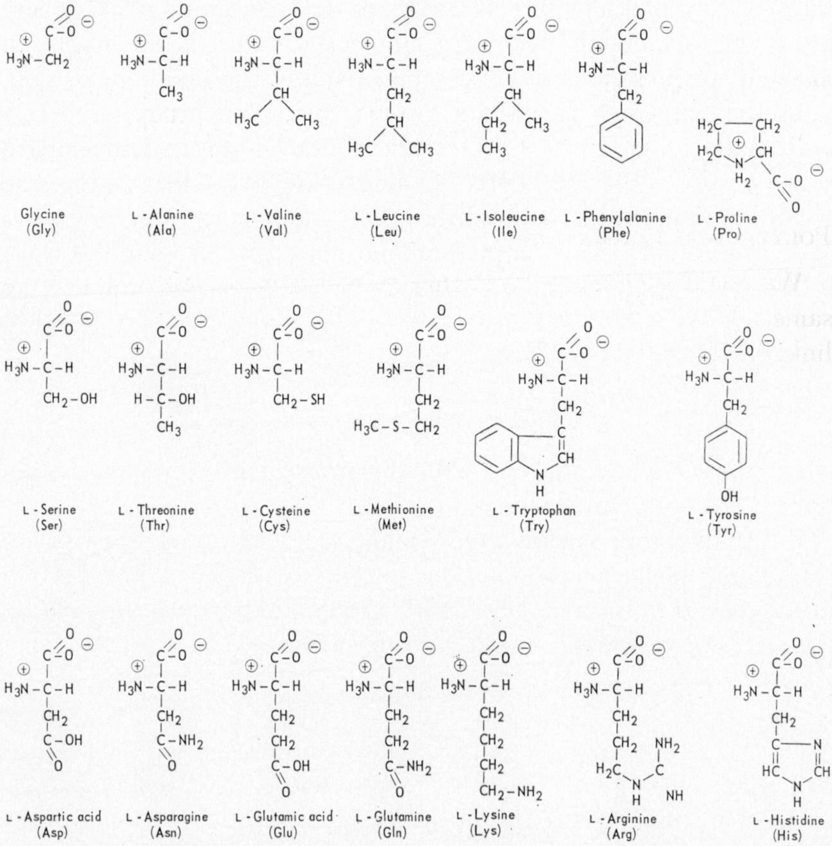

Glycine (Gly) L - Alanine (Ala) L - Valine (Val) L - Leucine (Leu) L - Isoleucine (Ile) L - Phenylalanine (Phe) L - Proline (Pro)

L - Serine (Ser) L - Threonine (Thr) L - Cysteine (Cys) L - Methionine (Met) L - Tryptophan (Try) L - Tyrosine (Tyr)

L - Aspartic acid (Asp) L - Asparagine (Asn) L - Glutamic acid (Glu) L - Glutamine (Gln) L - Lysine (Lys) L - Arginine (Arg) L - Histidine (His)

Fig. 3.4. The structural formulas of the important amino acids. Taken from "Introduction to Modern Biochemistry" by P. Karlson. Academic Press, New York, 1965.

of amino acids may be built up. Chains with more than about 100 amino acid residues are called proteins, rather than peptides, although the line of demarcation between the two is not distinct. Most proteins consist of one or more chains each 100–300 amino acids long. It should be noted that, in a chain of amino acids linked together by peptide bonds, the recurring sequence

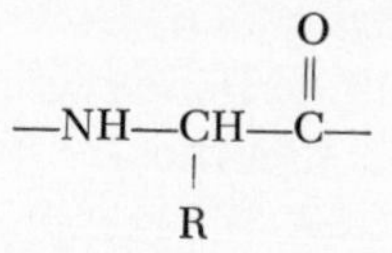

$$-NH-CH-\overset{\overset{\displaystyle O}{\|}}{C}-$$
$$\underset{R}{|}$$

constitutes a backbone for the chain, with the R groups coming off the backbone like ribs. At one end of the chain (conventionally written on the left) there is a free amino group, and at the other end (conventionally written on the right) there is a free carboxyl group.

POLYPEPTIDE FORMATION

We could synthesize a polymer in which many molecules of the same amino acid (R_1) combine with one another in peptide linkage:

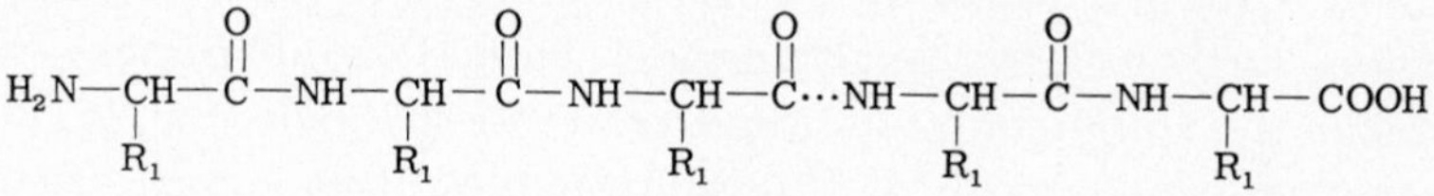

$$H_2N-\underset{R_1}{\overset{}{CH}}-\overset{\overset{O}{\|}}{C}-NH-\underset{R_1}{\overset{}{CH}}-\overset{\overset{O}{\|}}{C}-NH-\underset{R_1}{\overset{}{CH}}-\overset{\overset{O}{\|}}{C}\cdots NH-\underset{R_1}{\overset{}{CH}}-\overset{\overset{O}{\|}}{C}-NH-\underset{R_1}{\overset{}{CH}}-COOH$$

However, natural proteins are built up from molecules of different amino acids:

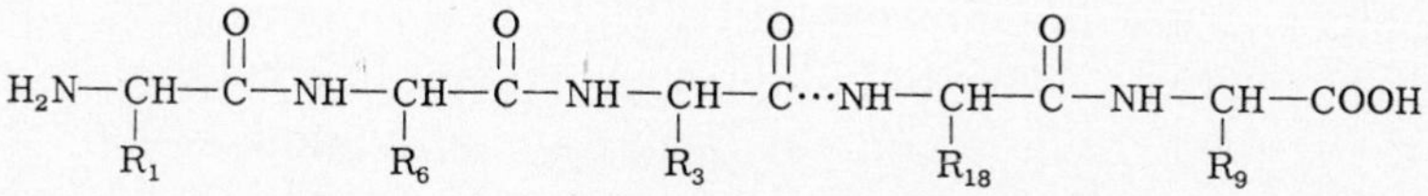

$$H_2N-\underset{R_1}{\overset{}{CH}}-\overset{\overset{O}{\|}}{C}-NH-\underset{R_6}{\overset{}{CH}}-\overset{\overset{O}{\|}}{C}-NH-\underset{R_3}{\overset{}{CH}}-\overset{\overset{O}{\|}}{C}\cdots NH-\underset{R_{18}}{\overset{}{CH}}-\overset{\overset{O}{\|}}{C}-NH-\underset{R_9}{\overset{}{CH}}-COOH$$

Since there are twenty common amino acids, there are almost unlimited possibilities of sequence. The polypeptide chain of each natural protein is made up of characteristic amino acids; the sequence and relative numbers of these units are unique for each protein.

The Structure of Proteins

PRIMARY STRUCTURE

The covalent structure of a protein molecule is referred to as the *primary structure*. This term encompasses not only the peptide bonds which bind each amino acid to its neighbors, but also (when present) the covalent disulfide bonds which bind the sulfur atoms of pairs of cysteine residues together. Although disulfide bonds are part of the primary structure of proteins, we shall discuss them together with tertiary structure (see below).

SECONDARY STRUCTURE

Polypeptide chains have a tendency to form two different kinds of organized conformation. First, and by far the most commonly occurring in nature, is the helix. The predominant variety of helix found in proteins is the α-helix, illustrated in Figure 3.5. The path of the backbone of a polypeptide chain in helical conformation describes a spiral similar to the thread of a screw, 3.6 amino acid residues comprising each turn. The carbonyl group of each amino acid forms a hydrogen bond with the imino group of the amino acid four residues farther along the polypetide chain. These hydrogen bonds stabilize the spiral conformation. Certain of the amino acids cannot be accommodated easily in this conformation; thus, when one such amino acid occurs in a polypeptide chain, the helix must end, and the chain must proceed in some other conformation, at least for a short span, before another helical segment can occur farther along the chain. Some proteins contain a great deal of helix, while others contain relatively little, but all proteins appear to have some portion of their polypeptide chains in helical conformation.

The second regular conformation in which polypeptide chains may arrange themselves is known as β-structure. This conformation consists of several segments of extended (nonhelical) polypeptide chain lying parallel to each other and held together in sheets by hydrogen bonds. This variety of conformation is uncommon in nature, occurring chiefly in silk proteins.

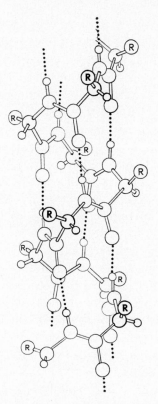

Fig. 3.5. The α-helical conformation of a polypeptide chain. Hydrogen bonds are represented by dotted lines. Redrawn with permission from "The Nature of the Chemical Bond" by L. Pauling, Cornell University Press, Ithaca, New York, 1960.

TERTIARY STRUCTURE

The most complex way in which the structure of one protein differs from that of every other protein is that of three-dimensional shape. The three-dimensional shape of a protein is defined as the *tertiary structure*. If the polypeptide chain of a protein were stretched out in a straight line, it would be very long and narrow. Nevertheless, many proteins as they exist in nature (*native* proteins) are not long, narrow molecules; they are compact and globular. Even the most elongated proteins have the proportions of a flute, rather than those of a piano string. Proteins are compact and not filamentous structures because their polypeptide chains are folded. It is, primarily, the particular way in which a polypeptide chain is folded that gives a protein its characteristic three-dimensional shape. The problem of how polypeptide chains fold after being synthesized as linear molecules has only recently come under direct investigation; further discussion is reserved for Chapter 11. They do not fold any which way. A given chain of amino acids under proper environmental conditions folds in only *one* way to yield the form corresponding to that of the native protein. It is extremely important that the folding be accomplished with accuracy, in order that the functional properties of each protein may be fully realized.

The many individual forces involved in guiding the folding process are, at the present time, understood only in the broadest terms. It is known, for instance, that polypeptide chains tend to fold in such a way as to expose a maximal number of hydrophilic amino acid residues to the aqueous environment and to enclose a maximal number of hydrophobic residues. Thus, one finds predominantly polar chemical groups on the surface of protein molecules and nonpolar groups in the interior.

Once a polypeptide chain has folded into the form that corresponds to the native protein, its three-dimensional shape is stabilized by multiple bonds between the various atoms of the amino acid side chains, such as hydrogen bonds (Figure 3.6), hydrophobic bonds (Figure 3.7), and ionic bonds. In addition to these, the three-dimensional shapes of some proteins are stabilized by disulfide bonds (Figure 3.8). The disulfide bond usually is a covalent bond between the sulfur atoms of two residues of the amino acid, cysteine, and is therefore actually part of the primary structure of proteins. The cysteine residues may have been widely separated when the linear polypeptide chain was originally assembled, but once the chain folds they come to lie sufficiently close to one another to join together by forming a disulfide bond, as shown in Figure 3.9.

The prevailing opinion of physical chemists is that, of all the types of noncovalent interactions, the hydrophobic bond makes by far the largest contribution to the stabilization of the tertiary structure of proteins. The role of both the hydrogen bond and the ionic bond in this stabilization appears to be far less important. Whether this generalization is applicable to all proteins, is still an open question.

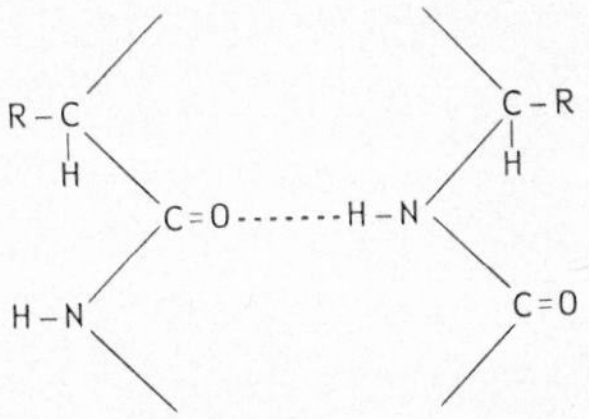

Fig. 3.6. Example of a hydrogen bond (represented as a dashed line) between two peptide groups.

The interaction between two adjacent parafinic amino acid residues, which underlies the hydrophobic bond, is often visualized in terms of the coalescence of oil droplets. This extrapolation from the macroscopic to the molecular level appears to be unjustified. Irving Klotz is one of the physical biochemists who have made major con-

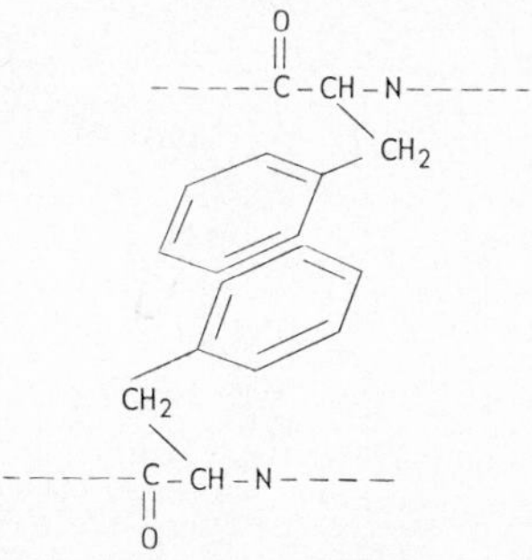

Fig. 3.7. Example of a hydrophobic bond between the benzene rings of two phenylalanine residues.

tributions to our knowledge of the forces that underlie the hydrophobic bond in proteins. His interpretation of hydrophobic interactions in proteins may be summarized as follows. The hydrophobic side chains abutting into the aqueous medium in which the protein is dissolved are enveloped in a structured layer of water existing in an ice-like (crystal-like) arrangement. That is to say, water molecules in the envelope have fewer degrees of translational and rotational freedom than do water molecules in the liquid state.

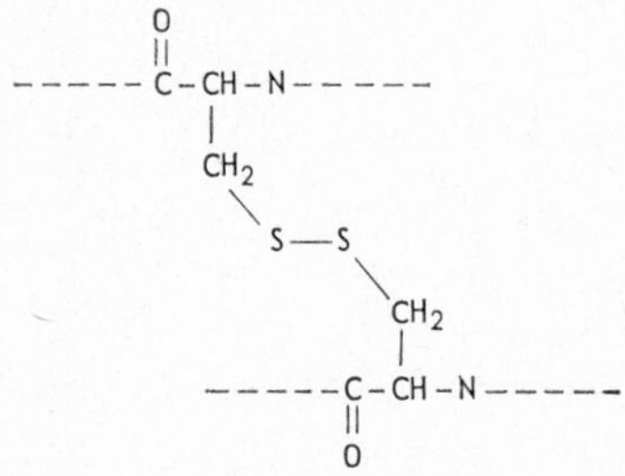

$$
\begin{array}{c}
O \\
\| \\
----\,C-CH-N------ \\
| \\
CH_2 \\
\backslash \\
S-S \\
\backslash \\
CH_2 \\
| \\
-----C-CH-N----- \\
\| \\
O
\end{array}
$$

Fig. 3.8. Example of a disulfide bond between the sulfur atoms of two cysteine residues.

The properties of water molecules of the former category approximate those of the molecules within the lattice of ice. According to this view, when two hydrophobic residues interact, the total amount of ice-like water associated with the residues that have combined

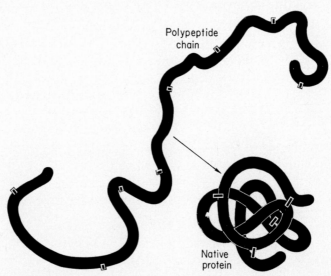

Polypeptide chain

Native protein

Fig. 3.9. Disulfide bonds (represented by rectangles) are formed between pairs of cysteine residues (represented as squares) when these residues come into proximity during the folding of the polypeptide chain.

is reduced in amount. It is the accompanying release of free energy (mainly an entropy change) that drives the reaction. Since free energy is required to orient water at a hydrophobic interface, free energy is released when the amount of such water in the system is reduced. Thus, it is not the avoidance of water *per se* but the reduction in the total area of surfaces at which water is oriented that drives the coalescence of hydrophobic residues. This is the essence of the hydrophobic bond. A simple way to visualize hydrophobic interactions is in terms of a special form of structured water enveloping all paraffinic residues exposed to the aqueous solvent. The free energy required for the formation of such ordered structures is sufficiently large to discourage solubility of hydrophobic residues in water and to encourage coalescing of such residues.

There is some evidence to support the view that there are holes present in the lattice of the ice-like water which envelopes the hydrophobic residues of proteins, and that the hydrophobic side chains can fit into these holes. It is this interpenetrability of the structured water layer by hydrophobic residues that accounts for the large contribution made by the ice-like water layers to the stability of the tertiary structure of protein. The thermal denaturation of proteins appears to be determined primarily by sharp transitions in the stability of the ordered water associated with the side chains of hydrophobic amino acids in the protein. Reagents such as urea, which lower the stability of protein-bound water structures, are the very ones which readily induce denaturation of proteins.

The older representation of a protein in solution involved the notion of a unit penetrable by the molecules of the solvent. It is probably much more realistic to think of a protein molecule in solution as an impenetrable unit. The solvent comes into contact with the protein, but only with those groups that are exposed at the surface, whereas the hydrophobic interior of the protein is buried and out of reach of the solvent.

QUATERNARY STRUCTURE

The *quaternary* structure of proteins is the structural relationship between two or more nonfunctional proteins which are bound together to form a functional unit. All proteins made of single polypeptide chains have primary, secondary, and tertiary structures. Only those proteins composed of more than one polypeptide chain, however, may have the added feature of quaternary structure.

The two or more polypeptide chains of such a protein may be identical or nonidentical. In either case, their structural relationships to each other must be determined entirely by noncovalent interactions if the protein is to be considered to have quaternary structure. In the case of the more complex proteins, the functional molecule may be composed of subunits, each of which contains more than one polypeptide chain. The presence of quaternary structure in a protein may have important functional consequences. For instance, by changing the arrangement of the subunits of such a protein, function may be altered drastically, and these alterations could allow for important biological control mechanisms (see Chapter 12).

The Ways of Studying a Protein

There are many ways of studying and analyzing a protein. One can cleave the peptide bonds in a protein and determine which amino acids are present and in what amounts. By special techniques the protein chemist can determine the complete amino acid sequence of a protein. The physical biochemist can measure the physical properties of proteins and is thus able to decide whether a molecule is positively or negatively charged, spherical or elongated, tightly folded or "spongy," and composed of one or more than one polypeptide chain. There is a large number of selective reagents which can modify or eliminate functional groups in the molecule, and from the effects of these reagents on the biological activity of the protein one can deduce the essentiality of particular functional groups for biological activity. The X-ray crystallographer can, with relative ease, recognize certain regularities in the protein molecule such as helix and parallel chains of amino acids (β-structures). Though considerably more difficult, he may be able to determine the exact disposition of every atom in the protein. All these different aspects of the protein molecule are pertinent to a complete understanding of its properties.

X-RAY CRYSTALLOGRAPHY

At the present time, the only method by which the three-dimensional structure of a protein can be determined in detail is that of X-ray crystallography. X-Rays may be used to probe the exact positions of the atoms in a protein molecule because X-rays are of extremely short wave lengths—wave lengths of the same order of magnitude as interatomic distances.

The first completely successful analysis of protein structure by X-ray crystallography was accomplished by J. C. Kendrew and his colleagues at Cambridge University in 1957. They were able to determine the structure of sperm-whale myoglobin, a heme protein with a molecular weight of approximately 16,000. Two years later, Max Perutz and his colleagues succeeded in defining the three-dimensional structure of hemoglobin, a considerably more complex molecule composed of four subunits, each closely resembling the myoglobin molecule. Perutz was able to demonstrate the fact that very definite, though small, changes in the shape of the hemoglobin molecule occur when it associates with, and dissociates from, oxygen—a finding that had been predicted on the basis of previous biochemical investigations of hemoglobin.

In 1965, D. C. Phillips and his collaborators at the Faraday Research Laboratory obtained detailed information on the structure of the enzyme lysozyme (molecular weight of approximately 14,000). Although not all of the data have yet been analyzed, many important conclusions have already been drawn from them. Aided by the known amino acid sequence of lysozyme (which had been determined by R. Canfield using classical techniques of protein chemistry), the Faraday group was able to locate, from their X-ray data, the atoms of all the 129 amino acid residues in the molecule, and to build a three-dimensional model.

The X-ray crystallographic work on lysozyme has been especially interesting because the active site of this enzyme could be studied. Due to the fact that no substrate of low molecular weight is available, competitive inhibitors of lysozyme have been used for this purpose. These inhibitors, which bind to lysozyme at the active site, can be localized on the enzyme by applying the techniques of X-ray crystallography to the enzyme-inhibitor complex. In this way the active site has been identified as a deep cleft in the surface of the enzyme. A three-dimensional model of lysozyme is shown in Figure 3.10; the active site cleft is indicated by the arrow.

Up to now, complete resolution of the three-dimensional struc-

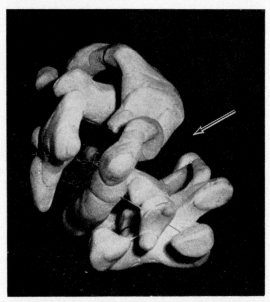

Fig. 3.10. Three-dimensional model of enzyme, lysozyme, constructed on the basis of X-ray crystallographic data with 6Å resolution. The deep cleft indicated by the arrow is the active site of the protein. The photograph was kindly provided by Dr. D. C. Phillips.

tures of proteins by X-ray crystallography has been accomplished only with relatively small proteins. Theoretically, however, there is no reason why such studies cannot be extended to larger and more complex ones. Of special interest would be those proteins which not only have catalytic sites, but also have special sites for combination with specific small molecules that regulate their functions (cf. Chapter 12). From studies on molecules of the latter type, it might be possible to identify the location and chemical characteristics of such "regulator sites" and to study changes in the three-dimensional structures of the proteins that might result from combination with regulator molecules. Biochemical investigations indicate that conformational changes in the proteins occur upon combination with such molecules, but only by X-ray crystallographic studies could these changes be defined with precision.

Although X-ray crystallography provides the most detailed information about protein structure, it is a laborious and time-consuming technique; it cannot be expected to become a routine laboratory procedure. However, the application of this technique to protein molecules of special interest will undoubtedly contribute immensely to our knowledge of protein structure and function in general. In addition, X-rays may be used to obtain less detailed but often very interesting and meaningful information about proteins. For example, by simply studying *changes* in the X-ray diffraction patterns produced by an insoluble protein crystal under several different conditions, F. Richards has been able to draw important conclusions about the function of the protein without knowing, or even attempting to know, anything about its three-dimensional structure. This and perhaps other modifications of the techniques of X-ray crystallography hold great promise for research on the structure and function of proteins in the future.

MULTIPLE ROLES FOR PROTEIN

There are large numbers of different proteins in every cell. Each one has a specific role to play, such as catalytic, structural, or transporting. Why are proteins suited for this wide spectrum of uses? As we mentioned above, there are twenty different varieties of amino acids which are commonly found in proteins. Some of the side chains of the amino acid residues are positively charged, others are negatively charged; some are hydrophobic, others are polar; some are short, others are relatively long. It is clearly the diversity of the amino acid building blocks which underlies the great diversity of proteins. There are twenty different ingredients to mix, so to speak, in the protein pot; by judicious selection of the kind and number of ingredients, and the sequence in which they are arranged, there is no limit to the possible number of gourmet dishes that may result.

Nucleic Acids

The determinants of heredity, and the custodian of biological information in the cell, are the class of macromolecules known as nucleic acids. These macromolecules bear the same relation to their repeating units, the nucleotides, as do the proteins to the amino acids and the polysaccharides to the simple sugars. Each nucleotide is made up of three component molecules linked together (Figure 3.11): (1) a basic heterocyclic ring compound

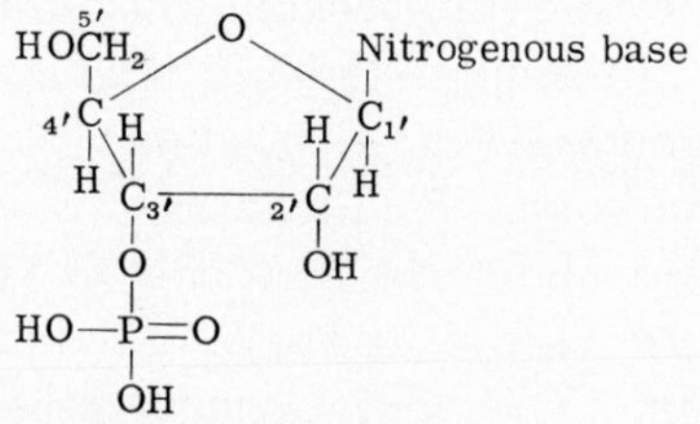

Fig. 3.11. The arrangement of the constituent parts of a nucleotide. The phosphate group can also be in the 5' position.

(purine or pyrimidine); (2) a pentose sugar (ribose or deoxyribose); and (3) orthophosphate. The bases that occur in nucleic acids are the purines, adenine and guanine, and the pyrimidines, cytosine, thymine, and uracil (cf. Figure 3.12). When combined with pentose and phosphate to form nucleotides, they are known, respectively, as adenylic acid, guanylic acid, cytidylic acid, thymidylic acid, and uridylic acid. One nucleotide is linked to another through the phosphate group (cf. Figure 3.13) which is covalently linked to carbon atom 3' of the pentose ring of one nucleotide and to carbon atom 5' of the pentose ring of the adjacent nucleotide.

Nucleic acids are of two types: ribonucleic acid (RNA), in which the sugar of the component nucleotides is ribose, and deoxyribonucleic acid (DNA), in which the sugar is deoxyribose.

Carbon atom 2 of ribose has a substituent (—OH) group which is replaced by a hydrogen atom in deoxyribose.

The nucleic acid RNA is built up mainly from four nucleotides: cytidylic acid, uridylic acid, adenylic acid, and guanylic acid. The corresponding set of nucleotides found in DNA consists of d-cytidylic acid,* thymidylic acid, d-adenylic acid, and d-guanylic acid. Thus, RNA and DNA share three of the four bases (adenine, guanine, and cytosine), but uracil is peculiar to RNA, and thymine is peculiar to DNA.

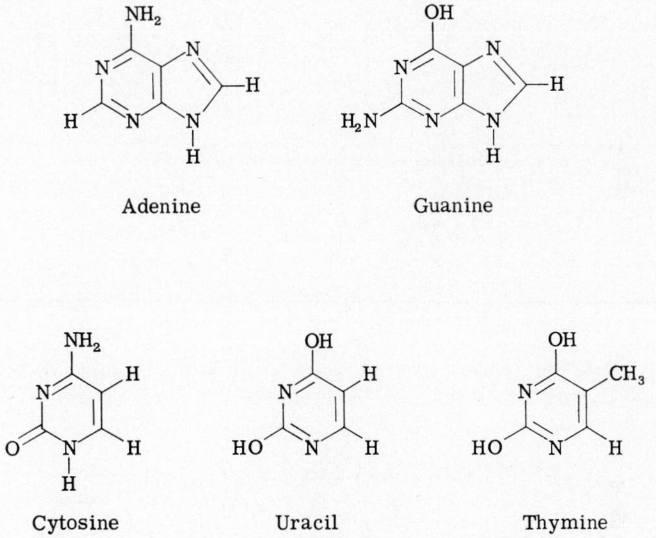

Fig. 3.12. Purine and pyrimidine bases in nucleic acids.

In Chapter 11 we shall be dealing with the functions of DNA and RNA. For the purpose of the present discussion it will be sufficient merely to point out that nucleic acids are macromolecules built up of relatively large numbers of nucleotides, linked one to the other in linear fashion. Because they are composed of several different nucleotide building blocks, the nucleic acids, like the proteins, have the possibility for enormous variation in structure. There

* The lower case d prefixed before the name of the nucleotide signifies that the sugar moiety is deoxyribose rather than ribose.

are, e.g., 64 different sequences possible for a chain of only three different nucleotides. When one considers actual nucleic acids, which contain many nucleotides (80–30,000), the number of possible different sequences becomes astronomically high. As we shall see in Chapter 11, this possibility for a huge number of different unique structures is one of the most important features of nucleic acids in relation to their functions.

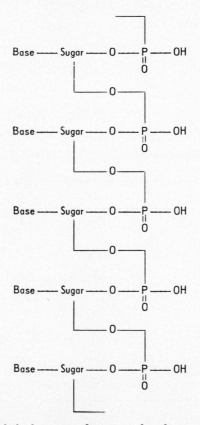

Fig. 3.13. The links between adjacent nucleotides in nucleic acids.

Phospholipids

Phospholipids are complex molecules which are among the building blocks of membranes and other key polymeric materials found in all living cells. Typically, all phospholipids contain three essential parts: (1) glycerol; (2) a pair of fatty acids; and (3) orthophosphate (Figure 3.14). The three parts are linked together by ester bonds. In most phospholipids the orthophosphate is further substituted. The additional substituent may be choline, as

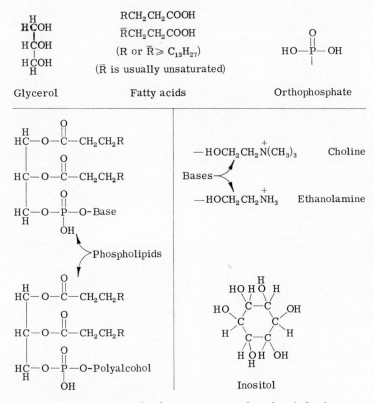

Fig. 3.14. The molecular constituents of a phospholipid.

in phosphatidylcholine (lecithin); ethanolamine, as in phosphatidylethanolamine; glycerol, as in cardiolipin; or inositol, as in phosphatidylinositol.

There are many other possible variations in the structures of phospholipids. The essential point is that a phospholipid may be regarded as a composite of two parts: a hydrophobic part, which

3. *Macromolecules*

includes the two long-chain fatty acid residues (enclosed by a dotted line in Figure 3.15) and a charged or polar part (the rest of the molecule). Many molecules have a bimodal character to some degree, but phospholipids have it to a very high degree; this bimodality is the basis of the extraordinary arrays which phospholipids form in water. We find in nature other bimodal molecules which can substitute for phospholipids. Two examples of these are the sulfalipids and glycolipids. In these lipids, phosphate is replaced by a sulfate and sugar residue, respectively.

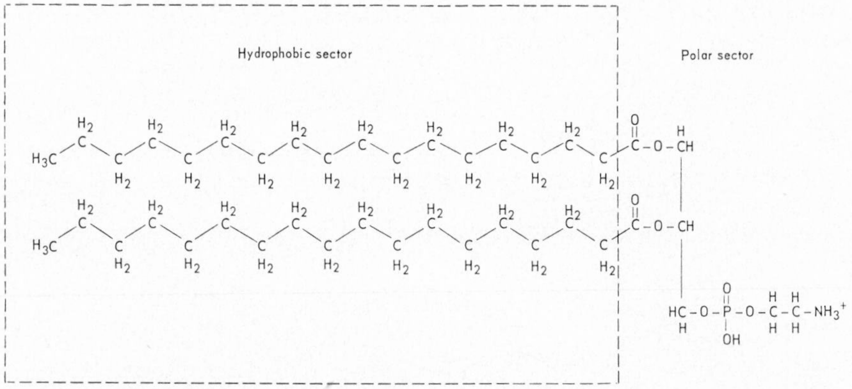

Fig. 3.15. Hydrophobic and polar sectors of phosphatidyl ethanolamine.

MICELLE FORMATION

Any phospholipid with two long-chain fatty acid residues (C_{18} or higher) is utterly insoluble in water. Nevertheless, when a set of phospholipid molecules is made to assume the proper arrangement in an aqueous environment, the whole array achieves water solubility. This trick is accomplished by orienting all the charged groups on the outside of the array and all the hydrophobic groups in the interior (Figure 3.16). In this way the aqueous solvent "sees" only the charged ends of the phospholipid molecules; the hydrophobic groups are buried in the interior and, in effect, are screened from contact with water. This oriented array of phospholipid molecules is known as a *micelle*. In a sense, the micelle is similar to a macromolecule (for example, a protein) in respect to solubility in water and to being more than a collection of separate molecules. The hydrophobic side chains of the amino acids of a protein in aqueous solution are buried in the interior of the molecule, whereas the charged groups are concentrated on the outside; because of this orientation the protein is soluble in water. The same applies to the micelle. The amino acids of a protein are held together by many varieties of bonds, whereas the micelle

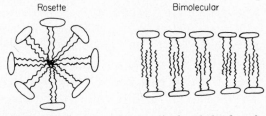

Fig. 3.16. Micellar arrangement of phospholipid molecules.

is held together by hydrophobic bonds alone. Admittedly, the individual bonds of the micelle are weak, yet collectively they are strong enough to maintain the micelle as a stable unit.

In biological systems the preferred micelle is the bimolecular micelle (Figure 3.16), which consists of paired two-dimensional arrays of oriented phospholipid molecules, with the arrays stacked in three dimensions. These micelles are fundamental to the performance of all biological membranes and also to all the cellular systems concerned with energy transformations.

Some Concluding Comments

The realm of biological macromolecules involves such a wealth of detail that the important take-home lessons may easily have been overlooked. Nature has found in the macromolecules the molecular means for accomplishing the multiple tasks of the cell. Each class of macromolecules has its own set of properties and its own set of rules for variation in structure and function. Let us consider some of the strategic considerations in the process of selecting macromolecules with the desired biological properties.

It is extremely important to understand what is meant by the word *selection* in the context of the present discussion. Throughout the process of evolution, starting with the earliest cells, natural selection has been an extremely efficient device for screening out unsatisfactory solutions to biological problems. However, such selection operates at the level of populations of organisms, not at the molecular level. Only the greater or lesser ability of organisms to survive and procreate determines their greater or lesser ability to compete with other organisms. One may discuss the selection of molecules, then, only in the sense that the characteristics of organisms are ultimately produced by the nature of the molecules which comprise them. One must never forget, however, that no actual selection of molecules *per se* is involved in the evolutionary process. Similarly, Nature does not *design* molecules with any foreknowledge of their possible usefulness. When one speaks of the process by which the molecules of the cell are designed one must keep in mind that the final product is the result of numerous and random variations, each of which was tested by selection for or against retention (at the population level).

In the design of polysaccharides the three possibilities for variation are the chemical nature of the repeating sugar, the geometric and optical form of the repeating sugar, and the nature of the covalent links between repeating sugars. Most of the natural innovation and experimentation in polysaccharide structure resulted in the design of macromolecules that are suitable either as storage forms of sugar (capable of rapid mobilization and convenient packaging) or as tough structural materials, either for enclosing cells or protecting soft tissues.

The proteins have no single repeating units; however, there is a repeating structural feature of proteins, namely, the peptide bond. The important variables which can be manipulated in the quest for new varieties of protein are: the sequence of amino acids; the formation of disulfide bonds; the formation of helix and β structures; the folding of peptide chains; the association of two or more protein subunits; and, finally, the incorporation of a particular coenzyme in a selective fashion. Variations in these modalities have led to a fantastic number of highly selective molecules well suited to a wide variety of purposes (catalytic, structural, immunological, etc.).

The nucleic acids are not multipurpose macromolecules. These were selected and perfected for one exclusive use, to serve as the repository of information and as a vehicle for the transcription and translation of this information (see Chapter 11). There are, in fact, but two *types* of nucleic acids which differ only in a few chemical details. The nature of the bonding between one nucleotide and the next, the orientation and optical form of the ribose or deoxyribose, and the nature of the five major purine and pyrimidine bases* are chemical features that are seldom varied. These are the features that make nucleic acids highly stable, linear macromolecules.

The phospholipids, like the nucleic acids, are more restricted in function than are the proteins. Phospholipids are as essential to membranes as nucleic acids are to the hereditary apparatus. All membranes require phospholipids as integral components, the properties of membranes being in large measure determined by the component phospholipids. The micellar associations formed by phospholipids, and the interaction of these micellar arrays with proteins, are properties which are fundamental to the building of membranes. The variables that can lead to changes in the properties of phospholipid micelles are: the number of carbon atoms

---

* Several additional purine and pyrimidine bases are being identified as minor constituents of nucleic acid.

in the fatty acid chains, the number of double bonds in the fatty acids, and the nature of the nitrogenous base or polyalcohol bound to the phosphate group in ester linkage. When more is known of the molecular architecture of membranes, some of the fine points in the design of phospholipid molecules may be better appreciated.

Suggested Reading

Books

Anfinsen, C. B., "Molecular Basis of Evolution," John Wiley and Sons, Inc., New York, 1959.

Ansell, G. B., and Hawthorne, J. N., "The Phospholipids," Elsevier Publishing Co., Amsterdam, 1964.

Chargaff, E., and Davidson, J. N., eds., "The Nucleic Acids," Vol. 1, Academic Press, New York, 1955.

Davidson, J. N., "The Biochemistry of Nucleic Acids," 4th ed., Methuen and Co. Ltd., London, 1960.

Dawson, R. M. C., and Rhodes, D. N., eds., "Metabolism and Physiological Significance of Lipids," John Wiley and Sons, Ltd., London, 1964.

Haggis, G. H., Michie, D., Muir, A. R., Roberts, K. B., and Walker, P. M. B., "Introduction to Molecular Biology," John Wiley and Sons, Inc., New York, 1964.

Hanahan, D. J., "Lipide Chemistry," John Wiley and Sons, Inc., New York, 1960.

Haurowitz, F., "The Chemistry and Function of Proteins," Academic Press, New York, 1963.

Ingram, V., "The Biosynthesis of Macromolecules," W. A. Benjamin, Inc., New York, 1965.

Perutz, M. F., "Proteins and Nucleic Acids: Structure and Function," Elsevier Publishing Co., Amsterdam, 1962.

"Protein Structure and Function," Brookhaven National Laboratory, Upton, New York, 1960.

Tanford, C., "Physical Chemistry of Macromolecules," John Wiley and Sons, Inc., New York, 1961.

Special Articles

Anfinsen, C. B., *Brookhaven Symp. Biol.* **15**, 184 (1962): on the three-dimensional structure of ribonuclease.

Crick, F. H. C., and Kendrew, J. C., *Advan. Protein Chem.* **12**, 133 (1957): X-ray analysis and protein structure.

Fisher, H. F., *Proc. Natl. Acad. Sci. U. S.* **51**, 1285 (1964): on the polarity ratio relating size and shape of protein molecules to their composition.

Goldberger, R. F., Epstein, C. J., and Anfinsen, C. B., *J. Biol. Chem.* **239**, 1406 (1964): enzyme for the proper folding of reduced proteins.

Green, D. E., and Fleischer, S., *in* "Metabolism and Physiological Significance of Lipids" (R. M. C. Dawson and D. N. Rhodes, eds.), John Wiley and Sons, Ltd., London, 1964: properties of phospholipid micelles.

Kauzmann, W., *Advan. Protein Chem.* **14**, 1 (1959): on hydrophobic bonding in proteins.

Kendrew, J. C., *Sci. Am.* **205**, 96 (1961): The three-dimensional structure of a protein molecule.

Klotz, I., *Brookhaven Symp. Biol.* **13** (1960): non-covalent bonds in proteins, protein structure, and function.

Klotz, I., *Federation Proc.* **24**, S24 (1965): discussion of ice-like water in macromolecules.

Perutz, M. F., *Sci. Am.* **211**, 64 (1964): X-ray crystallography of proteins, particularly of hemoglobin.

Manners, D. J., *Advan. Carbohydrate Chem.* **17**, (1962): on the enzymic synthesis and degradation of starch and glycogen.

Pauling, Linus, *in* "The Scientific Endeavor," The Rockefeller Institute Press, New York, 1965: on the architecture of molecules.

Spackman, D. H., Stein, W. H., and Moore, S., *J. Biol. Chem.* **235**, 633 (1960): the disulfide bonds of ribonuclease.

CHAPTER 4 _____

Enzymes

ENZYMES AND CELL CHEMISTRY

Many hundreds of different chemical reactions are constantly proceeding in every living cell. Only a few of these reactions would go on to any meaningful extent under conditions of temperature and pH which exist in living cells were they not facilitated by catalysts. The catalysts of living systems are known as enzymes. Essentially every new reaction developed during evolution required the development of a new enzyme. In general, enzymes display a high degree of specificity; most catalyze only a single chemical reaction; a few catalyze several related reactions. The large number and extensive variety of enzymes within any one cell mirror the number and variety of metabolic processes.

All enzymes are proteins varying in size from a molecular weight of approximately 10,000 to a molecular weight of 1,000,000. Each enzyme protein has a characteristic amino acid sequence and three-dimensional structural pattern that distinguishes it from all other enzymes. The unique structure of each enzyme is the ultimate key to its unique function.

Enzymes are usually named according to the nature of the reactions they catalyze. Thus, dehydrogenases catalyze dehydrogenations; carboxylases, the decarboxylation of keto or amino acids; ribonucleases, the hydrolysis of ribonucleic acid. The suffix *ase* is usually incorporated into the name of enzymes.

THE ROLE OF THE ENZYME IN CATALYSIS

The enzyme and the substance upon which it acts—the substrate—stand in a lock and key relationship to one another. This molecular fit goes to the very heart of enzyme specificity; in general, only one substrate "fits" any given enzyme. Most of the substances which undergo chemical reaction in the living cell are relatively inert (unreactive), chemically speaking, at physiological pH, temperatures, and concentrations. However, the same molecules become highly reactive when bonded to their appropriate enzymes. The enzyme provides a unique chemical environment in which a variety of forces can exert an influence on the group in the substrate molecule which is to undergo reaction. By virtue of these forces the group in question becomes highly susceptible to chemical change. The nature of the directive influences of the enzyme is such that only one type of chemical change is induced in the susceptible group of the substrate; this is the basis of enzyme specificity. We shall consider directive influences in greater detail later in this chapter.

When the enzyme interacts with its appropriate substrate, both may undergo some kind of structural deformation. Some proteins appear to have a certain degree of plasticity, and the processes leading up to, and including, the actual chemical change in the substrate molecule may involve changes in shape and contour of the protein. The enzyme is not always a static macromolecule; rather, it may puff and heave in the course of catalysis. This puffing and heaving may involve a sequential opening and closing of certain sites. If the enzyme protein has a series of active groups which come into play in sequence, this sequential process could be implemented by sequential changes in the conformation of the protein.

SPECIFICITY OF ENZYMES

There is some variation among different enzymes with respect to specificity. Some, like L-malic dehydrogenase, catalyze the oxidation, or dehydrogenation, of only one substance, namely L-malic acid; even the D-isomer of malic acid is not attacked. Others, like alcohol dehydrogenase, catalyze the oxidation of almost any organic compound which contains a primary alcohol group (R—OH). Alcohol dehydrogenase is specific for the —OH group that undergoes oxidation and is largely indifferent to the nature of the R chain. which could be ethyl, propyl, benzyl, or what have you. In general, enzymes attack only one of the two optical isomers of a given substrate (D- and L-forms). In cases of geometric isomers (*cis* and *trans* forms, Figure 4.1), the same discrimination by enzymes is usually shown. Thus, fumarase catalyzes the addition of water at the double bond of fumaric acid, the *trans* isomer, but not at the double bond of maleic acid, the *cis* isomer.

In most cases each molecule of enzyme takes on one molecule of substrate at a time, catalyzes the appropriate chemical reaction, releases the product, and then starts all over again on the next molecule of substrate. This process is repeated billions of times

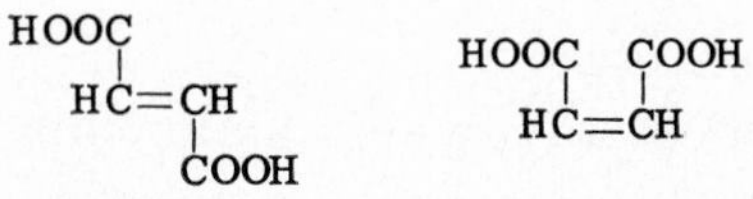

Maleic acid *trans* **form** — **Fumaric acid** *cis* **form**

Fig. 4.1. Geometrical isomers—*trans*-maleic acid and *cis*-fumaric acid. Fumarase catalyzes the hydration of fumaric acid only. Succinic dehydrogenase catalyzes the oxidation of succinic to fumaric acid only.

until either the supply of substrate is exhausted or the molecule of enzyme becomes damaged or degraded. Enzymes have a limited life span in the cell, which may vary from days to years. Eventually, however, they are degraded by proteolytic enzymes, and the component amino acids may be reused for synthesis of other protein molecules.

Effect of Temperature and Hydrogen Ion Concentration

In general, the rate of an enzymic reaction increases as the temperature is raised. There is, however, a practical limit to this increase. Above 40–50° C the enzyme may become unstable; the rate of its destruction then counterbalances the increased activity. This is the well-known "heat denaturation" of protein, a form of which is observed in the coagulation of egg white. Denaturation of an enzyme does not necessarily lead to the formation of a water-insoluble coagulum, but in some cases the two go hand in hand.

Usually enzymes are active only within a limited range of pH. Above or below this critical range they may be not only inactivated but damaged permanently, unable to regain activity even when optimal conditions are restored. For catalysis to take place both the enzyme and the substrate have to be in a proper form; the proper form may obtain only within a limited range of hydrogen ion concentration.* In general, the optimal hydrogen ion concentration and temperature for an enzyme are close to those in the living cell, but there are many exceptions.

Amount of Enzyme per Cell

The amounts of the individual enzymes found in each cell are variable. Enzymes that are intimately connected with main-line metabolic sequences—sets of chemical processes which go on all the time, and at a substantial rate—are usually present in relatively high concentration, whereas enzymes that implement metabolic sequences of secondary importance or of inconstant need are usually present in relatively low concentration. Since many main-line sequences involve constant molecular proportions of the various enzymes that implement the sequence, the particular sets of enzymes that carry out these sequences are always present at the same concentration levels, or multiples thereof (1 : 1, 1 : 2, etc.). Any main-line enzyme may number in the thousands of molecules per cell, whereas an enzyme outside the mainstream of metabolism may number less than one hundred. The smaller the size of the cell, the smaller the number of molecules of a given enzyme to be expected in that cell.

Rate of Enzyme Reactions

The rate of catalysis may be measured by the number of catalytic cycles which one molecule of an enzyme undergoes per unit of time

---

* Some enzymic reactions may require electrostatic interaction between enzyme and substrate. For this kind of interaction there may be a sharp pH-dependence curve. The optimal pH would be the point of maximal electrostatic differential between enzyme and substrate.

under specified conditions, each catalytic cycle representing the completion of the set of operations that lead to the transformation of one molecule of substrate into product. Some enzymes may undergo less than one hundred such cycles per minute at 38°C, whereas other enzymes may undergo more than one million cycles per minute. The cycling speed, or *turnover,* of an enzyme is determined, among other things, by the nature of the reaction catalyzed. A reaction involving the rearrangement or decomposition of a relatively small molecule, such as the decomposition of hydrogen peroxide to water and oxygen, can be catalyzed very rapidly. The greater the size and complexity of the substrate molecule, the slower the catalytic cycle is likely to be. The more species of substrate molecules participating in an integrated enzymic sequence, the slower the reaction is likely to be. These broad generalizations are not without exceptions.

SPECIES DIFFERENCES AMONG ENZYMES

In general, enzymes which catalyze the same reaction by similar mechanisms have much the same properties, regardless of origin, whether animal, plant, or microbial. However, there are distinctive chemical signs characteristic of the source of the enzyme. There are some enzymes which are chemically identical in a given species, regardless of the cell of origin, and others which are different and characteristic of the cell from which derived. Still other enzymes may be found in several forms within the same cell.

STRUCTURE OF THE ENZYME

The structure of the enzyme protein often depends on a delicate balance of factors that may be difficult to define and to control experimentally. That is why exact control of temperature, salt concentration, and hydrogen ion concentration is essential when such enzymes are studied outside the cell. Gross alterations in the structure of an enzyme may affect the "fit" between enzyme and substrate, and thus may lead to loss of activity. By appropriate laboratory methods it is possible to isolate many of the known enzymes of the cell and to separate any one enzyme more or less completely from the rest. One of the most difficult questions to evaluate is the extent of change in the structure and properties of an enzyme induced by, or consequent to, the rupture of the cell and the isolation procedure. There are many methods available for separating individual proteins from mixtures and bringing them to the state of pure compounds, but it is an exceedingly difficult task to establish unequivocally that the isolated enzyme has properties identical with those of the same enzyme in its natural setting within the cell.

SUBUNIT STRUCTURE OF ENZYMES

Enzymes are often found to be composites of two or more sub-units. The activity of the enzyme may depend upon the way in which the subunits are linked together. If the subunits can exist in more than one form, then a set of similar, but not identical, forms of the same enzyme (isoenzymes) may exist. For example, if one of the two subunits can exist in forms α and α', and the other in forms β and β', the active enzyme could be $\alpha\beta$, $\alpha'\beta$, $\alpha\beta'$, or $\alpha'\beta'$. Some composite enzymes have the active group spread over two non-identical subunits (cf. Figure 4.2). Thus, neither subunit alone will show the characteristic activity of the composite enzyme.

The concept of the unit of enzymic action needs some clarifying

One active group in
one protein subunit

One active group distributed
over two protein subunits

Fig. 4.2. The localization of the active group within a single protein subunit of an enzyme vs. the distribution of the active group over two protein subunits of an enzyme.

when the enzyme is a composite of two or more protein subunits. In some instances, the subunits are identical copies, each with a catalytic site. β-Galactosidase is an enzyme of this kind, with four identical subunits. Whether or not the component subunits are enzymically active individually, an enzyme of this type is defined as the polymeric unit. The polymeric nature of such enzymes opens up new possibilities for control of activity; it may be only in the polymeric form that the enzyme can be properly inhibited or activated, or can display the proper specificity for its function *in vivo*.

In other instances, the subunits are nonidentical. If each of the subunits is inactive in monomeric form, then there is no problem in defining what the enzyme is—it is the composite molecule, since only the composite can function as an enzyme. However, when each of the monomeric subunits has its own enzymic activity, then one must be careful in defining the enzyme according to the activity in question—the activity of one of the subunits or the activity of the composite enzyme. Tryptophan synthetase, for instance, is an enzyme built up of two dissimilar protein molecules bonded together. In this case, each of the two molecular parts does have an intrinsic enzymic activity, but only the two linked together in unique fashion show tryptophan synthetase activity. The unit of tryptophan synthetase is clearly the composite molecule made up of the two dissimilar component enzymes. In later chapters we shall discuss composite enzymes in which the number of participating subunits is still larger. These are more properly called *enzyme complexes,* since they are composed of several whole enzymes. One of the interesting features of such complexes is that some of their properties depend on the bonding together of the entire set of enzymes according to a unique structural pattern.

ENZYMES AND MEMBRANES

Many of the enzymes of the cell are built into the fabric of membrane systems. When the cell, ruptured by experimental means, is disintegrated, these enzymes may be torn from their structural setting. In the form isolated, an enzyme of this sort may retain some, but not all, of its original properties. This is not to say that the isolated enzyme is an artifact. The mechanism of the catalysis is not necessarily modified in any important respect by the isolation procedure, but some secondary features may, indeed, be modified or obliterated—features, for example, that involve the kinetics of the reaction or the control of the enzyme by regulators. Subtle modifications of these kinds must be borne in mind when extrapolating from the properties of isolated enzymes to those of their counterparts in intact cells.

CONTROL OF ENZYMES

In a later chapter we shall be exploring the mechanisms by which enzymic action can be regulated and controlled in the cell. Some of these control features can be built directly into the protein molecule(s) of the enzyme. Imagine an enzyme that converts substrate A into product B. This enzyme may be catalytically inactive unless exposed to a regulator molecule which we shall call X. When the enzymic protein comes into contact with X it may undergo rearrangement whereby the catalytic site becomes available to the substrate. This is one type of regulatory device by which the action of an enzyme can be controlled by a substance which itself does not undergo chemical change. The regulating molecule transforms the enzyme from a conformation that is wrong for catalysis into one that is right. An inhibitor of the enzyme might be a molecule which binds to the catalytic site and thereby simply blocks its accessibility to substrate. Alternatively, the inhibitor may interact with some other site on the enzyme and thereby distort the conformation of the catalytic site sufficiently to render it nonfunctional.

Another way to visualize the activation and inhibition of enzymes is as follows. Suppose that there are two forms of the enzyme, the active and inactive forms, and these two forms are in equilibrium with one another—that is, at any moment there is some of the enzyme in each form. An activator could then be any molecule that would stabilize only the active form and thereby pull the equilibrium toward that form. An inhibitor could be any molecule that would stabilize only the inactive form and thereby pull the equilibrium in the other direction.

We shall illustrate several features of the control problem by discussing some of the regulatory mechanisms involved in the action
of muscle phosphorylase. The breakdown of glycogen in animal
tissues is mediated by an enzyme, phosphorylase, which catalyzes
the following reversible phosphorylytic reaction.

Polyglucose (glycogen) $+ n$ orthosphosphate $\rightleftharpoons n$ glucose 1-phosphate

Five different control features have been built into the phosphorylase
system. Naturally, the question arises: Why this multiplicity of
controls? Nature apparently relies on the strategy of multiple controls whenever a process must be delicately maintained. Phosphorylase is the first known instance in which multiple controls
have been discovered to operate at the level of a single enzyme.

Most of our knowledge about phosphorylase is derived from
studies on the enzyme isolated from muscle tissue; this enzyme
occurs in two forms, a and b. The b-form is a dimer; the a-form
is a tetramer (the monomeric subunit has a molecular weight of
125,000). The tetrameric a-form is fully active in the absence of
any activating compound; the dimeric b-form is totally inactive
per se, but becomes fully active in the presence of adenosine
monophosphate (see Figure 4.3). The tetrameric form can be con-

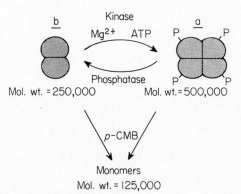

Molecular forms of muscle phosphorylase

Fig. 4.3. Interconversion of phosphorylases a and b. In the diagram, p-CMB
represents *para*-chlormercuribenzoate and —P represents a phosphate ester of a seryl
group in the protein. Figure kindly provided by Dr. Edmund H. Fischer of the
Department of Biochemistry, University of Washington in Seattle.

verted into the dimeric form by an enzyme known as phosphorylase
a phosphatase. Concomitant with this conversion, four molecules
of inorganic phosphate are released per molecule of tetramer. The
dimeric form can be converted back to the tetrameric form by an
enzyme known as phosphorylase *b* kinase, in the presence of ATP
and Mg^{2+}. During this conversion four molecules of phosphate are
introduced into the tetrameric enzyme—one molecule for each of
the four subunits that eventually make up the tetramer (ATP serves
as the phosphorylating agent in this reaction). Thus, two enzymes
(a specific kinase and a specific phosphatase) and one small molecule (four molecules of ATP in presence of Mg^{2+}) regulate the
form in which muscle phosphorylase will exist; in turn, this form
determines whether the enzyme will be highly active or essentially
inactive. As mentioned above, the dimeric form of muscle phosphorylase becomes fully active in presence of AMP. This activating effect is believed to be a consequence of an AMP-induced
rearrangement of the subunits of phosphorylase *b*. The AMP has
no such effect on phosphorylase *a*.

The *a* form of phosphorylase contains four residues of pyridoxal
phosphate, the *b* form, two residues (in both forms there is one
residue of pyridoxal phosphate per unit with a molecular weight
of 125,000). No catalytic function for pyridoxal phosphate has yet
been discovered in the reaction catalyzed by phosphorylase. The
studies of E. H. Fischer and E. G. Krebs strongly suggest that
pyridoxal phosphate plays an important role in determining the
overall conformation of the protein. When pyridoxal phosphate is
removed from the enzyme by appropriate means, the apoprotein
tends to polymerize to the tetramer whereas the corresponding enzyme with its full complement of pyridoxal phosphate does not
show this tendency to polymerize. It is of interest that low
temperature (0°–4°C) favors polymerization; at 38°C, the mo-
nomer is the preferred form even for the pyridoxal phosphate-free
apoenzyme.

Figure 4.4 points up two key features of phosphorylase: (1) the
multiplicity of sites that affect enzymic activity and (2) the influence of events at one site on the properties of neighboring
sites. Some of these intersite interactions are summarized in tabular

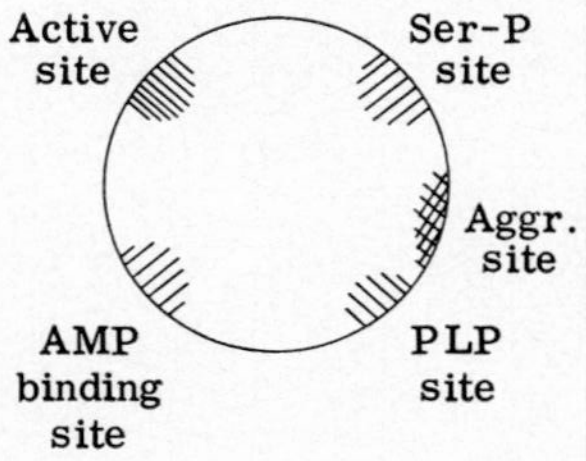

Additions and Their Effects	Interactions
Adenosine 5-phosphate Active site AMP ↗→ P-Ser site ↘ Aggregation site	Activates in absence of seryl phosphate Prevents attack by phosphorylase phosphatase and by trypsin Favors aggregation
Reagents that phosphorylate the serine group adjacent to the active group Active site P-Ser ↗→ AMP site ↘ Aggregation site	Activates in absence of AMP Increases 20 X affinity for AMP Dimer ⟶ Tetramer

Active site Ser-P site Aggr. site PLP site AMP binding site

Fig. 4.4. The influence of the addition of adenosine 5-phosphate and of reagents for phosphorylating the reactive seryl group on the properties of phosphorylase. In the diagram, P-Ser represents phosphoryl serine; PLP represents pyridoxyl phosphate. The arrows in the left-hand boxes in the Table denote the influence exerted by AMP or seryl phosphate on the various sites indicated. Figure kindly provided by Dr. Edmund H. Fischer of the Department of Biochemistry, University of Washington in Seattle.

form in the figure. The active site of an enzyme is, of course, the only site directly concerned in the catalytic process, but this critical site can be profoundly influenced by changes introduced at neighboring sites which do not participate in the catalytic process. A site which controls conformation or polymerization can indirectly control enzymic activity.

Finally, we must consider the requirements for the synthesis of glycogen from glucose 1-phosphate.* The preferred pathway for synthesis of glycogen in animal cells generally is by way of uridine diphosphoglucose (UDPG), rather than glucose 1-phosphate.† The preference reflects the fact that the direct conversion of glucose 1-phosphate to glycogen has an unfavorable equilibrium, whereas the equilibrium for the conversion of UDPG to glycogen is highly favorable. However, limited participation of muscle phosphorylase in glycogen synthesis cannot be excluded. Muscle phosphorylase *does not* catalyze the synthesis of glycogen from glucose 1-phosphate (that is, the reverse of the equation on page 68) in the absence of glycogen. The synthesis requires the presence of a polyglucose molecule, preferably one containing multiple branch points. The branch points *per se* are not the sites of the action of phosphorylase; rather, it is the terminal glucose residues of the many chains to which additional glucose units are added. The greater the degree of branching in the "primer," the more effective the priming properties because of the greater number of terminal acceptor residues. In this way, the presence or absence of primer can determine whether glycogen synthesis will take place. Also, the efficiency of priming is ultimately determined by yet another enzyme (the branching enzyme) which introduces the branch points into the polyglucose molecule. Thus, the necessities for priming the synthesis of glycogen permit the operation of yet another set of controls.

EXTRACELLULAR ENZYMES

Most of the enzymes of the body are present inside the cell and never leave as such. However, in certain cases special enzymes

---

* Glucose 1-phosphate + G—G—G . . . $\rightleftarrows$ G—G—G—G . . . + P$_i$

† Glucose 1-phosphate + uridine triphosphate (UTP) $\rightleftharpoons$ UDPG + pyrophosphate
UDPG + G—G—G . . . $\rightarrow$ G—G—G—G . . . + UDP

are secreted by cells. For instance, digestive enzymes are secreted into the gastrointestinal tract by the pancreas and the salivary glands. These are extracellular, "one-shot" enzymes, since they are lost to the body when their job is completed. Microorganisms also secrete enzymes into the medium in which they grow; usually such secreted enzymes have degradative activities.

Enzymes in Different Types of Cells

No one cell contains all of the known enzymes, but all cells contain essentially the same set of basic enzymes. The enzymes that implement the processes that are common to all cells (such as protein synthesis, synthesis of RNA and DNA, and glycolysis) will of course be present in all cells. The enzymes that are concerned with the function of specialized cells may be found exclusively in such cells. Also highly variable is the amount of an enzyme in different cells. Some cells may produce an enormous amount of a particular enzyme, whereas the same enzyme may be found only in trace amounts in another cell. There is, in fact, a pattern characteristic of any cell for the amounts and relative proportions of different enzymes. In microorganisms and in some animal cells, synthesis of enzymes may be induced by some triggering molecule. These inducible enzymes will be found in variable amounts depending upon the level of induction (see Chapter 13).

Reversibility of Enzymic Reactions

The great majority of enzyme-catalyzed reactions are reversible. Thus, fumarase catalyzes both the hydration of fumarate to malate and the dehydration of malate to fumarate.

$$\text{Fumarate} + H_2O \rightleftharpoons \text{malate}$$

The double arrows pointing in opposite directions signify this reversibility. There are, nevertheless, many enzymic reactions that are not reversible to any appreciable extent. For example, proteolytic enzymes can break down proteins, but cannot resynthesize a significant amount of protein from the fragmentation products. Amylase breaks down starch to smaller sugar units, but it cannot resynthesize starch from such units. In general, complex molecules are not synthesized to an appreciable extent by the reversal of the method of enzymic degradation. Thus, proteins, polysaccharides, nucleic acids, and lipids are synthesized by one set of reactions and broken down by a completely different set. The fact that there are two different pathways, one for breakdown and one for synthesis, does not necessarily mean that the pathway for breakdown is completely irreversible. Rather, the apparent irreversibility is due to the fact that the equilibrium for the degradative reaction strongly favors the formation of breakdown products.

Classification of Enzymes

The following five categories encompass virtually all the chemical reactions catalyzed by enzymes: (1) *hydrolysis*—breaking a bond with the addition of the elements of water, and separation into two molecules (phosphorolysis is an analogous process involving the addition of the elements of phosphoric acid instead of water); (2) *group transfer*—transfer of an integrated group of atoms from one molecule (donor) to another molecule (acceptor); (3) *oxidation and reduction*—transfer of one or more electrons, or hydrogen atoms (electron + proton), from one molecule (the molecule undergoing oxidation) to another molecule (the molecule undergoing reduction); (4) *isomerization*—rearrangement of the position of some atom, or group of atoms, within a molecule; and (5) *condensation*—linking, by covalent bonds, of two molecules (like or unlike) to form a new molecule.* Tables 4.1 through 4.5 provide examples of enzymic processes which fall within each category. The points at which the substrates are modified are indicated in the case of carbohydrases. It should be pointed out that the classification of enzymes into these five categories is not intended to be all inclusive; it is based merely on convenience and is quite arbitrary in the sense that, at the mechanistic level, the distinction among the different categories becomes blurred, or may even disappear. Eventually, a rational classification of enzymes may

---

* The reverse of condensation would entail the breaking of a carbon-carbon bond, as, for example, in decarboxylation.

TABLE 4.1

Representative Hydrolytic Enzymes

Class of Enzyme	Substrate	Bond attacked	Equation for reaction[a]
Proteases	Proteins, polypeptides, peptides	Peptide	$\bar{R}\underset{\underset{O}{\Vert}}{C}\wr NH-CH_2R + H_2O \longrightarrow \bar{R}COOH + NH_2CH_2R$
Carbohydrases	Polysaccharides, disaccharides	Glycoside	$\bar{R}\underset{H}{\overset{\vert}{C}}\wr O\wr\underset{H}{\overset{\vert}{C}}R + H_2O \longrightarrow \bar{R}\underset{H}{\overset{\vert}{C}}OH + HO\underset{H}{\overset{\vert}{C}}R$
Lipases	Neutral lipids, phospholipids	Ester	$\bar{R}\underset{\underset{O}{\Vert}}{C}\wr O-CH_2R + H_2O \longrightarrow \bar{R}COOH + HOCH_2R$
Ribonucleases	Ribonucleic acid	Ester	$\bar{R}-O-\underset{\underset{OH}{\vert}}{\overset{\overset{O}{\Vert}}{P}}\wr OR + H_2O \longrightarrow \bar{R}O-\underset{\underset{OH}{\vert}}{\overset{\overset{O}{\Vert}}{P}}-OH + HOR$
Phosphatases	Phosphate esters	Ester	$\bar{R}-O\wr\underset{\underset{OH}{\vert}}{\overset{\overset{O}{\Vert}}{P}}-OH + H_2O \longrightarrow \bar{R}OH + HO-\underset{\underset{OH}{\vert}}{\overset{\overset{O}{\Vert}}{P}}-OH$

[a]The notation $\wr$ represents the fracture point.

TABLE 4.2

Group Transferring Enzymes

Class of enzyme	Group transferred	Equation for reaction
Phosphotransferases	Phosphate	$\bar{R}O\wr\underset{\underset{OH}{\vert}}{\overset{\overset{O}{\Vert}}{P}}-OH + HOR \longrightarrow \bar{R}OH + HO-\underset{\underset{OH}{\vert}}{\overset{\overset{O}{\Vert}}{P}}-OR$
Aminotransferases	Amino	$\bar{R}\underset{\underset{H}{\vert}}{C}=O + NH_2CH_2R \longrightarrow \bar{R}CH_2NH_2 + O=\underset{\underset{H}{\vert}}{C}R$
Sulfatetransferases	Sulfate	$\bar{R}-\underset{\underset{OH}{\vert}}{\overset{\overset{O}{\Vert}}{P}}-O\wr\underset{\underset{O}{\Vert}}{\overset{\overset{O}{\Vert}}{S}}-OH + HOR \longrightarrow \bar{R}-\underset{\underset{OH}{\vert}}{\overset{\overset{O}{\Vert}}{P}}-OH + HO-\underset{\underset{O}{\Vert}}{\overset{\overset{O}{\Vert}}{S}}-OR$
Acyltransferases	Acetyl, Succinyl, etc.	$\bar{R}-S\wr\underset{\underset{O}{\Vert}}{C}CH_3 + HSR \longrightarrow \bar{R}SH + CH_3\underset{\underset{O}{\Vert}}{C}-S-R$

be anticipated—one that is based on the characteristic molecular mechanisms of enzymic catalysis; such a classification would cut across the boundaries of the arbitrary systems now used.

The very multiplicity of enzymic processes might appear to exclude any general theory of catalysis. Nevertheless, it is now possible to recognize certain principles that apply with equal force to all enzymic processes. Admittedly, there are major mechanistic

TABLE 4.3

Dehydrogenases and Cytochrome Oxidase

Enzyme	Type of oxidation	Formulation
Succinic dehydrogenase	Double bond formation	$COOHCH_2CH_2COOH \longrightarrow COOHCH{=}CHCOOH$ Loss of two hydrogen atoms
Alcohol dehydrogenase	Alcohol to aldehyde	$CH_3CH_2OH \longrightarrow CH_3C\begin{smallmatrix}O\\H\end{smallmatrix}$ Loss of two hydrogen atoms
Aldehyde dehydrogenase	Aldehyde to acid	$CH_3C\begin{smallmatrix}O\\H\end{smallmatrix} \longrightarrow CH_3COOH$ Loss of two hydrogen atoms from the hydrated aldehyde
Cytochrome oxidase	Ferrous to ferric porphyrin	$R\text{-}Fe^{2+} \longrightarrow R\text{-}Fe^{3+}$ $[R\text{-}Fe]$ = heme; $[R\text{-}]$ = porphyrin ring Loss of one electron
DPNH dehydrogenase	Dihydro-pyridine to pyridine ring	$R{-}N \diagup \bigcirc \diagup \longrightarrow R{-}N^+ \diagup \bigcirc \diagup$ Loss of two electrons and one proton (or one hydrion)

differences among enzymes of various types, but, as one penetrates deeply into the details of enzymic processes, the similarities overshadow these differences. It is to the similarities and the generalities that we shall direct our attention. All chemical reactions—at least of the kind which concerns us in living systems—involve the interplay of the valence electrons occurring in one or more substrate molecules. Be it group transfer or hydrolysis, oxidation or isomeri-

TABLE 4.4

Isomerases

Enzyme	Group isomerized	Alternative positions of group	Formulation
Hexosephosphate isomerase	Carbonyl	C-1 and C-2	$\overset{6}{C}-\overset{5}{C}-\overset{4}{C}-\overset{3}{C}-\overset{2}{C}-\overset{1}{C}=O$ (top) ⇅ $-C-C-C-C-C-C$ with O below C
Formyltetra-hydrofolate isomerase	Formyl	N-5 and N-10	$N^5 \quad ^{10}N^+ \rightleftharpoons {}^+N^5 \quad ^{10}N$ / HOC H H H H CHO
Enoyl hydrase[a]	Double bond	3,4 versus 2,3	$R\overset{4}{C}H=\overset{3}{C}H-\overset{2}{C}H_2-CO\cdots$ ⇅ $RCH_2-CH=CH-CO\cdots$
Aconitase[b]	Hydroxyl and hydrogen	C-2 and C-3	CH_2COOH CH_2COOH / $HO\overset{}{C}HCOOH \rightleftharpoons {}^2 CH_2COOH$ / $^3 CH_2COOH$ $HOCHCOOH$ / Citric acid Isocitric acid

[a] The elements of water add across the double bond at 3,4 and then the elements of water are eliminated from 2,3.

[b] The shift in the position of the –OH group is achieved by a cycle of dehydration and rehydration with reversal of the positions of the –OH and –H groups.

TABLE 4.5

Enzymes That Catalyze Condensations Involving the Formation of Carbon–Carbon Bonds

Enzyme	Condensing molecules	Formulation
Acetyl-CoA carboxylase	CO_2 + acetyl-CoA	$CO_2 + CH_3CO\overline{SCoA}$ $\longrightarrow HOOCCH_2CO\overline{SCoA}$
Thiolase	Acetyl-CoA + acetyl-CoA	$CH_3CO\overline{SCoA} + CH_3CO\overline{SCoA}$ $\longrightarrow CH_3COCH_2CO\overline{SCoA} + \overline{CoASH}$
Carbonic anhydrase	Carbon dioxide + water	$CO_2 + H_2O \rightleftharpoons H_2CO_3$
Aldolase	Dihydroxyacetone ℗ + glyceraldehyde ℗ ℗ = Phosphate	$HOCH_2COCH_2O℗ + ℗OCH_2CHOHCHO$ $\longrightarrow ℗OCH_2CHOHCHOHCHOHC CH_2O℗$ with O below

zation, the basic chemical problem is much the same—how to facilitate the movement of a valence electron from a certain atom of one molecule to an atom of another molecule.

Mechanism of Enzymic Catalysis

Through a detailed study of α-chymotrypsin, one of the proteolytic enzymes secreted into the intestinal tract by specialized cells of the pancreas, Myron L. Bender and his colleagues have attempted to describe what they aptly call "the anatomy of an enzymatic catalysis." They dissected out, one by one, the various factors that contribute to the catalytic properties of α-chymotrypsin. The overall catalytic efficiency of α-chymotrypsin can be accurately calculated by summing the contributions made by each of the structures or processes relevant to the catalysis. We shall draw heavily from Bender's interpretation of the *modus operandi* of α-chymotrypsin—not that this particular enzyme has special significance but, rather, because many of the features of enzymic catalyses in general closely follow those of the α-chymotrypsin model.

The Concept of Enzyme Fit

The list of requirements for efficient catalysis that are met by an enzyme, such as α-chymotrypsin, includes a very large number of items, all of which may be classified within three categories: (1) the fit of enzyme to substrate; (2) the thermodynamic consequences of close fit; and 3) the catalytic advantages derivable from close fit. The items in the first two categories are likely to be much the same for all enzymes. The third category will contain items not only of universal applicability but also of specific applicability to enzymes that catalyze particular classes of chemical reactions.

The notion of "fit" encompasses more than the kind of complementarity implicit in the close nesting of a finger in a snug glove. In addition to spatial or geometric fit, there has to be electrostatic complementarity because electrostatic repulsion between charged groups of the same sign can prevent close nesting of otherwise complementary surfaces. "Electrical fit" requires the pairing of oppositely charged groups in substrate and enzyme, respectively. A third kind of fit may be characterized by the phrase "the exact positioning of catalytic elements in the enzyme relative to the substrate." For example, an electron-withdrawing group, or a proton-donor group, in the enzyme must impinge upon one highly localized region of the substrate. The fit must lie within close tolerances, because the catalytic effect is inversely proportional to the *square* of the distance intervening between the reacting groups.

According to one likely model for α-chymotrypsin, four amino acid residues in the protein must be precisely positioned with respect to the substrate molecule, and also with respect to one another. These are two histidine residues, one serine residue, and one chain-terminal isoleucine residue. The imperative of positioning of those residues with specific catalytic function is one of the major factors which underlie the importance of enzyme conformation. The folding of the peptide chains to form the catalytically active enzyme molecule has to be sufficiently precise to meet these exacting spatial requirements. It is of interest to note that the above-mentioned isoleucine residue, which carries a positive charge by virtue of its chain-terminal position, plays a key role in the determination of the critical conformation of α-chymotrypsin. When this group is acetylated, catalytic activity is lost probably in consequence of improper conformation.

Finally, we have to introduce into this discussion of fit the notion of long-range fit, in contradistinction to the phenomenon of short-range fit implicit in the three categories discussed above. The chemical properties of the substrate molecule, once it is anchored to the active site of the enzyme, are significantly influenced by the electrostatic environment in the reaches of the enzyme beyond the active site. This environment, provided by the enzyme as a whole, determines which particular substrate can approach and penetrate into the active site; in that sense it helps in determining specificity. There are several enzymes known to have the same active site as α-chymotrypsin; each enzyme in this set has a different specificity. Thus, we may infer that the portion of the protein which does not include the specific active site is an eventual determinant of specificity.

ATOMIC MODEL OF α-CHYMOTRYPSIN

In our discussion thus far of the fitting of substrate to enzyme we have considered the relevant geometric, electrostatic, and positional factors that enter the picture only in general terms. A great deal of insight has been achieved into the fine details of enzyme-substrate fit by the elucidation of the complete amino acid sequence of α-chymotrypsin by Hans Neurath and his colleagues. From this known sequence, Myron Bender and his colleagues have constructed an atomic model of the enzyme which makes it possible to visualize the details of how the catalysis might proceed. Until the precise three-dimensional conformation of the enzyme has been determined by X-ray crystallography, such a model must be considered a hypothetical structure. However, there is a great deal to be learned from such a model since it is based upon all the biochemical facts known about the protein molecule. We shall now turn to a consideration of the Bender model of α-chymotrypsin, (Figure 4.5).

Suitable experimental substrates for α-chymotrypsin (an ester of tryptophan would serve well) are generally characterized by having a nonpolar aromatic side chain (in this case the tryptophan ring) and a polar ester group.* The aromatic sector of the substrate molecule fits into a hole within the enzyme molecule. This hole is formed by a disulfide link between two cysteine residues, separated from one another by fifteen amino acids. The interior of this cyclical structure has a hydrophobic character. Thus, the aromatic sector of the substrate may be firmly anchored to the protein by hydrophobic bonding to the hydrophobic side chains of the amino acid residues abutting into the hole. The polar ester group of the substrate rests on the exterior surface of the cyclical doughnut-like structure (cf. Figure 4.5).

The hydrophobic hole in chymotrypsin is a structural feature specific for the bimodal substrate. If, for instance, the substrate does not have a hydrophobic sector, there will probably be no

---

* Strictly speaking, the true substrate of α-chymotrypsin is a peptide rather than an ester. We are referring to the model esters that mimic the natural peptide groups in proteins which are attacked by α-chymotrypsin.

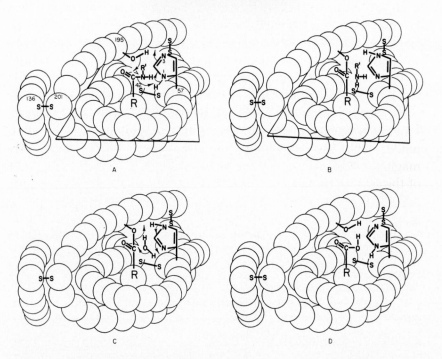

Fig. 4.5. A bead model of α-chymotrypsin constructed on the basis of the amino acid sequence as determined by H. Neurath and B. S. Hartley. In front of the white card are seen both components of the active site—the cycle, extending from cysteine 42 to cysteine 58 (these two residues are linked by an —S—S— bond), and the strand, extending from cysteine 191 to cysteine 201. Serine 195 (↓) is above and close to histidine 57 (↑).

A: This is only a sector of the bead model shown above. The relative position of the white card to the active site is shown for purposes of reference. The hydrophobic R group of the substrate is imbedded in the hydrophobic environment of the hole formed by the bonding of cysteine 42 to cysteine 58. The nearly contiguous serine hydroxyl and imidazole histidine are in position to react in a concerted fash-

provision in the structure of the enzyme for a hydrophobic hole within a cyclical structure. There will, however, have to be provision for the bonding of the polar substrate to an appropriately charged (or polar) active site in the enzyme.

FORMATION OF A COVALENT BOND

The fitting of substrate to enzyme is only the prologue to the formation of covalent bonding between the two reactants. Exact fit does not by itself compel covalent bonding, but it makes covalent bonding thermodynamically much more likely to occur. At the very least, we can say that exact fit *facilitates* the formation of a covalent bond between enzyme and substrate; when this bond is established, the battle is largely over.

When two molecules approach one another, the inherent "wriggling" (vibration) of all the rotating groups in each molecule imposes a barrier to interaction. If this wriggling could be eliminated, the barrier would be correspondingly reduced. The magnitude of the barrier can be quantitatively evaluated in terms of the thermodynamic parameter called entropy.* A wriggling mole-

---

ion with the peptide bond of the substrate. A new bond is formed between the oxygen of serine and the carbonyl group of the peptide bond; concomitantly the proton of the serine hydroxyl group is transferred to one of the imidazole nitrogens of histidine; the carbon-nitrogen bond of the peptide is cleaved, and the proton from the imidazole is transferred to the nitrogen atom of the liberated amino terminal group of the substrate (R'-NH_2).

B: The serine ester of the substrate and the liberated R'-NH_2. Note that the histidine imidazole ring is now in the tautomeric form in which the hydrogen is bonded to the nitrogen in position 3.

C: A water molecule, which now fills the position previously occupied by R'-NH_2, reacts with the serine ester to form an oxygen-carbon bond, and the serine ester bond is thereby cleaved. Simultaneously, the hydrogen on the nitrogen atom in position 3 of the imidazole ring is shifted to reestablish the hydroxyl group of serine. Also, a hydrogen atom from water becomes linked to the nitrogen at position 1 of the imidazole ring of histidine.

D: The carboxyl terminal portion of the substrate (RCOOH), shown in the diagram, is now free to leave. Note that the active site is restored to the original state in which serine has a free hydroxyl group, and the imidazole ring is in the proper tautomeric form.

* Entropy may be looked upon as a measure of the disorder in a system.

cule is, in the thermodynamic sense, a disordered system. To reduce wriggling of the groups in the molecule, energy has to be
put into the system, which then becomes more ordered. We shall
return to this point again.

THE GROUND AND TRANSITION STATE

In any chemical reaction the difference in energy content (in
respect to conformation) between the ground state of the molecules (just prior to the chemical reaction) and the transition state
(at the moment of interaction) is a crucial determinant of the
tendency to react. If the difference in energy content between
ground state and transition state is large, the tendency to interact
is small by virtue of this energy barrier. If, however, the energy
contents of the ground state and the transition state are nearly
identical, the energy barrier to interaction is all but eliminated.
Close fit of enzyme and substrate, in respect both to the geometry
of the nesting species and to the positioning of the catalytic
elements, ensures the near identity of the energy contents of the
ground and transition states. Given such near identity, the smooth
course of the catalysis is inexorable.

THERMODYNAMIC ADVANTAGES OF FIT

Let us now consider in more detail the thermodynamic advantages of exact fit for a substrate molecule, four of whose bonds
must be fixed in position before reaction can take place. Each of
the bonds is capable of rotation about an axis. The fixing of each
bond involves a significant entropy factor (about six entropy units
per bond). Thus, the fully aligned substrate-enzyme complex has
a thermodynamic advantage of twenty-four entropy units as compared to a nonaligned substrate molecule, none of whose bonds
is fixed by the enzyme. Interaction of the enzyme with the substrate
molecule, leading to the fixing of the groups in the substrate molecule, helps to reduce the activation barrier of the reaction. When
all the groups involved in the interaction of substrate and enzyme
are fixed in position by alignment, the energy barrier is reduced
essentially to zero. Thus, the fit of enzyme to substrate minimizes,
or eliminates, the entropy barrier to subsequent chemical reaction,

and this is accomplished, in part, by suppressing the wriggling of all reacting groups. The spatial constraints of the enzyme-substrate complex effectively prevent oscillatory fluctuations. The perfect, or specific, substrate is the maximally constrained and perfectly fitting molecule; a poor substrate is a marginally constrained and imperfectly fitting molecule. An interesting extension of this concept is that the perfect inhibitor would be one that fits as well as the perfect substrate but never leaves the enzyme because it undergoes no chemical change.

INTERMOLECULAR VERSUS INTRAMOLECULAR INTERACTIONS

As soon as a covalent bond is formed between enzyme and substrate the problem shifts from intermolecular interactions to intramolecular reactions. This transition has profound chemical repercussions. It is as if the concentration of enzyme became fantastically high, say 10 M, as compared to an actual concentration of 0.001 M or less. The effective concentration of enzyme is thus increased by a factor of ten thousand or more once a covalent bond with the substrate is formed. The dependence of the thermodynamic parameters on the concentration of reactants means that the transition to the intramolecular interaction carries a major thermodynamic advantage.

MULTISTEP CATALYSIS IN RELATION TO ACTIVATION ENERGY

In any chemical reaction a large activation energy is a powerful deterrent, regardless of how much free energy is released in the overall process. The enzyme solves this activation problem in a rather interesting fashion. The overall enzymic process is broken down into a series of component processes, each of which has a relatively small activation energy. Since the amount of activation energy to be paid in, before the free energy dividend is received, decreases with each subdivision of the overall process, a multistep catalysis has considerable kinetic advantage over a one-step catalysis (cf. Figure 4.6).

The best insurance for a smooth catalysis is that the drop in free energy between the system at the stage of the initial substrate(s) and the system at the stage of the final product(s) should describe a straight line. The acyl enzyme intermediate formed by the interaction of substrate with α-chymotrypsin lies, in fact, midway on the free-energy scale between the initial substrate and the final product. There are known exceptions to this optimal arrangement, but probably the graded unidirectional fall in free energy is fairly general for enzymic catalyses.

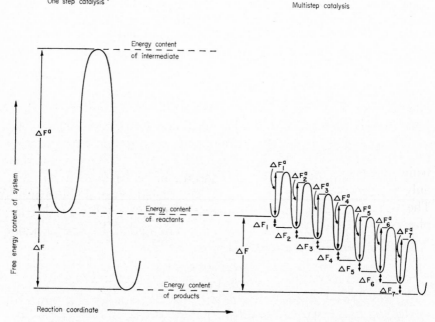

Fig. 4.6. The activation energies of a one step vs. a multistep catalysis. Abbreviations: ΔF^{a} = activation energy; ΔF = free-energy change between initial and intermediate steps.

THE CONCERTED REACTION IN CATALYSIS

The close fit of substrate and enzyme sets the scene for a concerted reaction in which protons or electrons are withdrawn from one group of atoms in the substrate and simultaneously delivered to another group of atoms separated in space from the first group. The synchronization of the withdrawal of protons or electrons at one point in the system with the delivery of protons or electrons at another point has enormous catalytic advantage, as compared to two sequential, independent steps. Synchronization of withdrawal and delivery leads to a major reduction of the activation barrier.

In the catalytic action of α-chymotrypsin, a proton is withdrawn from a histidine residue in the active group of the protein and simultaneously a proton is delivered to a serine residue (the serine and histidine residues are contiguous). This concerted action leads to the formation of an acyl ester between the substrate and the serine residue. In the second stage of the catalysis, a proton is withdrawn from the serine residue and simultaneously a proton is delivered to the histidine residue (cf. Figure 4.5). In this stage the acyl ester is hydrolyzed to set free the carboxylic acid and the —OH group on the serine residue.

The basic notion underlying the theory of concerted enzyme mechanisms is the simultaneity of bond breaking (for example, breaking of the original ester bond) and bond making (for example, forming the acyl ester of the enzyme). These two events are truly cooperative processes, and this cooperative effort is possible only in a system which behaves virtually as a single chemical unit. The basic process in α-chymotrypsin catalysis involves the interplay of four reacting species: (1) the substrate; (2) the histidine residue; (3) the serine residue; and (4) a molecule of water. All of these species form a single composite molecular system. Such a system provides the ideal instrument for synchronization of proton withdrawal and proton delivery, or of electron withdrawal and electron delivery. Catalysis within the framework of a composite molecular system approximates the conditions which are optimal for the operation of any catalytic process.

MECHANISTIC IDENTITY OF ACYL ENZYME FORMATION AND HYDROLYSIS

A typical synthetic substrate of α-chymotrypsin is an ester of a carboxylic acid and an alcohol. In the initial stage of the catalysis the carboxylic acid residue is transferred from the alcohol (to which it is originally linked) to the alcoholic —OH group of protein-bound serine. This reaction constitutes the formation of the acyl ester of the enzyme. In the final stage of the catalysis, water intervenes to

hydrolyze the acyl group away from the serine residue and thus release a carboxylic acid and simultaneously regenerate the —OH
group of serine. The same catalytic units intervene both in the
initial and final stages of the catalysis. In the initial reaction (acyl
enzyme formation) the histidine residue delivers a proton to the
potential acyl group of the ester and abstracts a proton from serine.
In the final reaction (hydrolysis of the acyl enzyme ester) a
histidine residue delivers a proton to the serine group of the acyl
enzymic ester and abstracts a proton from water. Thus, the initial
and final reactions are mechanistically identical. Both are trans-
esterifications of the acyl group. The first transfer of the acyl group
is from the substrate ester to enzyme-bound serine; the second
transfer of the acyl group is from serine to water (formally, water
may be looked upon as an alcohol, H-OH). The significance of
this symmetry in the two-step catalytic process is that the same type
of transition compound operates in both the acylation and deacyl-
ation steps. If this were not so, the two steps would have to involve
different catalytic mechanisms—extremely unlikely for a single
enzyme site. The important conclusion to be drawn is that, in a
two-step catalytic process, the same catalytic elements are always
operative; thus, the general mechanisms of both steps have to be
identical.

It is of value to note the kinds of chemical reactions that are
operative in a simple enzymic hydrolysis: proton transfers, trans-
esterifications, and addition reactions. At the mechanistic level the
line of demarcation among the various categories of enzymic processes becomes blurred. The fundamental principles of enzymic catalysis are in large measure independent of the particular enzymic
reaction under consideration.

THE GENERALITY OF THE MECHANISM OF α-CHYMOTRYPSIN CATALYSIS

The details of any enzymic catalysis will be determined by the
nature of the reaction catalyzed and by the nature of the catalytic
groups in the enzyme. Not all enzymic reactions involve the formation of covalent bonds between substrate and enzyme as in the
case for α-chymotrypsin. Histidine and serine residues are not catalytically active groups in all enzymes. We have to distinguish,

therefore, between the features of α-chymotrypsin catalysis that may apply only to a small group of hydrolytic reactions and the features that have general applicability to all enzymic reactions. The notions of the fit of enzyme to substrate, of the concerted reaction, of the intramolecular character of the enzyme-substrate complex or compound, and of multistep catalysis are among the universals of α-chymotrypsin catalysis. We may learn from the intensive study of one enzymic catalysis the ingredients to be found in all enzymic catalysis.

A Summarizing Comment

Since enzymes are the molecular instruments for all cellular activity, it is obvious that a complete treatment of enzymes must inevitably lead into every major area of biology. This central position of enzymes in the biological disciplines is pointed up in Figure 4.7.

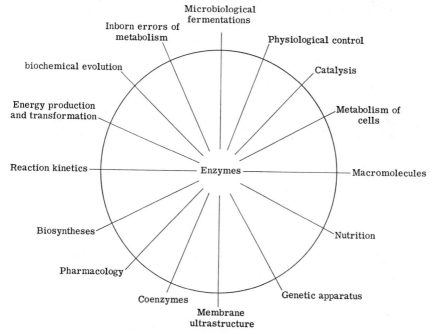

Fig. 4.7. The central position of enzymes and enzymology in biology.

The science of nutrition involves the nature and amounts of the dietary constituents required for the synthesis and replenishment of enzymes and their prosthetic groups. The science of pharmacology involves the capability of molecules to modify the enzymic machinery of organisms. The field of medicine is basically concerned with the abnormalities of cells, and these abnormalities may, in turn, involve derangements of the enzymic equipment of cells. The study of biological ultrastructure centers around the membrane systems which are the repositories of the basic enzymic machinery of the cell. The science of genetics is concerned with the hereditary apparatus and its operational principles. Among the key materials whose synthesis is controlled by the hereditary apparatus are the enzymes. Much of the science of physiology is focused on processes such as active transport, muscular contraction, and nerve conduction—processes which are uniformly enzyme-mediated. It is not surprising, therefore, that enzymology in its broadest sense has become, and probably will always remain, the hub of all biochemical and biological research.

Suggested Reading

Books

Dawson, R. M. C., and Rhodes D. N., eds., "Metabolism and Physiological Significance of Lipids," John Wiley, London, 1964.

Dixon, M., and Webb, E. C., "Enzymes," Academic Press, New York, 1958.

Goodwin, T. W., Harris, J. I., and Hartley, B. S., eds., "Structure and Activity of Enzymes," European Biochemical Societies Symposium, No. 1, Academic Press, New York, 1964: on the mechanism of enzymic catalysis and on the active sites of proteins.

Ingraham, L. L., "Biochemical Mechanism," John Wiley and Sons, Inc., New York, 1962.

Karlson, P., "Introduction to Modern Biochemistry," Academic Press, New York, 1963.

Mehler, A. H., "Introduction to Enzymology," Academic Press, New York, 1957.

Nielands, J. B., Stumpf, P. K., and Stanner, R. Y., "Outlines of Enzyme Chemistry," John Wiley and Sons, Inc., New York, 1955.

Special Articles

Bender, M. L., Kezdy, F. J., and Gunter, C. R., *J. Am. Chem. Soc.* **86**, 3669 (1964): the anatomy of an enzymatic catalysis, α-chymotrypsen.

Fischer, E. H., Forrey, A. W., Hedrick, J. L., Hughes, R. C., Kent, A. B., and Krebs, E. G. *In* "Proceedings of the Symposium on Chemical and Biological Aspects of Pyridoxal Catalysis," p. 543, Pergamon Press, London, 1962: pyridoxal-5′-phosphate in the structure and function of phosphorylase.

Grisolia, S., *Physiol. Rev.* **44**, 657 (1964): on the catalytic environment.

Hammes, G., *Nature* **204**, 342 (1962): chemical events at the catalytic site.

Hartley, B. S., *Brookhaven Symp. Biol.* **15**, 85 (1962): on the amino acid sequence of chymotrypsen.

Hartley, B. S. *In* "Structure and Activity of Enzymes" (T. W. Goodwin, J. I. Harris, and B. S. Hartley, eds., p. 47. Academic Press. New York, 1964: on the amino acid sequence of chymotrypsen.

Kaplan, N. O., *Bacteriol. Rev.* **27**, 155 (1963): multiple forms of enzymes.

Koshland, D. E., *Federation Proc.* **23**, 719 (1964): conformational changes at the active site during enzyme action.

Koshland, D. E., Jr., Yankeelov, J. A., Jr., and Thoma, J. A., *Federation Proc.* **21**, 1031 (1962): specificity and catalytic power in enzyme action.

Monod, J., Wyman, J., and Changeaux, J., *J. Mol. Biol.* **12**, 88 (1965): on the nature of allosteric transitions.

Multiple Forms of Enzymes and Control Mechanisms, *Bacteriol. Rev.* **27**, No. 2, 1963.

Stein, W. H., *Federation Proc.* **23**, 599 (1964): structure-activity relationship in ribonuclease.

Enzymes, Trace Substances, and Coenzymes

Prosthetic Groups

A considerable number of enzymes contain and require for their activity specific substances in addition to the protein moiety. Such a substance may represent less than 1% of the weight of its protein partner, but from the standpoint of essentiality it is on a par with the protein. Some twenty or more different substances of this kind have been discovered, with diverse chemical structures ranging from that of a complex organic molecule to that of a simple metal atom. They are referred to as prosthetic groups (working groups) or coenzymes. Each of the prosthetic groups is, with few exceptions, irreplaceable by any of the others. Thus, the protein moiety of an enzyme that has an absolute requirement for a particular prosthetic group will be inactive when supplemented with any other prosthetic group. There are many enzymes which neither contain nor require any additional nonprotein component. In general, the enzymes which catalyze oxidative reactions require prosthetic groups, whereas the enzymes which catalyze hydrolytic reactions do not.

ATTACHMENT OF THE PROSTHETIC GROUP TO THE PROTEIN

The prosthetic group in some cases is so firmly attached to the protein that the bond which holds the two together survives the rigors of an isolation procedure; in other cases the prosthetic group can readily be detached. In general, the term *coenzyme* is applied to a prosthetic group that may readily be detached from its protein.* The protein moiety—that is, the enzyme minus its appropriate prosthetic group—is often referred to as the *apoenzyme;* it is a potential enzyme which acquires activity only when supplemented with the appropriate coenzyme(s).

FUNCTIONS OF COENZYMES

The mechanism of action of coenzymes varies with the kind of reaction catalyzed. The prosthetic groups, or coenzymes, of those enzymes that catalyze oxidative reactions invariably undergo oxido-reduction; they serve as the first acceptors of electrons, or hydrogen atoms, from the substance which is oxidized by the enzyme. The prosthetic groups of enzymes that catalyze group-transfer reactions (such as the transfer of an amino or a formyl group) are capable of accepting the group in question from a substrate molecule which serves as the donor; they then transfer the group to another substrate molecule which serves as the acceptor. Some metal coenzymes, such as Mg and Zn, play a role as chemical junction points to which are attached both the protein and the substrate(s).

COENZYMES AND VITAMINS

All but a few of the vitamins have been demonstrated to be essential parts of the prosthetic groups of enzymes. There are some interesting consequences of this relationship. Certain animal species may not be able to synthesize some essential part of a coenzyme molecule. Unless this essential constituent is made available in the diet, the coenzyme cannot be formed, and its apoenzyme is then catalytically inactive. The organism would die if the coenzyme were not available since most of the enzymes that require coenzymes play a vital role in the economy of the cell. The need for continued supplementation of the diet with vitamins is due to the fact that enzymes have a limited lifetime.

---

* Coenzyme A, one of the few substances which carries the official designation of coenzyme, is in fact only a part of a substrate molecule, and strictly speaking is not a true coenzyme.

When animals are deprived of a given vitamin, they exhibit a wide variety of symptoms which are expressions of the damage sustained by the cells of particular organs when a key enzyme is nonfunctional. The pigeon deprived of vitamin B_1 shows symptoms of impaired brain function. Providing the deficiency state has not been too prolonged (a condition which leads to irreversible damage), the disturbance may be corrected in a matter of minutes merely by injecting vitamin B_1 into the bloodstream. First, the vitamin thus introduced into the body is readily converted into the coenzyme by attachment of inorganic pyrophosphate; this coenzyme then combines rapidly with the apoenzyme. As soon as the enzyme is reconstituted, brain function is restored, and the pigeon's behavior becomes normal again.

There is considerable variation in respect to the capacity of different animals to synthesize the essential parts of coenzymes. In other words, the vitamin requirements of different species of animals vary extensively. A vitamin requirement for man is not necessarily a requirement for a rat, the rat usually being the better synthetic chemist!

The ultimate dietary sources of all the substances that serve as vitamins for the animal kingdom are, of course, green plants or microorganisms. This has an important implication, namely, that the same functional or prosthetic groups are found in the enzymes of the plant, the microbial, and the animal cell. The plant cell can synthesize all its organic prosthetic groups, whereas animals are capable of synthesizing only a limited number of these essential molecules; thus, they are dependent on plant products for their supply.

METALS AND COENZYMES

Many of the prosthetic groups of enzymes are metals, such as Cu, Zn, Fe, Co, Mg, Mo, and Mn. Unless these metals are present in the diet, the formation of the appropriate enzymes, of which these metals are the primary functional groups, cannot proceed.

Generally, both vitamins and metals are required in the diet in very small amounts (less than 1 mg per kilogram of food). This is not surprising since each enzyme is present in relatively small amounts. Two corollaries of this obvious relationship are that any organic substance required in the diet in trace amounts is probably a vitamin, and that any substance which exerts a biological effect at a trace level is probably affecting some enzymic reaction.

The turnover number (number of molecules of substrate converted to product per minute per molecule of enzyme) is somewhat variable among different enzymes, ranging from a low of about one hundred to a high of a million or more. However, whether on the low or high side of the spectrum, each molecule of enzyme can catalyze an enormous amount of chemical change in, say, a 24-hour period. It is, indeed, the high activity of enzymes which underlies the fact that coenzymes are required in trace amounts.

MULTIPLE PROSTHETIC GROUPS

Some enzymes require more than one prosthetic group. For example, carboxylase, the enzyme which catalyzes the simple decarboxylation of pyruvic acid ($CH_3COCOOH$) to acetaldehyde (CH_3CHO) and carbon dioxide (CO_2), contains both cocarboxylase (vitamin B_1 pyrophosphate) and magnesium (Mg) as prosthetic groups. However, this is less of an anomaly than may appear. In this instance Mg merely subserves the role of chemical link between cocarboxylase and apoprotein. The coenzyme that actively implements the catalysis is cocarboxylase. Xanthine oxidase, which catalyzes the oxidation of hypoxanthine to uric acid by molecular oxygen, contains three prosthetic groups: flavin-adenine dinucleotide, Fe, and Mo. Here we are dealing with a complex, multienzyme system. The functional group of the primary enzyme in the system is flavin-adenine dinucleotide, which is, in turn, chemically bonded to a multiprotein electron-transfer chain, of which Fe and Mo are bound prosthetic groups. In a later chapter we shall be considering, in some detail, the electron-transfer chain of the mitochondrion, which also has a set of sequential catalysts bonded to a primary dehydrogenase containing flavin as functional group. Thus, we may conclude that in those cases in which more than one coenzyme is required for the enzymic reaction, we are dealing with a multistep process, and that each step involves only a single active prosthetic group.

Mechanisms of Coenzyme Action

Most of the coenzymes have rather elaborate structures. In any coenzyme one or two atoms are the primary instruments of the catalysis and the rest merely provide the molecular setting, so to speak, that ensures the desired behavior of these particular functional atoms. The chemist-specialist may recognize by inspection of a formula that a particular atom will have special properties. However, for the less specialized chemist the rest of the molecule merely is a distraction from the task of comprehending what is really going on. We shall follow the practice of presenting the various coenzymes only by reactive atoms or groups of atoms and using the symbol R or dotted lines to indicate the rest of the molecule.

COCARBOXYLASE

There is a set of enzymes that catalyze the formation or cleavage of carbon-to-carbon bonds; the functional group of these enzymes is cocarboxylase (also known as thiamine pyrophosphate). The various reactions catalyzed all have some formal resemblance:

Decarboxylation of pyruvic acid:

$$CH_3COCOOH \longrightarrow CH_3C\overset{\displaystyle O}{\underset{\displaystyle H}{\diagup}} + CO_2$$

Acetoin formation

$$2\ CH_3COCOOH \longrightarrow CH_3 \cdot CO \cdot CH(OH) \cdot CH_3 + 2\ CO_2$$

Transketolation

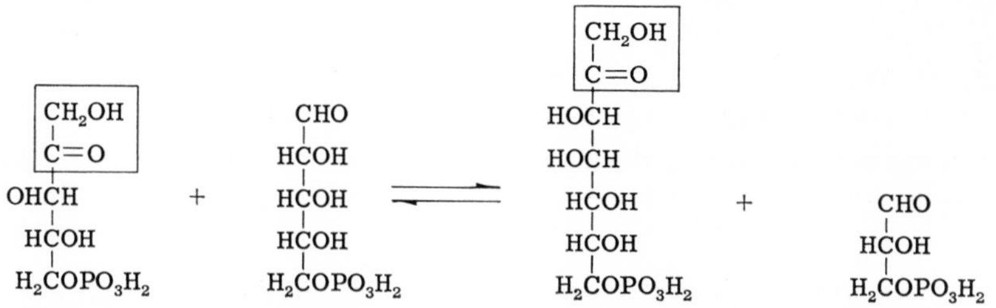

$\begin{array}{c}CH_2OH\\ \mid\\ C=O\end{array}$		$\begin{array}{c}CH_2OH\\ \mid\\ C=O\end{array}$	
$\begin{array}{l}OHCH\\ \mid\\ HCOH\\ \mid\\ H_2COPO_3H_2\end{array}$ +	$\begin{array}{c}CHO\\ \mid\\ HCOH\\ \mid\\ HCOH\\ \mid\\ HCOH\\ \mid\\ H_2COPO_3H_2\end{array}$	$\begin{array}{c}HOCH\\ \mid\\ HOCH\\ \mid\\ HCOH\\ \mid\\ HCOH\\ \mid\\ H_2COPO_3H_2\end{array}$ +	$\begin{array}{c}CHO\\ \mid\\ HCOH\\ \mid\\ H_2COPO_3H_2\end{array}$
D-Xylulose 5-phosphate	D-Ribose 5-phosphate	D-Sedoheptulose 7-phosphate	D-Glyceraldehyde 3-phosphate

In all cases a carbon-to-carbon bond is either made or broken; the bond that is formed is produced by interaction between carbon atoms, one of which carries a carbonyl function; the breaking of the carbon-carbon bond results in the formation of two moieties, each with a carbonyl function. The thiazole ring of the coenzyme (cf. formula below) contains a set of three linked atoms (—N—C—S—) which are the key atoms in the catalytic process:

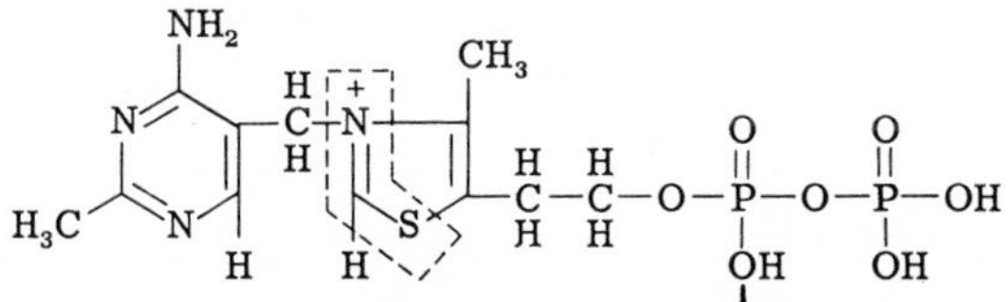

| Pyrimidine base | Thiazole ring | Pyrophosphate chain |

Cocarboxylase

We shall represent the coenzyme as

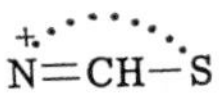

$$\overset{+}{N}=CH-S$$

where the dotted line represents the rest of the atoms in the molecule, and consider the role of the coenzyme in the decarboxylation of pyruvic acid to acetaldehyde and CO_2 (a reaction catalyzed by yeast carboxylase). In essence, the decarboxylation involves separation of the carboxyl group of pyruvic acid from the rest of the molecule, as shown in Eq. (1).

$$CH_3COCOOH \longrightarrow CH_3CO \cdots COOH \tag{1}$$

The separated carboxyl group comes off as CO_2; the other fragment is converted into acetaldehyde. The first essential feature of this catalysis is the displacement of the carboxyl group by the coenzyme, as shown in Eq. (2).

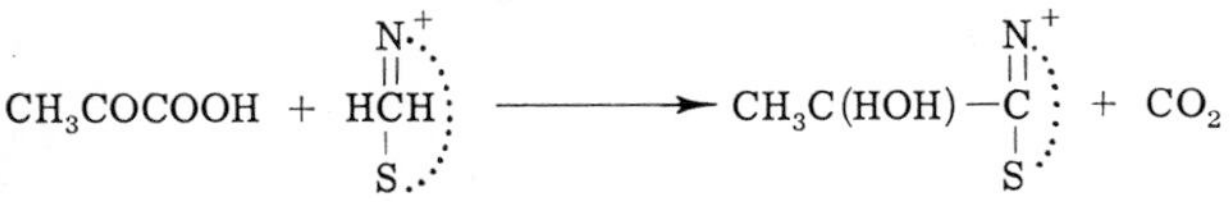

$$CH_3COCOOH + H\overset{\overset{+}{N}}{\underset{S}{C}}H \longrightarrow CH_3C(HOH)-\overset{\overset{+}{N}}{\underset{S}{C}} + CO_2 \tag{2}$$

The aldehyde-coenzyme complex then dissociates into acetaldehyde and the uncombined coenzyme, as shown in Eq. (3).

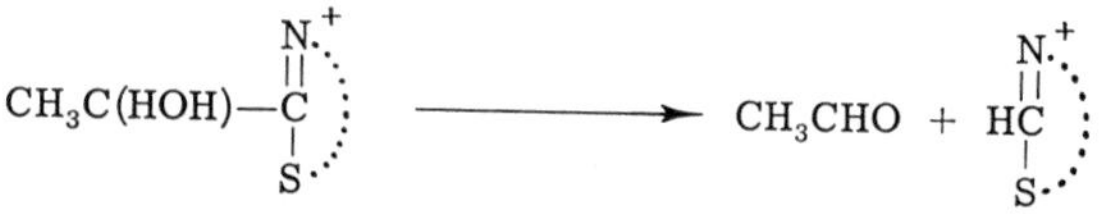

$$CH_3C(HOH)-\overset{\overset{N^+}{\|}}{\underset{\underset{S}{|}}{C}} \longrightarrow CH_3CHO + H\overset{\overset{N^+}{\|}}{\underset{\underset{S}{|}}{C}} \tag{3}$$

Inspection of the formula for cocarboxylase shows a pyrophosphate group attached to the thiazole ring. This group serves as the point of attachment of the coenzyme to Mg; in turn, Mg is attached to the apoprotein as indicated by the formulation:

Cocarboxylase · · · Mg · · · protein

Thiamine, which is similar to cocarboxylase but has no pyrophosphate group, is inactive as coenzyme for yeast carboxylase.

Coenzymes Containing Riboflavin

Many oxidative enzymes contain riboflavin as an essential component of their prosthetic groups. Riboflavin is a molecule made up of three fused rings (see formula below) and a sugar-like alcohol.

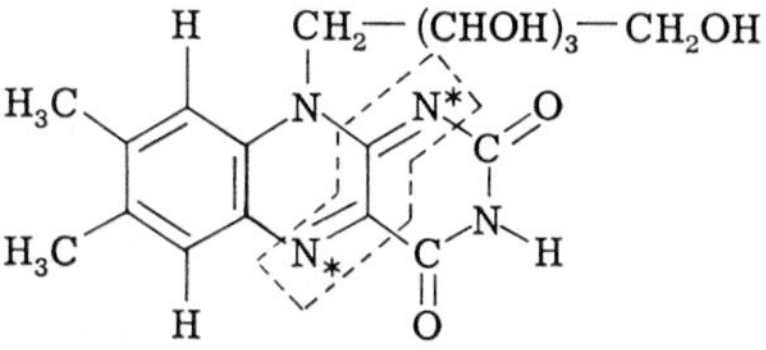

Riboflavin
(oxidized)

The two starred nitrogen atoms are the key atoms in the catalysis. We may represent the oxidized form of the coenzyme as

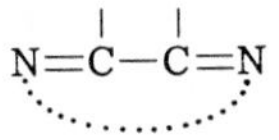

$$N=\overset{|}{C}-\overset{|}{C}=N$$

and the reduced form as

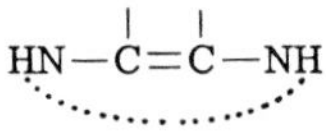

$$HN-\overset{|}{C}=\overset{|}{C}-NH$$

The reduced form is rapidly converted to the oxidized form by oxygen, the oxygen concomitantly being reduced to hydrogen peroxide (H_2O_2). The essence of the catalytic function of the flavin prosthetic group is the cyclic change from the oxidized to the reduced form and back again. During reduction of the coenzyme and the corresponding oxidation of the substrate, two atoms of hydrogen[*] are transferred from substrate to the oxidized coenzyme; during oxidation of the coenzyme, two atoms of hydrogen are transferred from the reduced coenzyme to an acceptor molecule. There is evidence that the hydrogen atoms can enter and leave the coenzyme one at a time. In other words, the reduction of the flavin coenzyme can proceed in two separate steps, shown in Eqs. (4) and (5), where the starred atom represents a trivalent carbon atom, or free radical.

$$N{=}C{-}C{=}N + H \longrightarrow HN{-}C^*{-}C{=}N \qquad (4)$$

$$HN{-}C^*{-}C{=}N + H \longrightarrow HN{-}C{=}C{-}NH \qquad (5)$$

Thus, there is a form intermediate between the fully reduced and the fully oxidized forms of the coenzyme. This intermediate, or semiquinone-like state, cannot be described adequately as a single stable state in which only one of the two nitrogen atoms is in the reduced form and the other in the oxidized form. On the contrary, there is an equilibrium, with equal probability that the lone hydrogen atom will be associated at a given instant with either N atom [Eq. (6)].

$$HN{-}C^*{-}C{=}N \rightleftharpoons N{=}C{-}C^*{-}NH \qquad (6)$$

With this fluctuation in position of one hydrogen between two nitrogens, the two carbon atoms adjacent to the two functional nitrogen atoms alternate (or resonate) between the trivalent state, in which there is an unpaired electron (marked with a star), and the normal tetravalent state. The unpaired electron fluctuates

---

[*] The transfer of one hydrogen atom is the equivalent of the transfer of one electron with simultaneous uptake of a proton from the medium.

among various possible sites, and this fluctuation contributes to the stabilization of the semiquinone type of free radical.

There are two common forms of coenzymes that contain riboflavin: the mononucleotide form, in which the ribityl group of riboflavin is linked to phosphate, and the dinucleotide form, in which riboflavin is linked to adenine-ribose-pyrophosphate. The mononucleotide is abbreviated as FMN, the dinucleotide as FAD.

Practically all the known coenzymes have a molecular "appendage," apparently designed in part to facilitate binding of the coenzyme to the enzyme. The appendage could be phosphate, pyrophosphate, sugar-phosphate, or adenine-ribose-pyrophosphate. The mononucleotide form of coenzymes may be represented by the formulations:

Base-sugar-phosphate   or   base-(sugar analogue*)-phosphate

The dinucleotide would be a pair of mononucleotides joined through their respective phosphate groups:

Base-sugar-phosphate-phosphate-sugar-base

In this formulation, molecules such as thiamine or flavin are represented as bases.

In principle, the flavin group of an enzyme may function as an electron "shuttle" in any of three ways which we may represent as follows: (1) flavin ⟷ flavin H; (2) flavin H ⟷ flavin H_2; and (3) flavin ⟷ flavin H_2. It is of interest to note that the flavin prosthetic group of D-amino acid oxidase undergoes a cycle which corresponds to shuttle (1); the flavin prosthetic group of TPNH†-cytochrome *c* reductase, a cycle which corresponds to shuttle (2); and the flavin prosthetic group of glucose oxidase, a cycle which corresponds with shuttle (3). These are not the only modes of flavoprotein catalysis. Reactions catalyzed by some flavoprotein enzymes involve a cooperative action between a flavin prosthetic group and neighboring dithiols, or between a flavin prosthetic group and a neighboring metal atom such as Fe.

---

* The sugar analogue could be a deoxy compound such as pantothenic acid (in coenzyme A) or ribitol (in riboflavin).

† Reduced triphosphopyridine nucleotide.

COENZYMES CONTAINING NICOTINAMIDE

There are two coenzymes containing nicotinamide that play a key role in biological oxidations. The catalytic cycle of these coenzymes involves the reduction and oxidation of the pyridine ring:

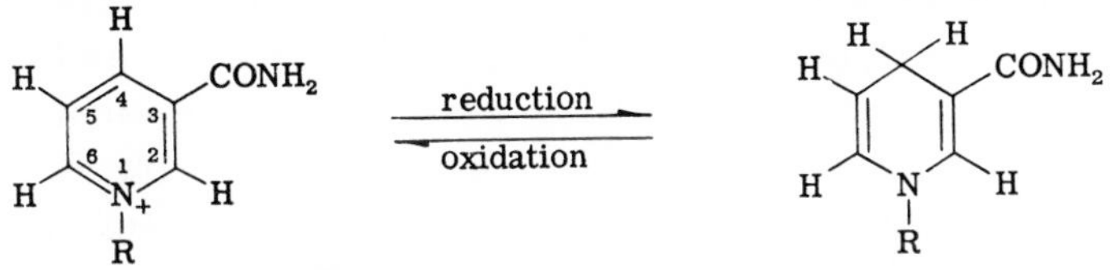

$$\text{reduction} \rightleftharpoons \text{oxidation}$$

When R is adenine-ribose-phosphate-phosphate-ribose, the compound is known as diphosphopyridine nucleotide, or DPN^+. When R is adenine-ribose-($2'$-phosphate)-phosphate-phosphate-ribose, the compound is known as triphosphopyridine nucleotide, or TPN^+. An International Commission on nomenclature has recommended that DPN^+ be designated as NAD^+ and TPN^+ as $NADP^+$. However, we shall adhere in this book to the older designations, DPN^+ and TPN^+.

The reduction of DPN^+ or TPN^+ to the corresponding reduced form involves the transfer of two electrons and one proton from a substrate molecule (represented as SH_2) to the coenzyme, and the concomitant liberation of one proton into the medium.

$$SH_2 + DPN^+ (TPN^+) \rightarrow S + DPNH(TPNH) + H^+$$

Thus, only one of the two hydrogen atoms originating in the substrate is incorporated into the coenzyme; the proton and electron of the second hydrogen atom are separated during the transfer. Indeed, the transfer may equally well be described in terms of the addition of a hydride ion (hydrogen with two electrons, represented as H^-). The reduction process is usually represented as a 1 : 4 addition—that is, one electron is added to the nitrogen atom in position 1 (N-1) and a hydrogen atom is added to the carbon atom at position 4 (C-4). Under some conditions, possibly in mitochondrial electron transfer, the addition may be 1 : 6—that is, one electron is added to the nitrogen atom at position 1 and a hydrogen atom to the carbon atom at position 6.

There are many enzymes which require DPN^+ or TPN^+ as prosthetic group. Each enzyme protein is specific for a particular substrate or group of related substrates. Thus, the protein moiety determines the substrate specificity. The prosthetic group serves the same function for each of these numerous oxidoreductive enzymes regardless of the nature of the substrate oxidized or reduced. Since the coenzymes containing nicotinamide are usually readily dissociable from their apoenzymes, it is possible to have an interaction (electron transfer) between the reduced substrate of one enzyme and the oxidized substrate of a second enzyme through the intermediation of a shared or communal coenzyme. In other words, two reactions can be *coupled* by virtue of a shared coenzyme. Consider the two reactions catalyzed, respectively, by alcohol dehydrogenase and β-hydroxybutyric dehydrogenase, shown in Eqs. (7) and (8).

$$CH_3CH_2OH + DPN^+ \rightleftharpoons CH_3CHO + DPNH + H^+ \tag{7}$$
Ethanol   Acetaldehyde

$$CH_3CHOHCH_2COOH + DPN^+ \rightleftharpoons CH_3COCH_2COOH + DPNH + H^+ \tag{8}$$
β-Hydroxybutyric acid   Acetoacetic acid

When acetaldehyde and β-hydroxybutyrate are mixed in presence of the two respective enzymes and DPN^+, the following net reaction ensues [Eq. (9)].

$$CH_3CHOHCH_2COOH + CH_3CHO \rightleftharpoons CH_3COCH_2COOH + CH_3CH_2OH \tag{9}$$

The coenzyme undergoes a cycle of reduction by β-hydroxybutyrate and oxidation by acetaldehyde. As a consequence β-hydroxybutyrate is oxidized to acetoacetate and acetaldehyde is reduced to ethanol. This type of oxidoreduction reaction—known as a coenzyme-linked reaction—plays an important role in several metabolic reaction sequences.

PYRIDOXAL PHOSPHATE

Pyridoxol (vitamin B_6) is a building block of a coenzyme known as pyridoxal phosphate.

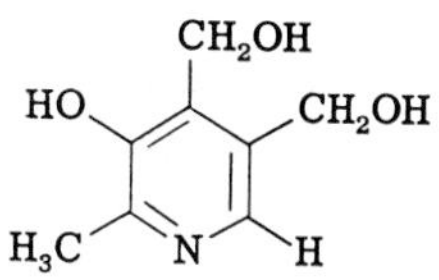

Pyridoxol

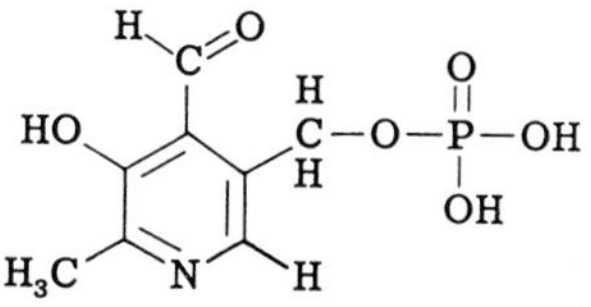

Pyridoxal phosphate

The key functional atom in the coenzyme is the carbon atom with the carbonyl function. We shall represent the coenzyme by the symbol RCHO, where R includes the entire ring system to which the aldehyde group is attached. Practically all the processes catalyzed by enzymes requiring pyridoxal phosphate involve a combination of the enzyme-bound coenzyme with the amino group of any of the various substrate molecules, the latter being represented by $NH_2\bar{R}$ [Eq. (10)].

$$RCHO + NH_2\bar{R} \rightarrow RCH{=}N\bar{R}$$

| Aldehydic coenzyme | Amine | Schiff base | (10) |

The product of the condensation (Schiff base) can rearrange in several ways, depending upon the catalytic influence of the apoprotein to which the pyridoxal phosphate is linked.

Transaminase is an enzyme in which pyridoxal phosphate is bound to the apoprotein. It catalyzes the transfer of an amino group from an amino acid, such as glutamate, to a keto acid, such as oxaloacetate. The reverse of this type of reaction is also catalyzed by the same enzyme, for example, the transfer of an amino group from aspartate to α-ketoglutarate, shown in Eq. (11).

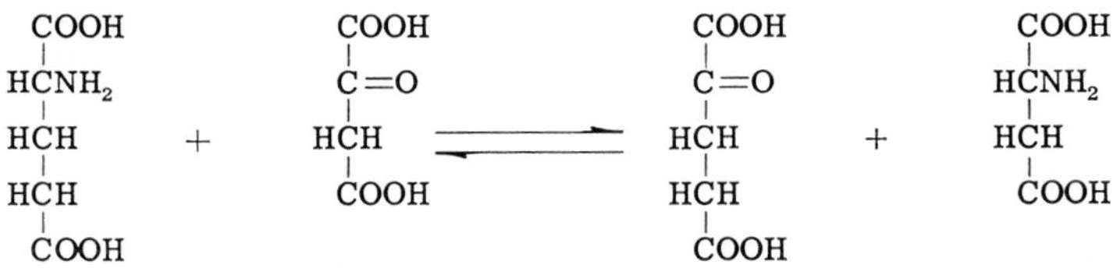

| Glutamic acid | Oxaloacetic acid | α-Ketoglutaric acid | Aspartic acid |

The catalysis may be represented by the sequence of reactions shown by Eqs. (12)–(17).

$$\underset{\substack{\text{Aldehydic} \\ \text{coenzyme}}}{\overset{\text{H}}{\underset{|}{\text{RC}}}{=}\text{O}} + \underset{\text{Glutamic acid}}{\overset{\text{H}}{\underset{|}{\text{H}_2\text{N}-\text{C}}}(\text{COOH})\text{CH}_2\text{CH}_2\text{COOH}} \longrightarrow \underset{\text{Schiff base}}{\overset{\text{H}}{\underset{|}{\text{RC}}}{=}\text{N}-\overset{\text{H}}{\underset{|}{\text{C}}}(\text{COOH})\text{CH}_2\text{CH}_2\text{COOH}} + \text{H}_2\text{O} \tag{12}$$

$$\overset{\text{H}}{\underset{|}{\text{RC}}}{=}\text{N}-\overset{\text{H}}{\underset{|}{\text{C}}}(\text{COOH})\text{CH}_2\text{CH}_2\text{COOH} \rightleftharpoons \overset{\text{H}}{\underset{\underset{\text{H}}{|}}{\text{RC}}}-\text{N}{=}\text{C}(\text{COOH})\text{CH}_2\text{CH}_2\text{COOH} \tag{13}$$

$$\overset{\text{H}}{\underset{\underset{\text{H}}{|}}{\text{RC}}}-\text{N}{=}\text{C}(\text{COOH})\text{CH}_2\text{CH}_2\text{COOH} + \text{H}_2\text{O} \longrightarrow \underset{\substack{\text{Aminated} \\ \text{coenzyme}}}{\overset{\text{H}}{\underset{\underset{\text{H}}{|}}{\text{RC}}}\text{NH}_2} + \underset{\substack{\alpha\text{-Ketoglutaric} \\ \text{acid}}}{\text{O}{=}\text{C}(\text{COOH})\text{CH}_2\text{CH}_2\text{COOH}} \tag{14}$$

$$\overset{\text{H}}{\underset{\underset{\text{H}}{|}}{\text{RC}}}-\text{NH}_2 + \underset{\text{Oxaloacetic acid}}{\text{O}{=}\text{C}(\text{COOH})\text{CH}_2\text{COOH}} \longrightarrow \overset{\text{H}}{\underset{\underset{\text{H}}{|}}{\text{RC}}}-\text{N}{=}\text{C}(\text{COOH})\text{CH}_2\text{COOH} + \text{H}_2\text{O} \tag{15}$$

$$\overset{\text{H}}{\underset{\underset{\text{H}}{|}}{\text{RC}}}-\text{N}{=}\text{C}(\text{COOH})\text{CH}_2\text{COOH} \rightleftharpoons \overset{\text{H}}{\underset{|}{\text{RC}}}{=}\text{N}-\overset{\text{H}}{\underset{|}{\text{C}}}(\text{COOH})\text{CH}_2\text{COOH} \tag{16}$$

$$\overset{\text{H}}{\underset{|}{\text{RC}}}{=}\text{N}-\overset{\text{H}}{\underset{|}{\text{C}}}(\text{COOH})\text{CH}_2\text{COOH} + \text{H}_2\text{O} \longrightarrow \underset{\substack{\text{Aldehydic} \\ \text{coenzyme}}}{\overset{\text{H}}{\underset{|}{\text{RC}}}{=}\text{O}} + \underset{\substack{\text{Aspartic} \\ \text{acid}}}{\text{H}_2\text{NC}(\text{COOH})\text{CH}_2\text{COOH}} \tag{17}$$

The amino group of glutamate forms a Schiff base with the aldehyde group of the coenzyme. The Schiff base rearranges and then undergoes hydrolysis, with release of the aminated coenzyme. The latter form of the coenzyme, known as pyridoxamine, can then transfer its amino group to oxaloacetate; in forming aspartate it regenerates the aldehydic form of the coenzyme. The cycle is then ready for a repeat performance.

Several other types of catalytic processes are carried out by enzymes requiring pyridoxal phosphate. Consider, for example, the

enzymic conversion of serine to glycine with release of formaldehyde, shown in Eqs. (18)–(20).

$$
\overset{H}{\underset{|}{R\overset{|}{C}}}=O \ + \ H_2\overset{H}{\underset{|}{N}}CH_2(COOH)\cdot CH_2OH \longrightarrow R\overset{H}{\underset{|}{C}}=N-\overset{H}{\underset{|}{C}}(COOH)\cdot CH_2OH \quad (18)
$$

Serine   Schiff base

$$
R\overset{H}{\underset{|}{C}}=N-\overset{H}{\underset{|}{C}}(COOH)\cdot CH_2OH \longrightarrow R\overset{H}{\underset{|}{C}}=N-\underset{\underset{H}{|}}{\overset{H}{\underset{|}{C}}}(COOH) \ + \ \overset{H}{\underset{H}{C}}{=}O \quad (19)
$$

Formaldehyde

$$
R\overset{H}{\underset{|}{C}}=N-\underset{\underset{H}{|}}{\overset{H}{\underset{|}{C}}}(COOH) + H_2O \longrightarrow R\overset{H}{\underset{|}{C}}=O + H_2NCH_2COOH \quad (20)
$$

Glycine

This particular cycle involves first formation and then cleavage of
the Schiff base. Formaldehyde is detached from the serine moiety
not as such but as a derivative of yet another coenzyme, tetrahydrofolate. Finally, the complex of glycine and the coenzyme is
hydrolyzed, and the coenzyme is regenerated. The net catalysis
is the conversion of serine to glycine by removal of a hydroxymethyl group.

The fate undergone by a given Schiff base (transamination, decarboxylation, or yet another conversion) will be determined by
the protein moiety of the enzyme. It should be stressed that the
protein is an essential participant in the catalytic process. Although
the coenzyme is involved in the actual shifting of chemical groups,
the apoprotein orients the coenzyme and the participating molecules, directs the specificity of the reaction, and ensures the proper
steric relationships of all the reactants.

Coenzyme A

Inspection of the exploded representation of coenzyme A shown
in Figure 5.1 reveals great complexity, yet the mode of action of this
coenzyme is extremely simple. The key group in the molecule is a

thiol group (—SH) and we shall represent the coenzyme as R-SH. Now we come to the unusual feature of coenzyme A. It is not really a coenzyme for any known enzyme. Rather, it is (or becomes) an integral part of substrate molecules, its function being to confer upon such molecules a high degree of reactivity. Consider, for example, the enzyme that catalyzes the conversion of acetate to acetyl-CoA—a conversion that is coupled with the breakdown of

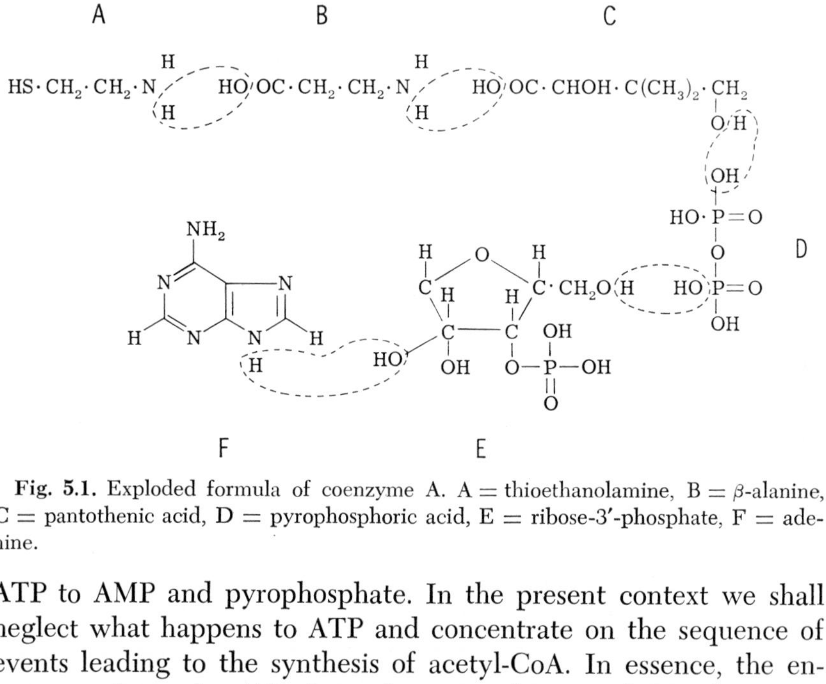

Fig. 5.1. Exploded formula of coenzyme A. A = thioethanolamine, B = β-alanine, C = pantothenic acid, D = pyrophosphoric acid, E = ribose-3′-phosphate, F = adenine.

ATP to AMP and pyrophosphate. In the present context we shall neglect what happens to ATP and concentrate on the sequence of events leading to the synthesis of acetyl-CoA. In essence, the enzyme catalyzes the ATP-dependent esterification of CoA by acetic acid, with elimination of water, as shown in Eq. (21).

$$CH_3COOH + HSR \quad \xrightarrow{\text{ATP}} \quad CH_3\underset{\underset{O}{\|}}{C}-S-R + H_2O \qquad (21)$$

The product of condensation is a thiol ester, formed from the coenzyme and acetic acid. The acetyl group in this thiol ester is highly reactive. Thus, this synthesis is a preliminary reaction, necessary for preparing acetic acid in a form in which it may participate in condensation reactions that lead, for example, to synthesis of citric acid.

In virtually all the reactions involving the oxidation or synthesis of fatty acids, the fatty acids participate in the form of their highly reactive CoA derivatives. In the oxidative decarboxylation of pyruvate and of α-ketoglutarate (both α-keto acids) the products are not simple acetate and succinate, respectively, but the CoA derivatives of these acids.

Acetyl-CoA plays a key role in a considerable number of synthetic condensation reactions, a few examples of which are shown in Eqs. (22)–(27).

$$CH_3CO\overline{SCoA} + CH_3CO\overline{SCoA} \rightarrow CH_3COCH_2CO\overline{SCoA} + \overline{CoASH} \tag{22}$$
$$\text{Acetoacetyl-CoA}$$

$$CH_3CO\overline{SCoA} + CO_2 \rightarrow COOHCH_2CO\overline{SCoA} \tag{23}$$
$$\text{Malonyl-CoA}$$

$$CH_3CO\overline{SCoA} + NH_2R \rightarrow CH_3CONHR + \overline{CoASH} \tag{24}$$
$$\text{Aromatic} \quad \text{Acetylated}$$
$$\text{amine} \quad \text{amine}$$

$$CH_3CO\overline{SCoA} + COOHCH_2CO\overline{SCoA} \rightarrow CH_3COCH_2CO\overline{SCoA} + \overline{CoASH} + CO_2 \tag{25}$$
$$\text{Malonyl-CoA} \qquad \text{Acetoacetyl-CoA}$$

$$CH_3CO\overline{SCoA} + COOHCOCH_2COOH \rightarrow$$
$$\text{Oxaloacetic acid}$$
$$COOHCOH(CH_2COOH)CH_2COOH + \overline{CoASH} \tag{26}$$
$$\text{Citric acid}$$

$$CH_3CO\overline{SCoA} + CH_3CH_2CH_2CO\overline{SCoA} \rightarrow$$
$$\text{Butyryl—CoA}$$
$$CH_3CH_2CH_2COCH_2CO\overline{SCoA} + \overline{CoASH} \tag{27}$$
$$\beta\text{-Ketohexanoyl—CoA}$$

Now, finally, we may consider the structure of coenzyme A, shown in Figure 5.1. This consists of seven component residues, arranged in the order

Adenine-(ribose-3′-phosphate)-pyrophosphate⌐
thioethanolamine-β-alanine-pantothenic acid⌐

This structure has some similarity to that of a dinucleotide; the "dipeptide," β-alanyl-thioethanolamine, is analogous to the usual base, and pantothenic acid is analogous to the usual sugar moiety of one of the component nucleotides. In addition, there is a third phosphate group in the coenzyme molecule—on C-3 of ribose. Thus, the structure of CoA is not unlike that of some of the other co-enzymes discussed above.

Lipoic Acid

As far as function is concerned, lipoic acid may be regarded as a cross between CoA and flavin—it serves both as a transfer agent for an acyl group and as an electron acceptor.[*] These two transfer functions are synchronized. Lipoic acid has the following structure:

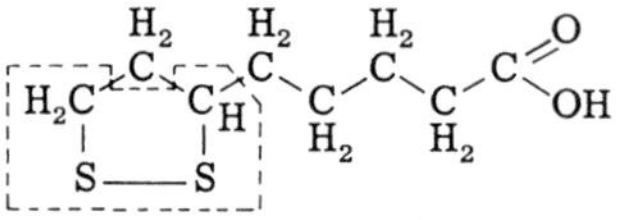

Lipoic acid   Lipoic acid
(oxidized)   (reduced)

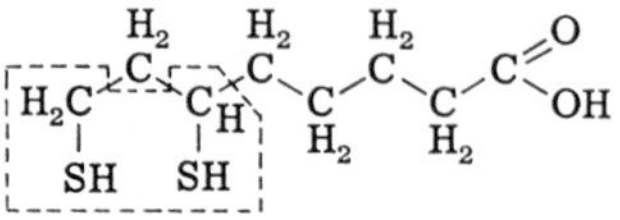

We shall represent the oxidized form as

L_{ox}

and the reduced form as

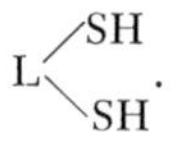

L_{red}

During the catalytic cycle of lipoic acid there is a transition from L_{ox} to L_{red} and back again; this is the electron-transfer cycle. However, in addition to electron transfer, there is a reductive acylation of L_{ox} by some α-keto acid, as shown in Eq. (28).

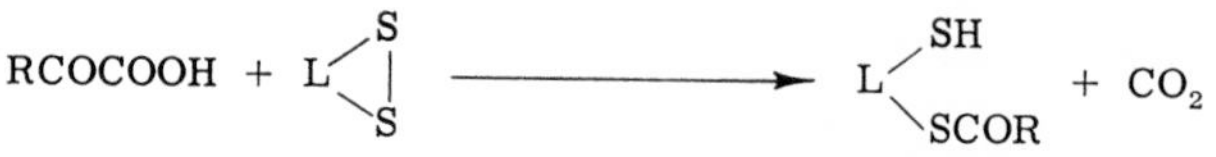

(28)

α-Keto   Acyllipoic
acid   acid

[*] Lipoic acid has formal analogies with tetrahydrofolate—a coenzyme which is a vehicle for a one-carbon fragment that undergoes oxidation-reduction while attached to the coenzyme.

Then there is a transfer of the acyl (acetyl or succinyl) group from the sulfur atom of lipoic acid to the thiol group of CoA, as shown in Eq. (29).

$$L \overset{SH}{\underset{SCOCH_3}{<}} + \overline{CoASH} \longrightarrow L \overset{SH}{\underset{SH}{<}} + CH_3CO\overline{SCoA} \qquad (29)$$

Finally, the reduced form of lipoic acid is converted back to the oxidized form by a flavoprotein enzyme, as shown in Eq. (30).

$$L \overset{SH}{\underset{SH}{<}} + \text{flavin enzyme} \longrightarrow L \overset{S}{\underset{S}{<}}| + \text{reduced flavin enzyme} \qquad (30)$$

The reduced flavoprotein is then reoxidized by DPN^+. In summary, the necessities of reductive acylation call for a set of four enzymes which sequentially catalyze: (1) the reductive acylation of L_{ox} by some α-keto acid; (2) the transfer of the acyl group from acyllipoic acid to $\overline{CoASH}$; (3) the flavin-dependent oxidation of L_{red} to L_{ox}; and (4) the oxidation of reduced flavin by DPN^+.

It is to be noted that lipoic acid is the prosthetic group of the first enzyme which catalyzes the reductive acylation; it is also the donor substrate for the second enzyme, which catalyzes the acyl transfer. In an analogous fashion, flavin is the electron acceptor for the reaction in which L_{red} is oxidized, and is also the electron donor for the subsequent reaction, in which DPN^+ is reduced to DPNH.

The two reaction sequences in which lipoic acid plays an intermediary role may be summarized as shown in Eqs. (31) and (32).

$$CH_3COCOOH + DPN^+ + \overline{CoASH} \rightarrow CH_3CO\overline{SCoA} + CO_2 + DPNH + H^+ \qquad (31)$$
Pyruvic acid   Acetyl—CoA

$$COOHCOCH_2CH_2COOH + DPN^+ + CoASH \rightarrow$$
$$COOHCH_2CH_2COSCoA + CO_2 + DPNH + H^+ \qquad (32)$$
α-Ketoglutaric acid   Succinyl—CoA

Both of these reaction sequences are catalyzed by similar, though distinctly different, macromolecular complexes, in each of which the four component enzymes are linked together like contiguous tiles in a mosaic.

We have first considered the reductive acetylation as a single process for reasons of simplicity. In point of fact, it is a two-step process, as shown in Eqs. (33) and (34).

$$
CH_3COCOOH + HC\overset{\overset{+}{N}}{\underset{S}{|}} \longrightarrow CH_3\overset{H}{\underset{OH}{C}}-C\overset{\overset{+}{N}}{\underset{S}{|}} + CO_2 \tag{33}
$$

Aldehyde adduct of
thiamine pyrophosphate

$$
CH_3\overset{H}{\underset{OH}{C}}-C\overset{\overset{+}{N}}{\underset{S}{|}} + L\overset{S}{\underset{S}{\langle}} \longrightarrow L\overset{SH}{\underset{SCOCH_3}{\langle}} + HC\overset{\overset{+}{N}}{\underset{S}{|}} \tag{34}
$$

Thiamine pyrophosphate is the catalytic instrument for the decarboxylation of pyruvic acid. It is the prosthetic group of a carboxylase which converts the α-keto acid into the aldehyde adduct, or complex of thiamine pyrophosphate. The actual reductant for L_{ox} is this aldehyde complex, not the α-keto acid. Thiamine pyrophosphate is the coenzyme for the decarboxylative aldehydolysis[*] of the keto acid and is also the substrate for the reductive acetylation of L_{ox}. When we add carboxylase to the set of enzymes enumerated above it brings the total number of enzymes required for the overall reaction sequence to five.

Lipoic acid cannot be detached from its protein apoenzyme by simple means because a peptide bond joins the carboxyl group of the prosthetic group with the amino group of a protein-bound lysine residue. The flavin prosthetic group of succinic dehydrogenase is similarly joined to its apoprotein by a "peptide bond," although a peptide bond is a comparatively unusual link between prosthetic group and apoprotein.

FOLIC ACID COENZYMES

In the synthesis of molecules such as purines, pyrimidines, amino acids, and nucleic acids, a key step is the introduction of groups containing only a single carbon atom. This is a special chemical

---

[*] Splitting of the keto acid into acetaldehyde and CO_2.

operation, for the implementation of which the cell has a specific coenzyme known as tetrahydrofolic acid (FH_4). Folic acid, a vitamin of the B group, is reduced to tetrahydrofolic acid, the structure of which is shown below:

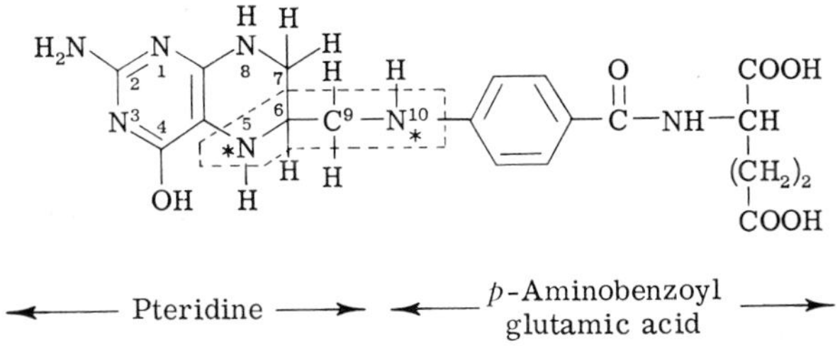

$$\longleftarrow \text{Pteridine} \longrightarrow \longleftarrow \begin{array}{c} p\text{-Aminobenzoyl} \\ \text{glutamic acid} \end{array} \longrightarrow$$

The coenzyme is built up of two parts—a pteridine ring moiety and a *p*-aminobenzoic acid residue joined in peptide linkage to glutamic acid. The two parts are joined through a —CH_2 group. The two nitrogen atoms marked with a star are the instruments of the catalysis. We may use the following shorthand notation for FH_4:

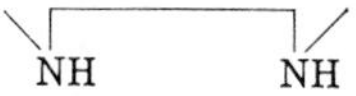

The group of the substrate molecule to be manipulated may be attached to the nitrogen at position 5 (N on the left hand side), or to that at position 10 (N on the right hand side), or to both. In fact, it is difficult to predict which of the three possibilities will apply in a given situation.

The formyl derivative (f) of FH_4 can exist in each of the following three forms:

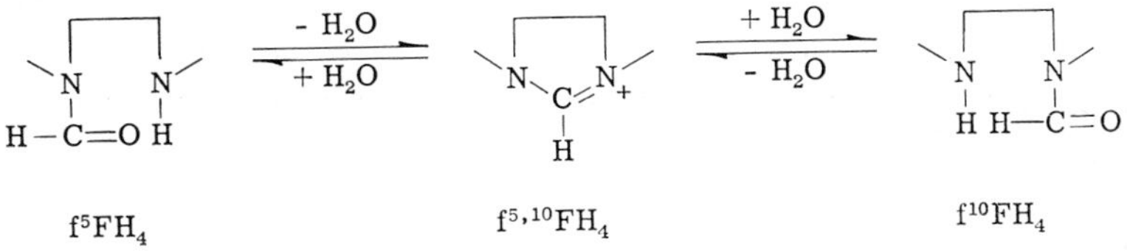

Enzymes have been found by Frank M. Huennekens which catalyze the conversion of $f^{5,10}FH_4$ to $f^{10}FH_4$, and the conversion of f^5FH_4 to $f^{10}FH_4$, the latter reaction occurring, presumably, with $f^{5,10}FH_4$ as an intermediate.

The hydroxymethyl derivative (h) of FH_4 could also exist, theoretically, in three forms:

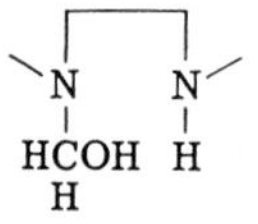

h⁵FH₄ ; h⁵,¹⁰FH₄ ; h¹⁰FH₄

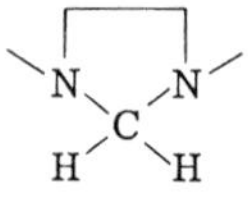

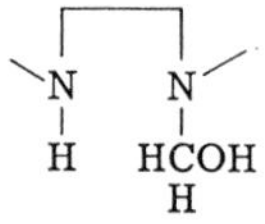

However, only the bridge methylene form (the middle formula shown above) has been detected experimentally.

Finally, the formimino derivative (fi) of FH_4 appears to exist exclusively in the form of the N-5 derivative:

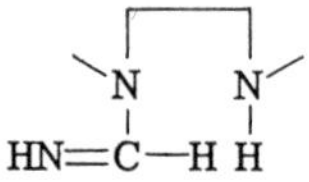

fi⁵FH₄

Formimine may be considered to be the imino derivative of formic acid. When fi⁵FH₄ is hydrolyzed in presence of the appropriate enzyme, f⁵,¹⁰FH₄ is formed, with liberation of ammonia (NH_3), as shown in Eq. (35).

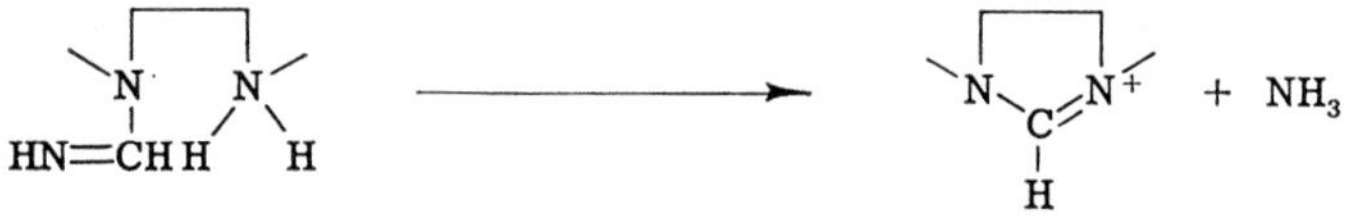

$$\text{fiFH}_4 \longrightarrow \text{f}^{5,10}\text{FH}_4 + \text{NH}_3 \qquad (35)$$

We may readily recognize the relation between the parent molecules and their derivative forms by inspection of the following series of one-carbon compounds, arranged in the order of decreasing states of oxidation (cf. Table 5.1). Formaldehyde gives rise to the hydroxymethyl derivative, formic acid to the formyl derivative, and formimine to the formimino derivative. Each of these interactions requires a special enzyme. The synthesis of f¹⁰FH₄ from formic acid requires ATP, whereas the synthesis of hFH₄ from

HCHO and FH_4 is not an energized process. Breakdown products of purines (formimimoglycine) or of histidine (formiminogluta-mate) are the actual donors of the formimino group to the co-enzyme.

ATP intervenes not only in the interaction of formic acid with FH_4, but also in the conversion of f^5FH_4 to $f^{10}FH_4$. The mechanism of this type of reaction will be dealt with extensively in Chapter VIII. For the present purpose we may assume that a phosphorylated derivative of FH_4 is formed first, and that the formyl group is then introduced by displacement of the phosphoryl group.

TABLE 5.1

States of Oxidation and Sites of Attachment of C_1 Groups [a]

Site of attachment			C_1 unit	Oxidation State
N-5	N-10	N-5 and N-10		
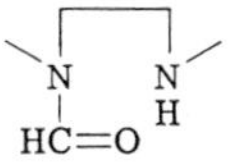 (N, N—H; HC=O)	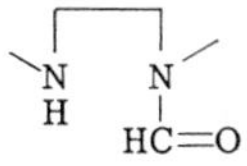 (N—H, N; HC=O)	—	Formyl	Formate
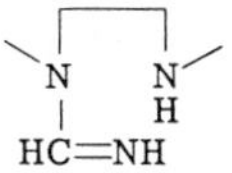 (N, N—H; HC=NH)	—	—	Formimino	Formate
—	—	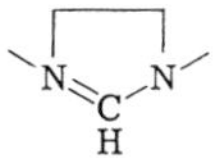 (N=C(H)—N ring)	Methenyl	Formate
—	—	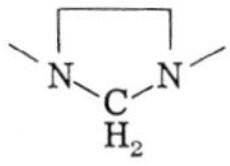 (N—C(H$_2$)—N ring)	Methylene (hydroxymethyl)	Formaldehyde
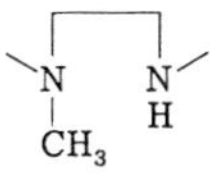 (N, N—H; CH$_3$)	—	—	Methyl	Methanol

[a] Adapted from Frank M. Huennekens in a "Symposium on Nutritional Anemias."

The conversion of $h^{5,10}FH_4$ to $f^{5,10}FH_4$ involves an oxidation of the methylene group to a methenyl group, as shown in Eq. (36).

There is, indeed, a specific dehydrogenase that catalyzes this oxidoreduction. Another enzyme catalyzes the TPNH (or DPNH)-dependent reduction of 5,10-methylene-FH_4 to the N-5 derivative.

We may summarize the catalytic role of FH_4 in terms of the general reactions described by Eqs. (37)–(45).

A. Hydroxymethyl donor $+ FH_4 \longrightarrow hFH_4$ (37)

   $hFH_4 +$ acceptor $\longrightarrow FH_4 +$ hydroxymethyl acceptor   (38)

   Donors (serine, hydroxymethyldeoxycytidylate); acceptors (glycine, deoxy-cytidylate)

B. Formyl donor $+ FH_4 \longrightarrow fFH_4$ (39)

   $fFH +$ acceptor $\longrightarrow + FH_4 +$ formyl acceptor   (40)

   Donor (formyl glutamate); acceptors (carboxamide ribotide, glycinamide ribotide)

C. Formimino donor $+ FH_4 \longrightarrow fiFH_4$ (41)

   $fiFH_4 +$ acceptor $\longrightarrow FH_4 +$ formimino acceptor   (42)

   Donors (formiminoglycine, formiminoglutamate); acceptors (glycine, glutamate)

D. Hydroxymethyl donor $+ FH_4 \longrightarrow 5,10\text{-}hFH_4$ (43)

   $5,10\text{-}hFH_4 + DPNH \longrightarrow$ 5-methyl FH_4 (44)

   5-methyl $FH_4 +$ acceptor $\longrightarrow FH_4 +$ methyl acceptor   (45)

   Donors (serine, glycine); acceptors (homocysteine)

These transfer reactions are steps in the synthesis of purines, pyrimidines, and amino acids.

In many respects FH_4 and CoA play similar catalytic roles as transfer agents, or shuttle agents, between donor and acceptor molecules. Bound to specific apoenzymes, they are capable of re-moving some appropriate group from a donor molecule and trans-ferring it to an acceptor molecule.

BIOTIN

Although biotin has long been known as one of the B vitamin group, it was only comparatively late in the development of en-zymology that its coenzymic function was defined. It has the struc-ture shown below—a double-ring system containing eight com-ponent atoms:

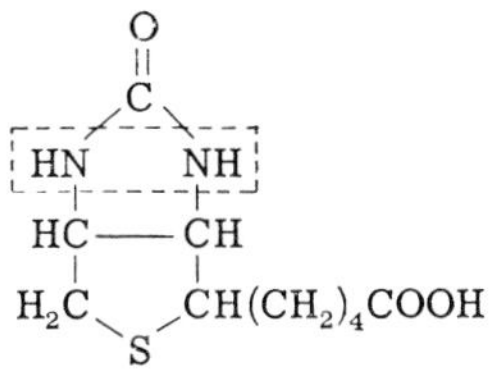

Biotin

The two nitrogen atoms separated by the carbonyl group are the key atoms in the catalytic role of biotin—namely, the activation of CO_2. We may represent this activation by the reactions shown in Eqs. (46)–(48), in which P represents an orthophosphate residue.

$$\text{Biotin} + \text{ATP} \longrightarrow \text{biotin-P} + \text{ADP} \tag{46}$$

$$\text{Biotin-P} + CO_2 \longrightarrow \text{biotin-}CO_2 + \text{P} \tag{47}$$

$$\text{Biotin-}CO_2 + \text{acceptor} \longrightarrow \text{biotin} + (\text{acceptor-}CO_2) \tag{48}$$

The first step in the activation of CO_2 is the formation of a phos-phorylated derivative of biotin. If we represent biotin as RN—H where —N—H is the reactive functional group, then the enzyme-bound intermediate is

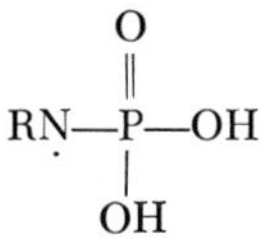

and the product is RN—CO_2. This set of reactions takes place on a single protein enzyme (kinase) to which biotin is bound. There is a whole series of enzymes which transfer biotin-bound CO_2 to some acceptor molecule. In fatty acid synthesis the following carboxylation reaction is of importance [Eq. (49)].

$$\text{Biotin-CO}_2 + \text{CH}_3\overline{\text{COSCoA}} \longrightarrow \text{biotin} + \text{COOHCH}_3\overline{\text{COSCoA}} \qquad (49)$$

Acetyl-CoA is carboxylated by biotin-CO_2 to yield malonyl-CoA. Usually, the enzyme which catalyzes the ATP-dependent carboxylation of biotin is structurally linked to the transferase enzyme implicated in the transfer of biotin-bound CO_2 to the acceptor molecule.

HEMOPROTEINS

The catalytic possibilities of the combination of an Fe atom with four pyrrole nuclei (cf. formula below) have been "explored" extensively throughout evolution.

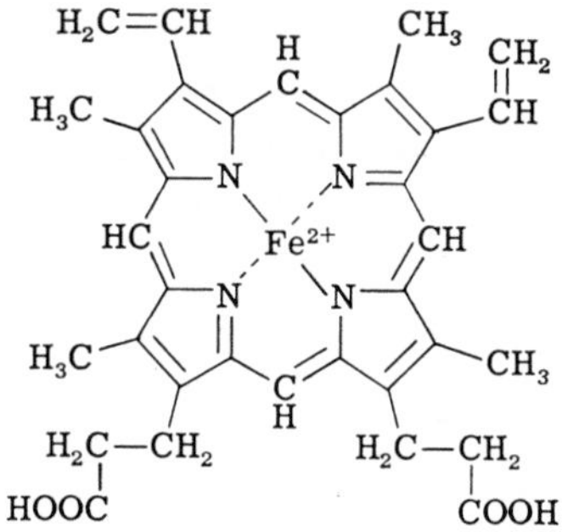

The hemoproteins—the general name applied to the set of proteins containing iron-tetrapyrrole as functional groups—participate in a wide variety of catalytic processes. The *hemoglobins* (and myoglobin) combine reversibly with molecular oxygen. *Catalase* catalyzes the decomposition of H_2O_2 into water and oxygen. The *peroxidases* catalyze the oxidation of various substrate molecules by H_2O_2. The *cytochromes* undergo cyclical reduction and oxidation in the electron-transfer chains of the mitochondrion and of the microsomal system. The nature of the link between the central Fe atom and the protein, the chemical and physical properties of the protein, and the nature and location of the substituents introduced into the pyrrole nuclei are the determinants of the catalytic function of the hemoprotein. Also, in two instances— chlorophyll and turacin—the central metal atom is different. In chlorophyll it is Mg; this variation has led to a molecule which can serve as the primary photoreceptor in the photosynthetic process. The central metal atom of turacin is Cu. This metalloporphyrin is combined with a protein which plays some structural function in the feathers of a bird.

In all the metalloporphyrins the central metal atom is the pivotal atom. It may undergo a cycle of reduction and oxidation involving the gain and loss of a single electron; a cycle of combination with, and dissociation from, molecular oxygen, without change in its state of oxidation; a cycle of combination with H_2O_2, followed by rearrangement of the complex leading to the evolution of oxygen; and so on. The hemoproteins point up the multiple possibilities for the genesis of new catalytic functions inherent in the combination of a protein with a particular functional group. There are at least four different naturally occurring forms of the tetrapyrrole nucleus—these forms differing in respect to the nature and position of the substituents attached to the pyrrole rings. The central atom may be one of three different species of metal. In practically every known metalloporphyrin-protein combination, the nature of the links between the iron-porphyrin and the protein is unique. The links may be covalent or electrostatic, and the number of links is variable.

In the hemoglobins we have to consider yet another basis for variation of function. The hemoglobin molecule of the human red blood corpuscle is built up by the combination of four protein subunits (two pairs of subunits), each with its own heme group. In myoglobin, the analogous compound indigenous to muscle tissue, there are no subunits—that is, the molecule corresponds to a single subunit of hemoglobin.

COBAMIDE COENZYMES

The prize for structural complexity is reserved, without a doubt, for the coenzymic forms of vitamin B_{12} (cf. Figure 5.2). In essence, vitamin B_{12} consists of a central atom of cobalt linked to

(a) four pyrrole nuclei (corrin ring); (b) dimethylbenzimidazole nucleotide; and (c) cyanide. One additional noteworthy feature of the molecule is that the benzimidazole nucleotide is doubly attached: at one end to the cobalt atom and at the other end to the side chain of one of the pyrrole nuclei. There are at least two forms of vitamin B_{12} that fulfill a coenzymic role. In one such form the cyanide group (attached to the central cobalt atom) is

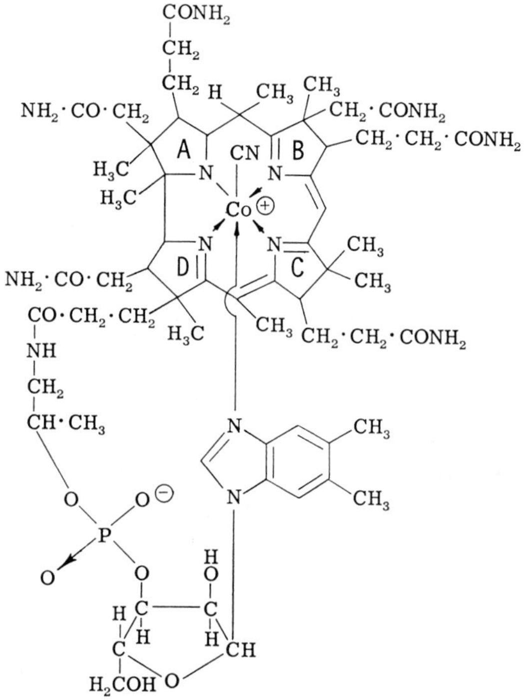

Fig. 5.2. Structure of vitamin B_{12} (cyanocobalamin).

replaced by an adenosyl residue. We shall refer to this form as adenosyl B_{12}. In the other form, the cyanide group of vitamin B_{12} is replaced by a methyl group. The term "cobamide coenzyme" is also applied to the functional forms of vitamin B_{12}. The cobalt atom in both coenzymic forms is in the trivalent state.

Adenosyl B_{12}* has been shown to be the functional coenzyme of three different enzymes which, respectively, catalyze the reactions shown in Figure 5.3. Each of these three reactions involves internal rearrangements in a given molecule: methylmalonyl-CoA to succinyl-CoA, glutamate to methyl aspartate, and propionaldehyde to 1,2-propanediol. The gross chemical mechanism is readily

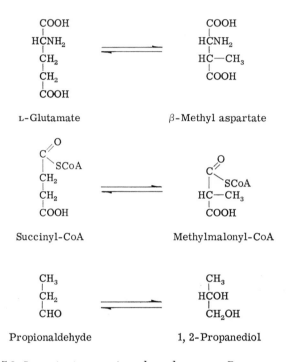

Fig. 5.3. Isomerization reactions dependent upon B_{12} coenzymes.

recognizable, but the fine details have yet to be worked out. In each of the three reactions a hydride ion is abstracted from the substrate molecule and finally returned to the modified, or isomerized, substrate. It is reasonable to assume that the cobalt atom is

* Strictly speaking it is deoxyadenosyl-B_{12} and not adenosyl B_{12}. Carbon atom 5 of the ribose moiety lacks a hydroxyl group.

the instrument of this abstraction. The hydrion mechanism for this abstraction, postulated by Frank M. Huennekens, is summarized in Figure 5.4.

Methyl B_{12} is formed from cyano B_{12} by the sequence of reactions shown in Figure 5.5. This coenzyme form of B_{12} is the functional group of an enzyme that catalyzes the methylation of homo-

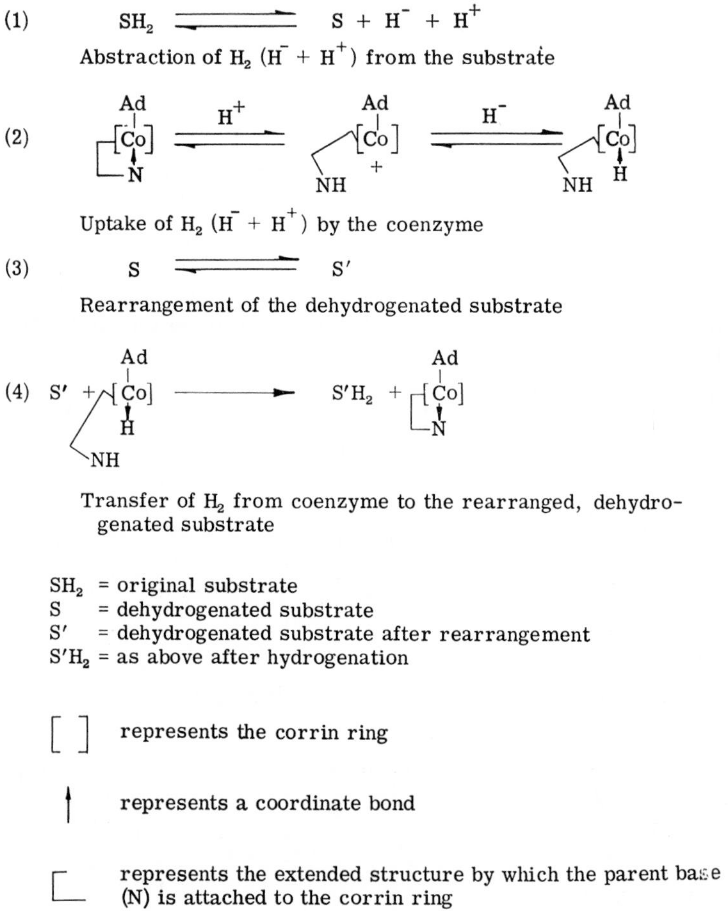

(1) $SH_2 \rightleftharpoons S + H^- + H^+$

Abstraction of H_2 ($H^- + H^+$) from the substrate

(2)

Uptake of H_2 ($H^- + H^+$) by the coenzyme

(3) $S \rightleftharpoons S'$

Rearrangement of the dehydrogenated substrate

(4)

Transfer of H_2 from coenzyme to the rearranged, dehydrogenated substrate

SH_2 = original substrate
S = dehydrogenated substrate
S' = dehydrogenated substrate after rearrangement
$S'H_2$ = as above after hydrogenation

[ ]   represents the corrin ring

| represents a coordinate bond

⌐_   represents the extended structure by which the parent base (N) is attached to the corrin ring

Fig. 5.4. Hypothetical mechanism for role of adenosyl B_{12} in isomerization reactions. From Frank M. Huennekens, Jr., *in* "Symposium on Nutritional Anemias" (see reference list).

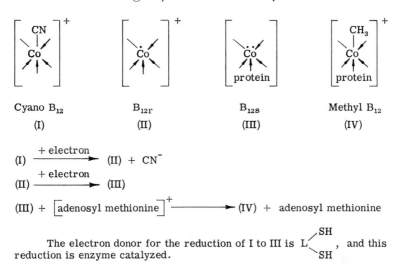

Cyano B_{12}	B_{12r}	B_{12s}	Methyl B_{12}
(I)	(II)	(III)	(IV)

$$(I) \xrightarrow{+ \text{ electron}} (II) + CN^-$$

$$(II) \xrightarrow{+ \text{ electron}} (III)$$

$$(III) + \left[\text{adenosyl methionine}\right]^+ \longrightarrow (IV) + \text{adenosyl methionine}$$

The electron donor for the reduction of I to III is $L{<}^{SH}_{SH}$, and this reduction is enzyme catalyzed.

Fig. 5.5. Sequence of reactions in the conversion of cyano B_{12} to methyl B_{12}.

cysteine by 5-methyltetrahydrofolate; the product of methylation of homocysteine is methionine. During the catalytic cycle, the methyl group of B_{12} itself is not transferred.

Design of Prosthetic Groups

We may think of the various prosthetic groups as a set of molecular tools, each eminently suited for a particular chemical maneuver. Cocarboxylase is specifically designed to break carbon-to-carbon bonds; pyridoxal phosphate for forming Schiff bases; lipoic acid for oxidative acylation; biotin for activating CO_2 (by conversion to a reactive carbonyl group); cobalt-porphyrin for reversibly abstracting and reinserting a proton, etc.

We are still only at the beginning of an understanding of how these chemical maneuvers reflect the design of the molecules concerned. The coenzyme, DPN^+ is a particularly good example of a molecule "tailored" by Nature for a specific kind of chemical reaction. The chemistry of reactions involving DPN^+ is sufficiently well understood that we can now perceive the near perfect design of the molecule for the catalytic processes in which it participates.

In the abbreviated formula of DPN^+, given on the following page, the R-group is concerned with holding the molecule in place on the enzyme surface and is not involved in the oxidoreduction. It is the pyridinium ring which is the "business-end" of the molecule.

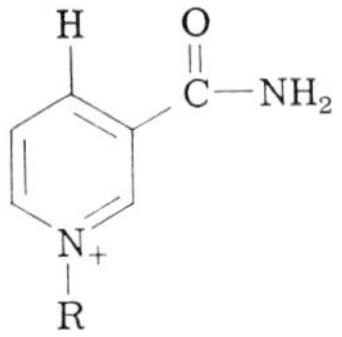

In the dehydrogenase reaction, DPN^+ acquires the elements of a hydride ion:

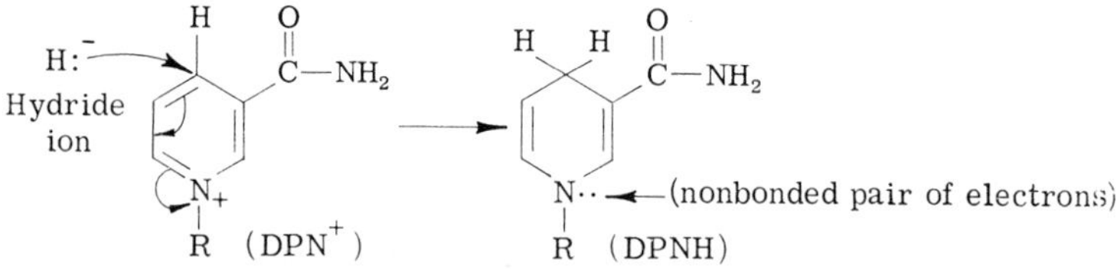

The addition of the hydride to DPN^+ results in the rearrangement of the double bonds in the molecule and in the consequent movement of a pair of electrons within the ring toward the nitrogen atom where these electrons take up a position in which they are *not bonding* any additional atom to nitrogen. Such a pair of electrons, which resides on an atom but which is not engaged in bonding, is called a nonbonding, or unshared, pair of electrons. The shift of electrons within the pyridinium ring to the nonbonding position of the nitrogen atom is associated with a profound change in the shape of the molecule, reflecting the change in the shape of the nitrogen atom.

The nitrogen atom of the pyridinium ring of DPN^+ is "flat." This means that the nitrogen atom, the two carbon atoms in the pyridinium ring to which the nitrogen atom is linked, and the carbon atom in the R-group to which the nitrogen atom is bonded, all lie in the same plane. However, when a hydride is added to DPN^+, the nitrogen atom no longer remains flat, but becomes tetrahedral, like a saturated carbon atom. This means that in the reduced molecule the three atoms bonded to the nitrogen atom occupy three apices of a regular tetrahedron, while the nonbonding pair of electrons is directed toward the fourth apex. This profound change in the shape of the nitrogen atom reflects itself in a change in the general shape of the molecule of DPNH as compared to that of DPN$^+$. The change in shape of the molecule takes on greater significance when it is considered in light of the manner in which the molecule is held on the enzyme surface. It is known that the carboxamide group

$$-C-NH_2$$
$$\overset{\|}{O}$$

is absolutely required for dehydrogenase activity, although it is not directly involved in the chemistry of the dehydrogenase reaction. Presumably, this group, similar in function to the R-group, is required for holding the molecule on the enzyme surface. This must mean that the binding of the carboxamide and R-group to the enzyme surface must remain essentially spatially constant despite the great change in the shape of the molecule during reduction. Such a restriction can be satisfied during the reduction only by the rotation or "flip" of the plane of the pyridinium ring, as shown in Figure 5.6.

It should be noticed that in the reduced form, the pyridinium ring is virtually parallel to the enzyme surface, and the hydrogen atom to be donated by DPNH is pointing downward. If an acceptor

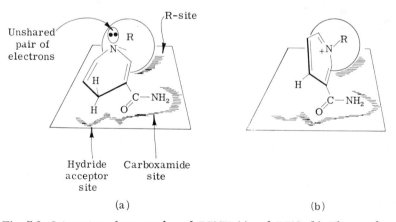

Fig. 5.6. Orientation of enzyme-bound DPNH (a) and DPN$^+$ (b). The pyridinium ring is bound to the enzyme via the carboxamide and R-group (represented as a sphere).

group, which is capable of picking off the elements of a hydride ion, is present at that site on the enzyme surface, DPNH will be oxidized and the "flip" will occur. The pyridinium ring of DPN^+, thus formed, will now be essentially perpendicular to the enzyme surface. In the perpendicular orientation, the pyridinium ring of DPN^+ is able to pick up a hydride from a donor which can donate to either "face" of the flat ring, although in most cases the enzymic donation is stereospecific for only one face of the ring. Such a hydride donation would *force* the flip of the ring from oxidized to reduced form, and thus bring the reduced ring again into perfect position to pass the hydride on to an enzyme-bound acceptor. Thus we have a system which flips back and forth upon reduction and reoxidation. Such a system, which is well adapted for the enzyme-bound passage of electrons through DPN^+ as an intermediate catalytic carrier, has great advantages with respect to the electron-transfer chain, which will be considered in detail in Chapter 9.

The near perfect design of DPN^+ can be further illustrated by asking the question why DPN^+ has a pyridinium rather than a benzene ring. Another way of stating this question is to ask why there is a nitrogen atom rather than a carbon atom in the position *para* to the carbon atom to which the hydride is transferred. The answer to this question becomes clear if we examine the differences between DPN^+ and the analogue in which a benzene ring replaces the pyridinium nucleus.

The benzene analogue of DPN^+ would have the structure:

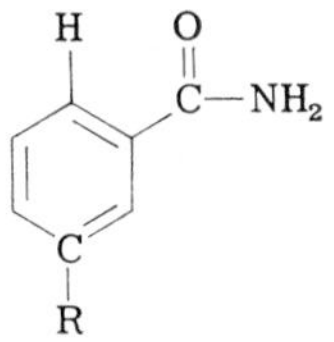

It will be immediately noticed that there is a profound difference between the benzene and pyridinium analogues. In the oxidized form of the molecules, the pyridinium analogue carries a positive charge on the nitrogen atom of the ring, whereas the carbon atom at the same position of the benzene analogue carries no net charge. The positive charge on the nitrogen atom tends to attract the mobile and easily displaced electrons of the pyridinium ring toward the nitrogen atom which acts as an electron sink. This attraction tends to give the carbon atom across the ring from the nitrogen (i.e., *para*) a partial positive charge. Since it is precisely at the *para* carbon atom that the reduction takes place by acquisition of the elements of a negatively charged hydride ion, the generation of a site of positive charge at *that very* carbon atom would tend to facilitate the reduction. Such facilitation by an electron sink is not possible in the benzene analogue. Indeed, the lack of a positive charge on the key carbon atom of the benzene analogue (the one linked to the R group), and the consequent difficulty of generating a positively charged center at the site of reduction, makes the acquisition of a hydride ion chemically very unlikely. In effect, the positively charged center is *required*. To generate this center, carbon in the place of nitrogen will just not do.

Let us also consider the question of shape change in the benzene analogue as compared to the pyridinium analogue. The carbon atom replacing the nitrogen atom in the ring is also "flat," and on this basis there seems to be no advantage in having a nitrogen atom. Let us imagine for the moment, although we know that hydride transfer to the benzene analogue is chemically unlikely, that such a transfer *were* possible. Such a hydride transfer could be written:

(Carbanion)

The reduced compound formed, with a nonbonding pair of electrons now on carbon, would be a negatively charged *carbanion*. Carbanions are known to be extremely strong bases, which means that such a molecule would have an enormous tendency to acquire a proton to form the saturated and tetrahedral carbon compound. Therefore, a benzene analogue, if enzyme-bound in the same fashion as the pyridinium analogue, could undergo the "flip" in the orientation of its ring. The nonbonding pair of electrons, however, is now a *bonding* pair, forming a bond between carbon and hydrogen.

Thus far, on the basis of considerations of change in shape, the nitrogen atom in the ring offers no advantage over a carbon atom. However, in the reoxidation of the benzene analogue, great difficulties would arise. Reoxidation requires the "feeding back" of electrons into the ring. In the benzene analogue this is not easily possible, since it would be necessary to regenerate the carbanion as the source of the nonbonded electrons to be fed back. The formation of a carbanion is extremely unfavorable on energetic grounds. In a sense, the nonbonded electrons required for feeding back are "trapped" in the very stable carbon-hydrogen bond formed during reduction of the benzene analogue. The reduced pyridinium analogue has none of this difficulty. The nitrogen atom of the ring is capable of tolerating a nonbonding pair of electrons very well, and yet does not restrict the ability of these electrons to feed back into the ring during reoxidation. The choice of nitrogen on this basis is quite clear.

Thus, we see that the DPN^+ molecule is extremely well designed. In particular, the nitrogen atom of this molecule is well chosen. Indeed it is difficult to imagine how such a molecule could operate with any atom other than nitrogen. Although it seems difficult to imagine at present, there might conceivably be better designed molecules than DPN^+ for the chemical role it fulfills, and as long as such a possibility exists, it is appropriate to describe the design of DPN^+ as "near" perfect.

Suggested Reading

Books

Boyer, P., Lardy, H., and Myrbäck, K., eds., "The Enzymes," Academic Press, New York, 1960: volumes 2 and 3 on prosthetic groups and cofactors.

Falk, J. E., "Porphyrins and Metalloporphyrins," Elsevier Publishing Co., Amsterdam, 1964.

Falk, J. E., Lemberg, R., and Morton, R. K., eds., "Hematin Enzymes," Pergamon Press, Oxford, 1961.

Hutchinson, D. W., "Nucleotides and Coenzymes," Methuen and Co., London, 1964.

Khorana, H. G., "Some Recent Developments in the Chemistry of Phosphate Esters of Biological Interest," John Wiley and Sons, Ltd., New York and London, 1961.

Kosower, E., "Molecular Biochemistry," McGraw-Hill, New York, 1962.

Smith, L. E., "Vitamin B_{12}," 3rd ed., Methuen and Co., London (1965).

Snell, E. E., "The Mechanism of Action of Water Soluble Vitamins," Churchill, London, 1961.

Strong, F. M., "Topics in Microbial Chemistry," John Wiley and Sons, Inc., New York, 1958: See chapter on coenzyme A.

Wagner, W. F., and Folkers, K., "Vitamins and Coenzymes," John Wiley and Sons, Inc., New York, 1964.

Special Articles

Abeles, R. H., and Lee, H. A., *Brookhaven Symp. Biol.* **15**, 310 (1962): studies on diol dehydrase.

Baddiley, J., *Advan. Enzymol.* **16**, 1(1955): on the structure of coenzyme A.

Barker, H. A., Weissbach, H., and Smyth, R. D., *Proc. Natl. Acad. Sci. U.S.* **44**, 1093 (1958): on a coenzyme form of vitamin B_{12}.

Breslow, R., *J. Am. Chem. Soc.* **80**, 3719 (1958): on the mechanism of action of thiamine.

Dolphin, D., Johnson, A. W., Rodrigo, R., and Shaw, N., *Pure and Appl. Chem.* **7**, 539 (1963): on the vitamin B_{12} coenzyme.

Fisher, H. F., Conn, E. E., Vennesland, B., and Westheimer, F., *J. Biol. Chem.* **202**, 687 (1953): on the stereospecific transfer of deuterium to DPN.

Green, D. E., *Advan. Enzymol.* **1**, 177 (1941): on the enzyme-trace substance concept.

Huennekens, F. M., Jr., *in* "Currents in Biochemical Research" (D. E. Green, ed.), Interscience Publishing Co., New York, 1956: on nucleotides and coenzymes in enzymatic processes.

Huennekens, F. M., Jr., *in* "Symposium on Nutritional Anemias," American Medical Association, St. Louis, Missouri, October 1964: on the biochemical functions and interrelationships of folic acid and vitamin B_{12}.

Huennekens, F. M., Jr., Whitely, H. R., and Osborn, M. J., *J. Cellular Comp. Physiol.* **54**, Suppl. 1, 109 (1959): mechanism of formylation and hydroxymethylation reactions.

Kaplan, N., Ciotti, M. M., and Stolzenbach, F. E., *J. Biol. Chem.* **221**, 833 (1956): on analogues of DPN^+.

Karlson, P., *in* "Introduction to Modern Biochemistry," Academic Press, New York, 1963: see Chapter VI on coenzymes.

Khorana, H. G., and Moffatt, J. H., *J. Am. Chem. Soc.* **83**, 663 (1961): total synthesis of coenzyme A.

Knappe, E., Ringelmann, J. E., and Lynen, F., *Biochem. Z.* **335**, 168 (1961): mechanism of action of biotin.

Koike, M., Reed, L. J., and Carroll, W. R., *J. Biol. Chem.* **235**, 1924 (1960); **235**, 1931 (1960): on dehydrogenation of ketoacids.

Krampitz, L. O., Suzuki, I., and Greull, G., *Proc. 5th Intern. Congr. Biochem.* Vol. IV, p. 321, Pergamon Press, London, 1963: on the mechanism of action of thiamine pyrophosphate.

Lynen, F., Reichert, E., and Rueff, L., *Ann.* **574,** 1 (1951): on the identification of acetyl coenzyme A.

Massey, V., and Gibson, Q. H., *Federation Proc.* **23,** 18 (1964): on the role of semiquinones in flavoprotein catalysis.

Massey, V., Gibson, Q. H., and Veeger, C., *Biochem. J.* **77,** 341 (1960): on intermediates in the catalytic action of lipoyl dehydrogenase.

Masters, B. S. S., Bilimoria, M. H., Kamin, H., and Gibson, Q. H., *J. Biol. Chem.* **240,** 4081 (1965): on electron transfer cycles in flavoproteins.

Metzler, D. E., Ikawa, M., and Snell, E. E., *J. Am. Chem. Soc.* **76,** 648 (1954): mechanism of catalysis by metal chelates of pyridoxal.

Perlman, D., ed., "Vitamin B_{12} Coenzymes," *Ann. N. Y. Acad. Sci.* **112,** 547 (1964).

Reed, L. J., *Vitamins and Hormones,* **20,** 1 (1962): on the biochemistry of lipoic acid.

Scrimegeour, K. G., and Huennekens, F. M., *in* "Pteridine Chemistry" (W. Pfleider and E. C. Taylor, eds.) Pergamon Press, New York, 1964: on the coenzyme of one-carbon metabolism.

Weissbach, H., and Barker, H. A., *Proc. 5th Intern. Congr. Biochem.,* Vol. IV, p. 255, Pergamon Press, London, 1963: the cobamide coenzymes.

Weissbach, H., and Dickerman, H. W., *Physiol. Rev.* **45,** 80 (1965): review of B_{12}-containing enzymes and coenzymes.

CHAPTER 6 ———————————————————

Bioenergetics

The cells of living organisms, like man-made machines, accomplish work. Like machines, cells require a source of energy (fuel) for the work they do. However, the energy changes in a given physiological process, such as the synthesis of a macromolecule or the contraction of a muscle, cannot always be specified with the same precision as are the energy changes involved in the operation of man-made machines. This is not because of any fundamental differences, but rather because of the complexity of living cells and the difficulty of studying energy changes at the molecular level. We know, in fact, that the basic relationship of an electric current to an electric motor is applicable to all biological energy transformations, and that many of the principles involved in the operation of man-made machines are closely analogous to the principles of bioenergetics. It is especially interesting to note that the efficiency of certain parts of the cellular machinery has never been exceeded in machines devised by man.

SOURCES OF BIOLOGICAL ENERGY

The animal body derives its energy ultimately from the chemical energy stored in the molecules of the diet. When a molecule is synthesized, energy is required for the assembly of its constituent atoms—bond formation. The animal body taps the stored chemical energy of such molecules by appropriate degradative processes. That is to say, the particular molecules that serve as biological fuel (such as glucose, fatty acids, and certain amino acids) undergo a sequence of chemical changes that are preparatory for the energy-yielding step *which is always an oxidation, or a conse-*

127

quence of an oxidation. * During these oxidative processes, utilizable energy is released, and a portion of this released energy is then conserved in an appropriate form.

STORAGE FORM OF BIOLOGICAL ENERGY

There is, in fact, only one form to which the utilizable energy released by oxidation is transformed. Oxidative release of utilizable energy is coupled to the synthesis of ATP from ADP and P_i (cf. Figure 6.1). The new bond formed between the terminal

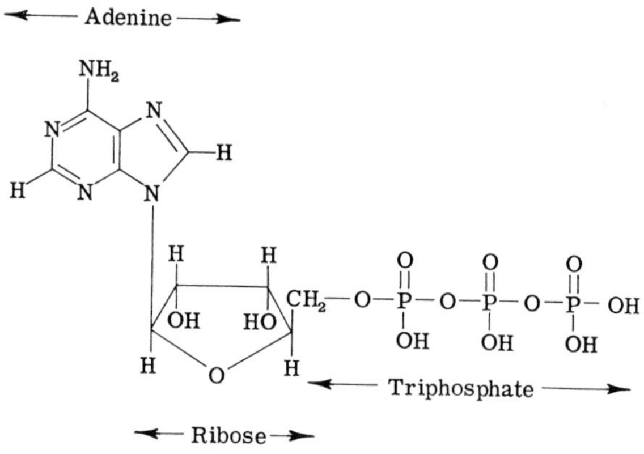

Fig. 6.1. Structural formula of adenosine triphosphate (ATP).

P of ADP and the P of inorganic phosphate (via an O atom) is the repository of the conserved energy. It may, at first glance, appear strange that the utilizable energy, locked in various molecules of the diet, should be converted into the energy of a P—O—P bond of only one molecule, namely, ATP. Why should the wealth of energy be cashed in for energy of one denomination? The answer is that ATP is to biochemical machines what electricity is to an electric motor; biochemical machines are designed to be energized exclusively by ATP.

---

* Oxidative reactions in general involve greater energy changes than nonoxidative reactions. The formation of a "high-energy" bond would have to be linked to a chemical reaction with a good yield of energy; oxidative reactions would then clearly be the most acceptable candidates.

RADIANT ENERGY AS THE ULTIMATE SOURCE OF BIOLOGICAL ENERGY

The source of the molecules that make up the diet of the animal kingdom is the green plant. The plant world is uniquely specialized for the assembly of complex molecules from simple molecules such as CO_2, H_2O, and NH_3. To accomplish this job (essentially a reductive synthesis), the green plant harnesses the radiant energy of sunlight. Although carnivores eat no vegetation, they prey ultimately on the herbivores who subsist entirely on plant products. Thus, the sun is the ultimate source of all energy in biological systems, at least for the animal and plant worlds. Some microorganisms are independent of solar energy by virtue of their capacity to liberate utilizable energy by oxidation of inorganic molecules in soil or in water.

Devices for Coupling Oxidation to ATP Synthesis

Relatively few substances can serve as fuel for the biological generation of energy; for practical purposes we need consider only three biochemical devices by which the synthesis of ATP can be coupled to oxidation. We shall discuss these devices in detail in the next chapter. One of them involves the oxidation of pyruvate to CO_2 and H_2O by molecular oxygen, as shown in Eq. (1).

$$CH_3COCOOH + 2.5O_2 + 15P_i + 15ADP \rightarrow 3CO_2 + 2H_2O + 15ATP \qquad (1)$$

The second involves the anaerobic cleavage of glucose to lactic acid, as shown in Eq. (2).

$$C_6H_{12}O_6 + 2P_i + 2ADP \rightarrow 2CH_3CHOHCOOH + 2ATP \qquad (2)$$

The first equation is an overall description of a process known as the *citric acid cycle* which takes place within a subcellular organelle—the mitochondrion. The second equation is an overall description of a process known as glycolysis, the enzymes for which are probably localized in the membrane that encloses the cell. Glycolysis and the citric cycle, though independent processes, very often are synchronized so that the end product of glycolysis (lactic acid) becomes available for oxidation in the citric cycle.*

---

* Lactic acid can be readily oxidized to pyruvic acid under aerobic conditions.

When such synchronization takes place, one molecule of glucose is converted to CO_2 and H_2O by six molecules of oxygen.

In green plants there is still another device by which energy can be obtained for living systems—photosynthesis. By this device, which is localized within a subcellular organelle (the chloroplast) solar radiant energy is utilized for the synthesis of ATP. In the light the chloroplast is the principal ATP-generating system of the plant cell, whereas in the dark the mitochondrion and the glycolytic apparatus are the predominant systems which supply ATP.[*]

Devices for Utilizing the Bond Energy of ATP

Not only is there a highly specialized biochemical apparatus for linking citric acid cycle oxidations, glycolysis, and photochemical oxidations to the synthesis of ATP, but there are other biochemical devices by which ATP can be used to power such processes as synthesis of complex molecules, excitation of nerve, contraction of muscle, and secretion by the tubule cells of the kidney. In Chapter 8 some of these processes will be considered in detail. Here we are concerned only with a few of the most basic principles of bioenergetics relevant to the coupling of oxidation to the synthesis of ATP, and to the powering of synthetic reactions by ATP.

Thermodynamics of Energy Conservation

In all chemical reactions there are energy changes. We are not concerned here with such changes in general, but only with the way in which energy, locked (or stored) in molecules, can be released and conserved in some suitable form for subsequent utilization. This conservation is a contrived operation which requires special equipment in the same sense that a turbine is needed to

[*] Bacteria and microorganisms that do not have a citric cycle, and lack the capacity for photochemical phosphorylation, have two alternative energy sources—either glycolysis or a modification of the mitochondrial system which permits the coupling of ATP synthesis to the oxidation of molecules other than those of the citric acid cycle.

convert water power into electric current. Given the necessary molecular equipment for conservation of oxidatively released energy, the efficiency of any conservation operation, however perfect, has certain limits, and these limits are rigorously defined by the laws of thermodynamics. Whether or not the utilizable energy will be conserved is a question of mechanism and equipment, but how much can be conserved is a question of thermodynamics. In living systems the efficiency with which utilizable energy is conserved after being released by oxidation is extremely high—approaching the theoretical thermodynamic limits.

Component Steps in Energy Conservation

We can subdivide the overall process of biologic energy conservation into four independent events which follow one another in sequence. (1) The electron donor for the coupling reaction is generated in a set of preparatory reactions. The donors include triose phosphate in glycolysis, DPNH and succinate in the citric cycle of the mitochondrion, and probably reduced ferredoxin in the chloroplast. (2) The appropriate electron donor interacts with the electron-transfer system, and this oxidoreduction is coupled to the formation of the first high-energy intermediate. (3) The high-energy bond of this intermediate is then, in effect, transferred from one pair of linked molecules (those forming the high-energy intermediate) to another pair of molecules, namely ADP and P_i. Thus, the high-energy bond finally comes to reside in the P—O—P link between ADP and P_i. (4) The P—O—P bond of ATP is manipulated by replacement reactions to give rise to bonds essential for synthetic processes. These four component events are summarized graphically in Figure 6.2. In the coupling reaction there is transformation in the form of the energy involved. Coupling channels the released energy of oxidation into the bond energy of a high-energy intermediate.

Thermodynamic Principles of the Coupling Reactions

In a coupled reaction an oxidative process is linked to the formation of a bond between two molecules. If the coupled reaction can be carried out reversibly—that is, under conditions close to equilibrium—then the free energy change of the system (δF) is exactly equal to the work capacity (δW), providing the system undergoes no volume change.

In common chemical applications of thermodynamic relations, work only in the form of $P\delta V$ is permitted, and then $\delta F = 0$ at equilibrium. However, if we exclude work in that form (we may assume that the volume change in the coupling systems is, in fact, zero) and allow other sorts of reversible work, then $\delta F = \delta W$. If we equate the δW term with the formation of a high-energy bond, then in a reversible coupled system at equilibrium the free energy change accompanying an oxidative reaction is translated into the equivalent energy of a bond linking two molecules. How this bond

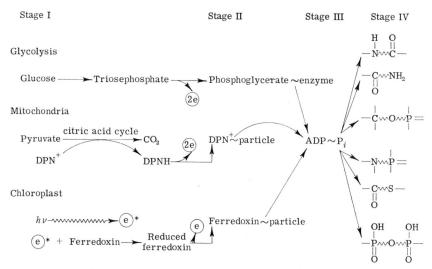

Fig. 6.2. The four stages in the transduction of oxidative energy. Stage I = the preparatory stage during which the electron donors are generated; Stage II = the formation of the high-energy bond by interaction of the electron donor with the coupling system; Stage III = the transfer of the bond from the pair of molecules in the first high-energy intermediate to the pair ADP-P$_i$; Stage IV = the formation of new bonds during ATP-energized synthetic reactions. The high energy intermediate is represented, arbitrarily, as DPN $\sim$ particle in the mitochondrion, and as ferredoxin $\sim$ particle in the chloroplast. The exact form of the intermediates is still unknown, and there are multiple forms. Radiant energy is designated as $h\nu$; an electron as an encircled e.

energy is distributed in the linked molecules is irrelevant to our discussion. We cannot specify precisely the intermediate form that δW assumes in a coupled system. It could be a reversible conformational change, a reversible flow of current, etc. Whatever the nature of this reversible work, its final expression is the formation of the new bond.

The thermodynamic dilemma posed to a cell may be stated as follows. At equilibrium, coupling efficiency is maximized since $\delta F = \delta W$. However, at complete equilibrium a reaction proceeds with infinite slowness, and, if a coupling reaction is slowed down to the point where the net production of the high energy intermediate is zero, the needs of the cell would never be satisfied. Is there some escape from this dilemma? There are experimental grounds for believing that the solution of the dilemma takes the following form. If the primary, reversible coupling reaction is at least two orders of magnitude faster than the irreversible processes by which the high-energy bond is delivered to the outside systems, then it is possible to achieve rapid equilibrium in the primary system (during which the full thermodynamic harvest is reaped) without this equilibrium being materially influenced by the much slower, irreversible secondary processes. The speed of the overall catalytic process is, of course, set by the slower secondary processes.

The dropping-mercury electrode provides an elegant demonstration of the feasibility of achieving near reversibility in a rapid, primary oxidation-reduction reaction at an electrode surface even though slower, irreversible (diffusion-controlled) processes are going on all the time. In this case δW takes the form of reversible electric current, in contrast to the coupled biological system where δW takes the form of a high-energy bond.

The primary coupling system is a single enzyme in the case of glycolysis, or a membrane-repeating unit in the case of the mitochondrion or the chloroplast. From the available evidence, a very convincing case can be made for the idea that the primary coupling act is a nearly reversible, intramolecular process, whereas the secondary delivery is necessarily an irreversible, intermolecular, diffusion-controlled process. The high-energy bond generated in the action of triose phosphate dehydrogenase has to undergo two diffusion-controlled intermolecular transfers before it ends up in the right pair of molecules, and one of these transfers involves interaction with an additional enzyme. The high-energy bond generated by the mitochondrial electron transfer chain has to undergo an even more extensive series of intermolecular transfers before delivery to the right pair of molecules on the outside of the mitochondrion. The electron-transfer process can proceed very many times faster when the mitochondrial system is uncoupled from this series of intermolecular transfers than when it is perfectly coupled. The speed of the uncoupled system is an approximate measure of the intramolecular process, whereas the speed of the coupled system is more nearly a measure of the intermolecular processes.

If the coupling systems have, in fact, achieved the maximal thermodynamic efficiency (that is, if $\delta F = \delta W$), then we would expect the bond energy of the primary high-energy compound to be equal to δF. The oxidation-reduction potential difference between the reductant and the oxidant in the primary coupling system is a measure of δF. However, the value for δW is more difficult to arrive at since this would be the bond energy for the first high-energy intermediate, and this could well be considerably higher than the bond energy of the first stable compound formed in the secondary processes. The instability of the primary enzyme-bound intermediate is the principal difficulty in the evaluation of δW. Another obstacle to a definitive test of the equivalence of δF and δW is the dilemma of assigning a value for the concentration and activity coefficient to an enzyme-bound intermediate.

The conversion of the first high-energy intermediates into ATP is essentially a *seriatim* replacement, by ADP and P_i, of the molecular partners joined by the bond. The enzymic mechanisms involved in these substitution reactions will be considered in more detail in Chapters 8 and 9.

Utilization of ATP for Synthetic Reactions

The final stage in the energy cycle involves the coupling of the hydrolysis of ATP to energy-requiring formation of bonds. Perhaps a simpler way of describing the processes involved in this stage would be in the following terms. Synthetic processes involve bringing two or more molecules together to form a larger molecule. The chemical linking of two molecules by covalent bonds has to be energized, and the energy of hydrolysis of the P—O—P bond of ATP is the source of that energy. In that sense, synthesis is driven by ATP. The actual mechanisms by which ATP powers the synthesis of various biologically important molecules will be dealt with in Chapter 8. Again, these ATP-driven synthetic reactions are replacement reactions. The difference between the free energy of hydrolysis of the pyrophosphate bond of ATP and that of the new bond formed may be small or large, depending on the nature of the reaction being energized.

UNIQUENESS OF ATP

ATP is not the only biological compound containing pyrophosphate bonds. From an energy standpoint, the pyrophosphate bonds of several other types of compounds are similar to those of ATP. However, the diphosphates of these bases cannot replace ADP in the primary processes in which ATP is synthesized, nor can the triphosphates replace ATP in the subsequent processes in which ATP is used to energize other reactions. This high degree of specificity may be an expression not so much of the unique properties of ATP as of the fact that the biochemical machinery has been uniquely designed for ATP (cf. Chapter 2).

The P—O—P bonds of ATP may be transferred to other nucleotides by enzymic means. Thus, adenosine triphosphate (adenosine-P—O—P—O—P) will interact with cytidine diphosphate (cytidine-P—O—P) to form adenosine diphosphate (adenosine-P—O—P) and cytidine triphosphate (cytidine-P—O—P—O—P). In fact, the triophosphates of all the purine- and pyrimidine-5′-nucleotides may be formed from the appropriate diphosphates by enzymic transfer of a phosphoryl group from ATP. For some selected synthetic processes, some triphosphonucleotides other than ATP, are the direct source of chemical energy; however, since they have to be synthesized by transfer of a phosphoryl or pyrophosphoryl group from ATP, they cannot qualify as *primary* energizers. Muscle tissue contains a molecule of another type, adapted for stor-

age of energy—phosphocreatine. This is an N-phosphoramide derivative of creatine and contains a high-energy bond.

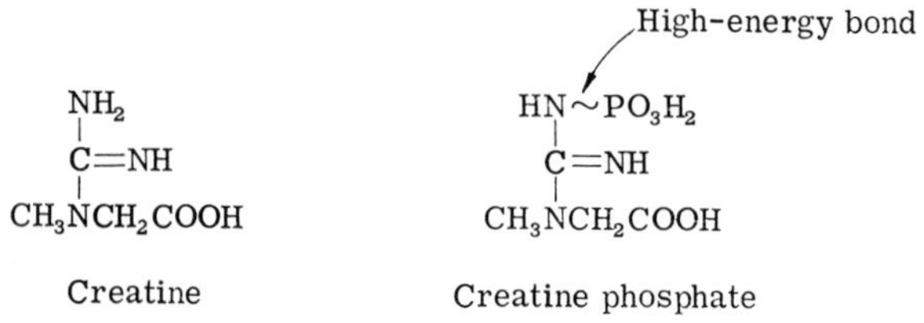

High-energy bond

NH_2
|
C=NH
|
CH_3NCH_2COOH

Creatine

HN∼PO_3H_2
|
C=NH
|
CH_3NCH_2COOH

Creatine phosphate

Because the source of its phosphoryl group is again ATP, creatine
phosphate cannot qualify as a *primary* energy source. There are
several other molecules with high-energy bonds that fall within
the same category as creatine phosphate: arginine phosphate,
acetyl phosphate, acetyl-CoA, histidine phosphate, and acetyl histidine.

The Nature of High Energy Bonds

In biological systems all the known high-energy bonds are found
in anhydride links between two molecules. Equations (3)–(7)
are examples of this relationship.

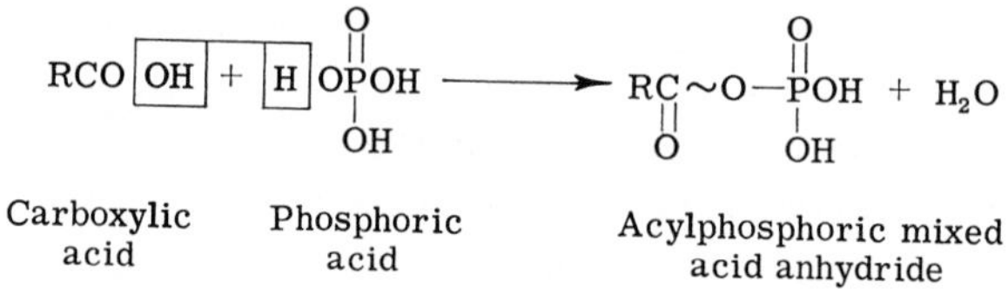

$$RCO\boxed{OH} + \boxed{H}OPOH \longrightarrow RC\sim O-POH + H_2O \tag{3}$$

| Carboxylic
acid | Phosphoric
acid | Acylphosphoric mixed
acid anhydride |

$$RCO\boxed{OH} + \boxed{H}SR \longrightarrow RC\sim S-R + H_2O \tag{4}$$

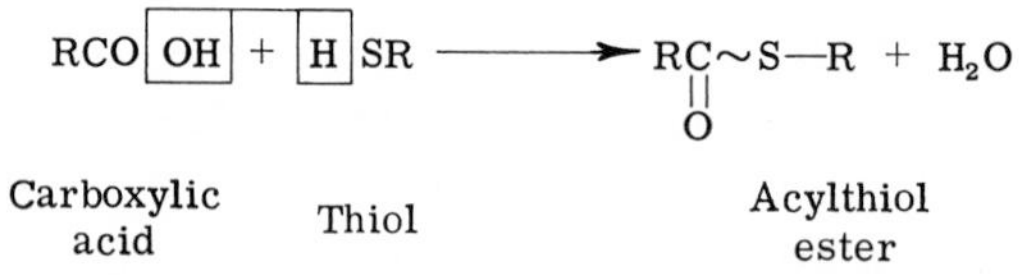

| Carboxylic
acid | Thiol | Acylthiol
ester |

$$C-N\boxed{H} + \boxed{HO}POH \longrightarrow C-N\sim POH + H_2O \tag{5}$$

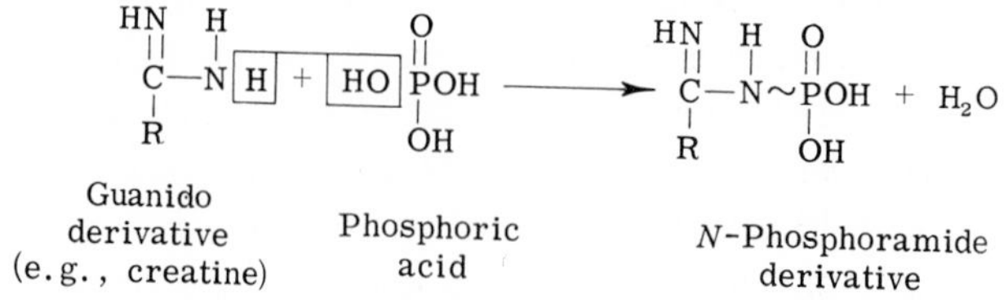

Guanido
derivative
(e.g., creatine)

Phosphoric
acid

N-Phosphoramide
derivative

$$\text{HOP}\boxed{\text{OH}} + \boxed{\text{H}}\,\text{OPOH} \longrightarrow \text{HOP}-\text{O}-\text{POH} + H_2O \qquad (6)$$

Phosphoric acid — Pyrophosphoric acid

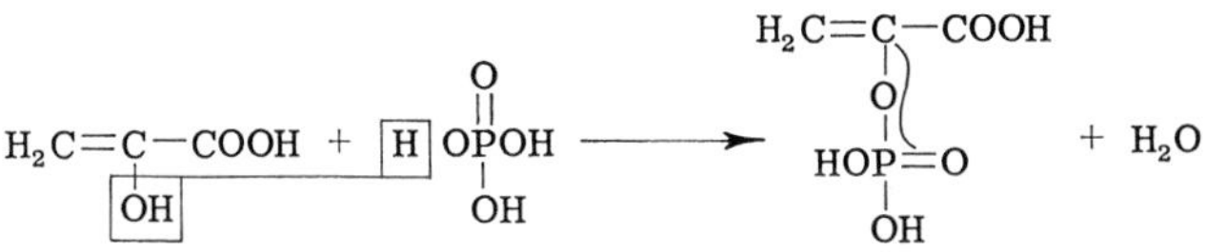

$$H_2C{=}C-COOH + \boxed{H}\,\text{OPOH} \longrightarrow \begin{array}{c} H_2C{=}C-COOH \\ \end{array} + H_2O \qquad (7)$$

Enolpyruvic acid — Phosphoenolpyruvic acid

It must be pointed out that not all compounds formed by elimination of water have a high-energy bond. For example, simple phosphoric esters, such as glucose 6-phosphate, have low-energy links between the carbon atom (via the intermediate oxygen atom) and the phosphorus atom. However, anhydride formation between phosphoric acid and either a carboxylic acid derivative or an enolate, or between two molecules of phosphoric acid, invariably leads to a high-energy bond. The underlying principle may be stated in simple terms. The molecules that can form partners to the high-energy bond (carboxylic acids, enolates, phosphoric acid, guanido derivatives, etc.) are characterized by a high degree of resonance in the region of the group that participates in anhydride formation. Thus, the carboxyl group and the phosphoric acid group, independently, can exist in multiple resonance forms. As soon as the anhydride bond is formed between them, the possible number of these resonance forms is greatly reduced. The reduction of resonance in a resonating system requires the input of energy. The greater the resonance of a group, the greater the energy required to eliminate this resonance. The high-energy character of the bonds formed as described above in Eq. (3)–(7) reflects the conservation in the system of the energy that had to be paid for the elimination of resonance consequent to anhydride formation. The conserved energy is ultimately derived from the internal energy of the two molecules participating in anhydride formation and may be regarded as being localized in the anhydride bond.

Strictly speaking, there is no such entity as a high-energy bond because the energy is distributed over the entire molecule. However, no violence will be done to the facts if we assume, for operational purposes, that the energy is preferentially concentrated in the anhydride bond. When there is a transfer of energy from the molecule with the high-energy bond to a receptor molecule, it is as if the energy were, in fact, localized in the anhydride bond. Thus, we can use very effectively the concept of a localized high-energy bond even though such localization is not borne out by quantum chemical theory and data.

The Molecular Basis of Biologic Energy Transformations

When we compare man-made techniques for transforming energy with the biological techniques we recognize one fundamental difference. Living systems do not depend upon *macro* devices for achieving these transformations. All biological transformations take place at the level of single molecules. There are no large mechanical contrivances to be found in cells. Even a muscle is not a single contrivance but, rather, the sum total of millions of component elements, each of which individually undergoes specific molecular rearrangements, and these are the basis of the performance of the overall system. Energy transformations in living systems lie in the domain of molecular changes, not of macro mechanical contrivances.

Suggested Reading

Books

Klotz, I. M., "Some Principles of Energetics in Biochemical Reactions," Academic Press, New York, 1957.
Lehninger, A. L., "Bioenergetics," W. A. Benjamin, Inc. New York, 1965.
McElroy, W. D., and Glass, B., eds., "A Symposium on Light and Life," The Johns Hopkins University Press, Baltimore, Maryland, 1961.
Szent-Györgyi, A., "Introduction to a Submolecular Biology," Academic Press, New York, 1960.

Special Articles

Hill, T. L., and Morales, M. F., *Arch. Biochem. Biophys.* 37, 425 (1952): on the thermodynamics of free energy transfer in certain models of muscle action.

Huennekens, F. M., and Whiteley, H. R., *in* "Comparative Biochemistry" (M. Florkin and H. S. Mason, eds.), Vol. I, Chapter IV, pp. 107–186, Academic Press, New York, 1960: on energy-rich compounds.

Kalckar, H. M., *Chem. Rev.* **28**, 229 (1941): on mesomeric concepts in the biological sciences.

Kalckar, H. M., *Chem. Rev.* **28**, 71 (1941b): on the nature of energetic coupling in biological synthesis.

Krebs, H. A., and Kornberg, H. L., *Ergeb. Physiol.* **49**, 212 (1957): a survey of the energy transformation in living matter.

Lipmann, F., *in* "Currents in Biochemical Research" (D. E. Green, ed.), p. 137, Interscience Publishing Co., New York, 1946: on metabolic process patterns.

CHAPTER 7 ───────────────────

Energy-Yielding
Biochemical Processes

There are two fundamental processes by which the chemical energy of molecules can be tapped in animal cells. These are the citric acid cycle (the aerobic oxidation of pyruvate), catalyzed by mitochondrial enzymes, and glycolysis (the anerobic splitting of glucose into lactic acid or other products), catalyzed by the glycolytic complex of enzymes. The first requires elementary oxygen, whereas the second can proceed in absence of oxygen. In any given cell both processes may go on simultaneously or one or the other may dominate. Cells that have a low oxygen supply may have to depend largely or entirely on glycolysis. Cells that implement some physiological process continuously, like those of heart or flight muscle, may depend to a preponderant degree on mitochondrial oxidations. In other cells, an even balance is struck between the contributions of the two systems.

Current thinking about biochemical evolution favors the view that glycolysis, the less efficient process for tapping chemical energy, was evolved prior to the citric cycle. There are many organisms that lack the citric cycle complex of enzymes, but none that does not have some form of glycolysis.

The skeletal muscles of higher animals have two types of contractile fibers—dark, or red, fibers which are energized predominantly by citric cycle oxidations, and light, or white, fibers, which are energized predominantly by glycolysis. It appears that muscle cells that depend exclusively on the glycolytic system are capable of powerful, but short-lived, bursts of activity, whereas muscle cells that are energized by citric acid cycle oxidations are capable of less powerful, but more sustained, contractions.

The Citric Cycle

PRINCIPLE OF THE CYCLE

This cycle, discovered by H. A. Krebs in the early 1940's, is a chemical device for oxidizing pyruvic acid completely to CO_2 and H_2O by means of oxygen. The principle of the cycle is readily recognizable from the simple diagram shown in Figure 7.1, in which

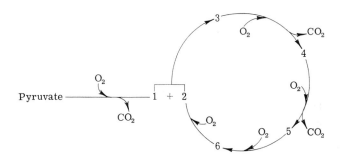

1.	Acetyl–CoA	$CH_3 \cdot CO \cdot \overline{SCoA}$
2.	Oxaloacetate	$COOH \cdot CH_2 \cdot CO \cdot COOH$
3.	Citrate	$COOH \cdot CH_2 \cdot COH(COOH) \cdot CH_2 \cdot COOH$
	Isocitrate	$COOH \cdot CH(OH) \cdot CH(COOH) \cdot CH_2 \cdot COOH$
4.	α-Ketoglutarate	$COOH \cdot CH_2 \cdot CH_2 \cdot CO \cdot COOH$
5.	Succinate	$COOH \cdot CH_2 \cdot CH_2 \cdot COOH$
6.	Fumarate	$COOH \cdot CH = CH \cdot COOH$
	Malate	$COOH \cdot CHOH \cdot CH_2 \cdot COOH$

Fig. 7.1. The citric acid cycle.

the chemical intermediates are represented by numbers. Before entering the cycle, pyruvate is oxidized to an acetyl derivative, 1, which condenses with 2 to form 3. Then 3 is oxidized progressively in four steps, each step involving an oxidation by elementary oxygen. At the end of one complete cycle a molecule of 1 has effectively been burned to CO_2 and H_2O, and a molecule of 2 has been regenerated. The cycle repeats itself (cf. Figure 7.2) until all available pyruvate has been oxidized to CO_2 and H_2O. It should be noted that pyruvate, as such, is not oxidized serially, carbon atom by carbon atom. The process begins that way, with oxidation of pyruvate to acetyl-CoA, but thereafter the mechanism appears to become more complex. It might simplify the understanding of the citric acid cycle to interpret the process in the following terms. The actual oxidations are, in essence, the stepwise oxidation of pyruvate to CO_2 and H_2O in five oxidative steps, but the last four of these oxidations involve the oxidation not of acetate but of the product

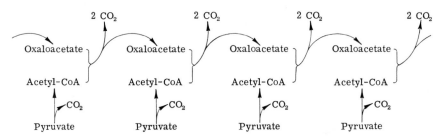

Fig. 7.2. The cyclical character of the citric acid cycle.

formed by condensation of acetyl-CoA with oxaloacetate. Acetate, in this bound form (as citrate or isocitrate), is then oxidized, carbon atom by carbon atom, until only oxaloacetate (the original condensing partner) is left. Thus, oxaloacetate is playing a kind of catalytic role, leading acetyl-CoA to the slaughter, as it were, and then, when the acetate moiety has been disposed of, taking on another molecule of acetyl-CoA.

ENTRY INTO THE CYCLE

It is helpful to think of the citric cycle as a furnace, the entry into which is restricted to all but the six members of the cycle. Any substance can be fully combusted to CO_2 and H_2O if it can give rise to one of these members. Let us consider the three major classes of utilizable molecules in foodstuffs—sugars, fats, and proteins. Sugars can give rise to pyruvate. The fatty acid chains of fats give rise to acetyl-CoA by oxidation. Several of the amino acids which make up proteins are convertible into certain members of the citric cycle: alanine (by transamination*) to pyruvate, proline

* Cf. page 101 in Chapter 5.

and glutamate (by oxidation and/or transamination) to α-ketoglutarate, and aspartate (by transamination) to oxaloacetate. Thus, portions of all three of the principal foodstuffs can be funnelled directly into the citric cycle combustion chamber.

THE RELEASE OF ENERGIZED ELECTRONS DURING THE COMBUSTION PROCESS

The citric cycle involves two separable processes: (1) the combustion process just discussed and (2) the release, during combustion, of electrons which provide the energy ultimately to be transformed into the bond energy of ATP. The combustion process is carried out by a set of enzymes localized exclusively in the repeating units of the outer mitochondrial membrane, whereas the coupling of electron flow to synthesis of ATP is the responsibility of enzymes restricted in localization to the repeating units of the inner membrane (cf. Chapter 10). There is, thus, a geographical as well as functional separation of the combustion process from the coupling phase of oxidation phosphorylation. How are the electrons, released during citric cycle oxidations in the outer membrane, transported to the electron-transfer chain in the inner membrane? These electrons are not free but are localized within two molecules, DPNH and succinate, both of which serve as vehicles for introducing the electrons into the electron-transfer chain (cf. Figure 7.3). The citric cycle oxidations do not involve molecular oxygen. Oxygen comes into the picture only in the terminal oxidations carried out by the electron-transfer chain in mitochondria.

The key oxidant in the oxidative reactions of the outer membrane is DPN^+. It plays the role of a shuttle between the units that carry out the citric cycle (and reduce the coenzyme to DPNH) and the units that house the electron-transfer chain (and regenerate the coenzyme by oxidizing it to DPN^+). The reader can be spared a great deal of confusion by thinking exclusively in terms of electron transfers and neglecting the hydrogen or proton balance sheet. In the reduction of DPN^+ by the substrates of the citric cycle, two electrons are transferred from substrate to DPN^+.

---

* Hydrogen ions liberated during the reduction of DPN^+ by substrate are picked up again during the reduction of oxygen to water.

When DPNH thus formed is oxidized by molecular oxygen in the electron-transfer chain, two electrons are transferred from DPNH ultimately to molecular oxygen.

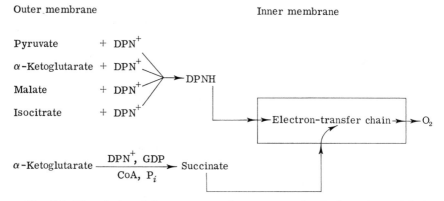

Fig. 7.3. The relation of the enzymes in the outer mitochondrial membrane (which catalyze the citric cycle) to the electron-transfer chain of the inner membrane.

Yield of ATP During Coupling

The ten electrons released for each molecule of pyruvate oxidized to CO_2 and H_2O energize the synthesis of fifteen molecules of ATP. Two of the ten electrons (those entering the chain by way of succinate) are responsible for synthesis of two molecules of ATP; the remaining eight electrons (those entering the chain by way of DPNH) contribute to the synthesis of twelve molecules of ATP. This comes to a total of fourteen molecules of ATP. The molecule of ATP as yet unaccounted for, is synthesized not in the electron-transfer chain at all, but in the outer membrane layer, by an entirely different mechanism (substrate-level phosphorylation).

All the steps of the citric cycle and of the electron-transfer process have been shown to be reversible except the final reaction involving molecular oxygen. The efficiency of the process whereby the utilizable energy released by oxidation of pyruvate is converted into the bond energy of ATP is estimated to be about 40%—that is, about 40% of the utilizable energy released in the oxidation of pyruvate can be conserved in the form of ATP. The reversible segment of the electron-transfer chain encompasses some 83% of the total drop in free energy between DPNH and oxygen. If we exclude the irreversible segment of the potential drop, the efficiency of conversion is about 53%. The gap between theory and experiment may be closed (a) if the bond energy of the first high-energy intermediate is considerably larger than that of the P—O—P bond in ATP and (b) if the full potential drop within each subdivision of the electron-transfer chain is not utilized during high-energy bond formation.

The eight steps of the citric cycle, and the requirements for each of these enzymic steps, are summarized in Table 7.1. To complete

Table 7.1

THE EIGHT ENZYMIC STEPS IN THE CITRIC ACID CYCLE, THE ENZYMES THAT IMPLEMENT THESE STEPS, AND THE FUNCTIONAL GROUPS OF THESE ENZYMES[a]

Step	Enzyme	Required functional groups
1. Pyruvate to acetyl-CoA	Pyruvic dehydrogenase complex	DPN^+, Mg^{2+}, cocarboxylase, CoA, lipoic acid
2. Acetyl-CoA + oxaloacetate to citrate	Condensing enzyme (acetyl-CoA-oxaloacetate)	None
3. Citrate to isocitrate	Aconitase	Fe^{2+}
4. Isocitrate to α-ketoglutarate	Isocitric dehydrogenase	DPN^+ (TPN^+), Mg^{2+} (Mn^{2+})
5. α-Ketoglutarate to succinate	α-Ketoglutaric dehydrogenase complex	DPN^+, Mg^{2+}, cocarboxylase, CoA, lipoic acid, P_i
6. Succinate to fumarate	Succinic dehydrogenase	Flavin, nonheme iron
7. Fumarate to malate	Fumarase	None
8. Malate to oxaloacetate	Malic dehydrogenase	DPN^+

[a] See Figure 7.1 for the structural formulas of the intermediates in the cycle.

the metabolic picture we are also including, in two companion tables, the steps by which fatty acids are oxidatively converted to acetyl-CoA (Table 7.2) and the reactions by which three of the amino acids are converted to intermediates of the citric cycle (Table 7.3).

Glycolysis (Fermentation) of Sugar

The process by which one molecule of glucose is cleaved into two molecules of lactic acid without the intervention of molecular oxygen is known as *glycolysis*. The fermentation of sugar by yeast

Table 7.2

THE FIVE ENZYMIC STEPS IN THE OXIDATIVE CONVERSION OF FATTY ACIDS
(RCH_2CH_2COOH) TO ACETYL-CoA

Step	Enzyme	Requirement
RCH_2CH_2COOH to $RCH_2CH_2CO\overline{SCoA}$[a]	Fatty acid-activating enzyme	CoASH, Mg^{2+}, ATP
2. $RCH_2CH_2CO\overline{SCoA}$ to $RCH{:}CHCO\overline{SCoA}$	Fatty acyl CoA dehydrogenase	Flavin (protein bound)
3. $RCH{:}CHCO\overline{SCoA}$ to $RCHOHCH_2CO\overline{SCoA}$	Enoyl hydrase	None
4. $RCHOHCH_2CO\overline{SCoA}$ to $RCOCH_2CO\overline{SCoA}$	β-Hydroxyacyl-CoA dehydrogenase	DPN$^+$
5. $RCOCH_2CO\overline{SCoA}$ to $RCO\overline{SCoA} + CH_3CO\overline{SCoA}$	β-Ketoacyl-CoA thiolase	CoASH

[a] The notation $\overline{SCoA}$ signifies the attachment of CoA to the group in question via the sulfur atom of its sulfhydryl group.

Table 7.3

THE CONVERSION OF ALANINE, GLUTAMIC ACID, AND PROLINE TO
INTERMEDIATES OF THE CITRIC CYCLE

Transformation		Enzyme
1. CH_3CHNH_2COOH (Alanine)	to $CH_3COCOOH$ (Pyruvic acid)	Alanine–glutamic transaminase (transfer of amino group from alanine to α–ketoglutarate)
2. $COOHCH_2CH_2CHNH_2COOH$ (Glutamic acid)	to $COOHCH_2CH_2COCOOH$ (α–Ketoglutaric acid)	Glutamic dehydrogenase
3. 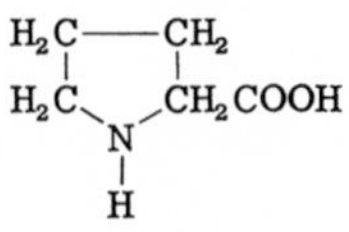 Proline	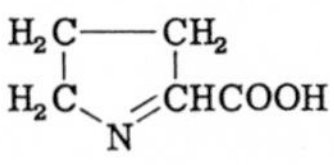 to Δ'-Pyrroline-5 carboxylic acid	Proline dehydrogenase
4. Δ'-Pyrroline-5– carboxylic acid	to Glutamic acid	Glutamic semialdehyde dehydrogenase

is a variation on the theme, in which ethyl alcohol, rather than lactic acid, is the end product.

Rationale of Glycolysis

The logic of the glycolytic process may be expressed in the following terms. Glycolysis is composed of ten consecutive enzymic reactions by means of which glucose is split into two molecules of lactic acid; for each molecule of lactic acid formed by this cleavage, one molecule of ATP is synthesized from ADP and P_i. In point of fact, glucose, as such, is not split. The actual sugar involved is fructose, after it has been converted into its diphosphoric ester (fructose 1,6-diphosphate). The conversion of glucose into fructose 1,6-diphosphate requires the outlay of two molecules of ATP, as shown in Eqs. (1)–(3).

$$\text{Glucose} + \text{ATP} \rightarrow \text{glucose 6-phosphate} + \text{ADP} \quad (1)$$

$$\text{Glucose 6-phosphate} \rightleftharpoons \text{fructose 6-phosphate} \quad (2)$$

$$\text{Fructose 6-phosphate} + \text{ATP} \rightleftharpoons \text{fructose 1,6-diphosphate} + \text{ADP} \quad (3)$$

At this point two molecules of ATP have been used up per molecule of glucose and none has been synthesized; the net production of ATP per molecule of glucose may be said to be minus two.

In the next phase of glycolysis, fructose 1,6-diphosphate is cleaved into two molecules of triose phosphate, one of which is aldotriose phosphate; the other is the corresponding ketotriose phosphate [Eq. (4)]:

Ketotriose phosphate

Aldotriose phosphate

Fructose 1,6-diphosphate

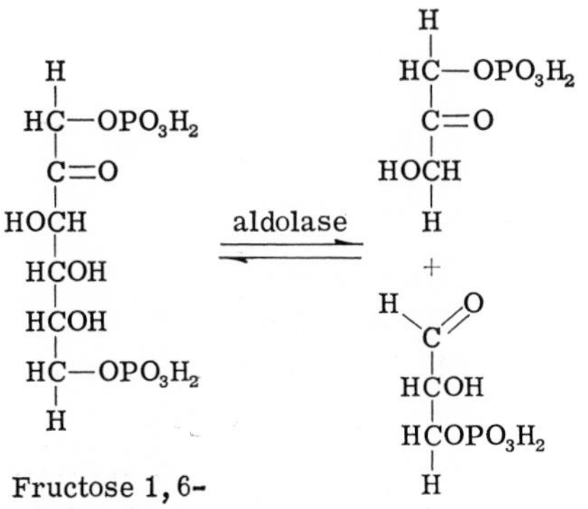

(4)

There is an isomerizing enzyme which catalyzes the interconversion of the two triose phosphates:

$$\text{Aldotriose phosphate} \rightleftharpoons \text{ke!otriose phosphate}$$

The aldotriose phosphate is then oxidized in a two-step reaction that leads to the synthesis of ATP, as shown in Eqs. (5) and (6).

$$\text{Aldotriose phosphate} + \text{oxidant} + P_i \rightleftharpoons \text{1,3-diphosphoglycerate} + \text{reductant} \quad (5)$$

$$\text{1,3-Diphosphoglycerate} + \text{ADP} \rightleftharpoons \text{3-phosphoglycerate} + \text{ATP} \quad (6)$$

The nature of these two reactions can readily be visualized from the structural formulas shown in Eq. (7a).

$$
\begin{array}{c}
\underset{\substack{\text{Aldotriose}\\\text{phosphate}}}{
\begin{array}{c}
H\diagdown\,_{\displaystyle C}\diagup O\\
|\\
HCOH\\
|\\
HCOPO_3H_2\\
|\\
H
\end{array}}
\quad
\xrightarrow[\substack{\text{+ phospho-}\\\text{rylation}}]{\text{oxidation}}
\quad
\underset{\substack{\text{1,3-Diphospho-}\\\text{glycerate}}}{
\begin{array}{c}
O{=}C{-}OPO_3H_2\\
|\\
HCOH\\
|\\
HCOPO_3H_2\\
|\\
H
\end{array}}
\quad
\xrightarrow[\substack{\text{phosphate to}\\\text{ADP}}]{\text{transfer of}}
\quad
\underset{\substack{\text{3-Phospho-}\\\text{glycerate}}}{
\begin{array}{c}
COOH\\
|\\
HCOH\\
|\\
HCOPO_3H_2\\
|\\
H
\end{array}}
\end{array}
\quad (7a)
$$

At this point the net production of ATP per molecule of glucose may be said to be zero (bear in mind that two molecules of aldotriose phosphate originate from one molecule of glucose).

Phosphoglycerate now undergoes two successive reactions [Eq. (7b)]; the first is a rearrangement yielding 2-phosphoglycerate; the second is a dehydration yielding phosphoenolpyruvate.

$$
\begin{array}{c}
\underset{\substack{\text{3-Phospho-}\\\text{glycerate}}}{
\begin{array}{c}
COOH\\
|\\
HCOH\\
|\\
HCOPO_3H_2\\
|\\
H
\end{array}}
\quad
\rightleftharpoons
\quad
\underset{\substack{\text{2-Phospho-}\\\text{glycerate}}}{
\begin{array}{c}
COOH\\
|\\
HCOPO_3H_2\\
|\\
HCOH\\
|\\
H
\end{array}}
\quad
\xrightarrow[\text{+ H}_2\text{O}]{\text{- H}_2\text{O}}
\quad
\underset{\substack{\text{Phosphoenol-}\\\text{pyruvate}}}{
\begin{array}{c}
COOH\\
|\\
COPO_3H_2\\
\|\\
CH_2
\end{array}}
\end{array}
\quad (7b)
$$

The end product of this set of reactions is phosphoenolpyruvate. In the transition from 3-phosphoglycerate to phosphoenolpyruvate the total energy content of the molecule is not changed appreciably, but the energy cake is cut differently in the two molecules; the phosphoryl group in phosphoenolpyruvate is given a larger slice than it had in the parent molecule. The phosphoryl group of phosphoenolpyruvate is, in fact, a high-energy phosphate capable of phosphorylating ADP, as shown in Eq. (8).

$$CH_2{=}C(OPO_3H_2){-}COOH + ADP \rightleftharpoons CH_3COCOOH + ATP \qquad (8)$$
$$\text{Phosphoenolpyruvate}$$

At this point the net production of ATP is plus two (per molecule of glucose), since two molecules of phosphoenolpyruvate are formed per molecule of glucose.

To complete the sequence, pyruvate is reduced to lactate, as shown in Eq. (9).

$$CH_3COCOOH + \text{reductant} \rightleftharpoons CH_3CHOHCOOH + \text{oxidant} \qquad (9)$$
$$\text{Pyruvate} \qquad\qquad\qquad \text{Lactate}$$

This reduction is coupled to the oxidation of aldotriose phosphate, as noted above. Thus, pyruvate is the oxidant for aldotriose phosphate; aldotriose phosphate is the reductant for pyruvate, as shown in Eq. (10).

$$\text{Aldotriose phosphate} + P_i + \text{pyruvate} \rightarrow \text{diphosphoglycerate} + \text{lactate} \qquad (10)$$

Although this formulation may serve as the overall statement of the oxidoreduction, it leaves out an important detail. The interaction between aldotriose phosphate and pyruvate involves two half-reactions, catalyzed by different enzymes, but sharing a common coenzyme (DPN^+), as shown in Eqs. (11) and (12).

$$\text{Aldotriose phosphate} + P_i + DPN^+ \rightleftharpoons \text{1,3-diphosphoglycerate} + DPNH + H^+ \qquad (11)$$

$$DPNH + \text{pyruvate} + H^+ \rightleftharpoons DPN^+ + \text{lactate} \qquad (12)$$

The DPN^+ thus acts in a shuttle capacity, being reduced by aldotriose phosphate (in the presence of the aldotriose phosphate dehydrogenase) and oxidized by pyruvate (in the presence of the lactic dehydrogenase). In sum, all the ten reactions we have discussed balance out to permit the conversion of one molecule of glucose into two molecules of lactic acid, two molecules of ADP being converted into two molecules of ATP.

COUPLING DURING OXIDATION OF TRIOSE PHOSPHATE

Of the two processes by which ATP is synthesized during glycolysis, the first is an oxidative process coupled to phosphorylation and the second involves an internal rearrangement of a phosphorylated molecule leading to the conversion of a phosphoryl group of low energy into one of high energy. The first step of the oxidative reaction which is coupled to ATP synthesis is the oxidation of aldotriose phosphate by some group in a dehydrogenase which is capable of being reduced (probably a disulfide group). Let us represent the enzyme as

$$E\diagup\!\!\!\overset{S}{\underset{S}{\diagdown}}\overset{|}{}$$

and aldotriose phosphate as RCHO. The oxidation would then be written as [Eq. (13)]:

$$\text{RCHO} + E\diagup\!\!\!\overset{S}{\underset{S}{\diagdown}} \longrightarrow R\overset{O}{\overset{\|}{C}}{\sim}S\diagup\!\!\!\overset{E}{\diagdown}\text{SH} \qquad (13)$$

Acyl enzyme

Next, the acyl enzyme interacts with inorganic phosphate to form the acyl phosphate and to set free the reduced form of the enzyme [Eq. (14)]:

$$R\overset{O}{\overset{\|}{C}}{\sim}S\diagup\!\!\!\overset{E}{\diagdown}\text{SH} + P_i \longrightarrow R\overset{O}{\overset{\|}{C}}{\sim}OPO_3H_2 + E\diagup\!\!\!\overset{SH}{\diagdown}\text{SH} \qquad (14)$$

The reduced enzyme is then oxidized by DPN^+ [Eq. (15)]:

$$E\diagup\!\!\!\overset{SH}{\underset{SH}{\diagdown}} + DPN^+ \longrightarrow E\diagup\!\!\!\overset{S}{\underset{S}{\diagdown}}\overset{|}{} + DPNH + H^+ \qquad (15)$$

It should be stressed that the oxidation and the phosphorylation take place simultaneously; in fact, the oxidation does not occur unless inorganic phosphate (or arsenate) is present. The net result of the oxidative sequence is that the energy of oxidation is conserved in the form of a high-energy bond between the enzyme and the acyl group, and this bond can be manipulated by phosphorolysis to give rise to a high-energy phosphoryl group. A specific enzyme catalyzes the transfer of this carboxyl-linked phosphoryl group to ADP.

Pentose Cycle

There is a complex system of enzymes, widespread in nature, which is capable of oxidizing glucose to CO_2 and H_2O by a pathway which involves neither the citric cycle nor glycolysis. None of the reactions in this sequence, the *pentose cycle*, leads to the synthesis of ATP. Does this mean that the pentose cycle is useless from the standpoint of energy conservation? In the preceding discussion, the role of ATP as the currency of biochemical energy has been stressed to the exclusion of other possibilities. The dilemma posed by the pentose cycle necessitates another look at the energy problem.

PENTOSE CYCLE AND ENERGY PRODUCTION

Virtually all synthetic processes—that is, processes in which larger molecules are made from smaller precursor molecules—involve one or more reductive steps (steps in which electrons have to be channeled into the reacting molecules). For example, fatty acid synthesis from acetate requires the outlay of twenty-eight electrons (fourteen reductive steps) for a fatty acid chain of sixteen carbon atoms. The synthesis of cholesterol from acetate is another example of a process which makes heavy demands for reducing electrons.

The pentose cycle leads to the formation of 12 moles of TPNH from TPN^+ for each mole of glucose oxidized to CO_2 and H_2O. The TPNH can provide electrons for various synthetic processes, including synthesis of fatty acids and cholesterol. Thus, TPNH may be looked upon as a source of chemical energy in much the same sense that ATP is a source of chemical energy. On the one hand, it is formed by the primary energy-producing system (in this case the set of enzymes that implement the pentose cycle); on the other hand, its energy can be utilized in energy-requiring synthetic processes. The exportable energy of ATP comes in the form of a highly reactive phosphoryl group, whereas the exportable energy of TPNH comes in the form of two electrons. Both DPNH and TPNH can qualify as electron donors that are generated in the primary energy-producing systems and are uniquely adapted for energizing certain synthetic reactions.

OXIDATION OF GLUCOSE TO CO_2 AND H_2O IN THE PENTOSE CYCLE

The chemical details of the pentose cycle may be summarized by Eqs. (16–20).

$$6 \text{ Glucose 6-phosphate} + 12 \text{ TPN}^+ \rightarrow 6 \text{ pentose-phosphate} +$$
$$6 \text{ CO}_2 + 6 \text{ H}_2\text{O} + 12 \text{ TPNH} \quad (16)$$

$$4 \text{ Pentose-phosphate} \rightarrow 2 \text{ fructose 6-phosphate} + 2 \text{ tetrose-phosphate} \quad (17)$$

$$2 \text{ Pentose-phosphate} + 2 \text{ tetrose-phosphate} \rightarrow 2 \text{ fructose 6-phosphate} +$$
$$2 \text{ triose-phosphate} \quad (18)$$

$$2 \text{ Triose-phosphate} \rightarrow \text{fructose 1,6-diphosphate} \quad (19)$$

$$\textit{Sum } 6 \text{ Glucose 6-phosphate} + 12 \text{ TPN}^+ \rightarrow 6 \text{ CO}_2 + 6 \text{ H}_2\text{O} + 12 \text{ TPNH} +$$
$$4 \text{ fructose 6-phosphate} + \text{fructose 1,6-diphosphate} \quad (20)$$

There are enzymes that can convert both fructose 6-phosphate and fructose 1,6-diphosphate into glucose 6-phosphate. Given these conversions, the overall pentose cycle may be described by Eq. (21).

$$\textit{Sum } 6 \text{ Glucose 6-phosphate} + 12 \text{ TPN}^+ \rightarrow 6 \text{ CO}_2 + 6 \text{ H}_2\text{O} +$$
$$12 \text{ TPNH} + 5 \text{ glucose 6-phosphate} \quad (21)$$

This equation states that, of every six molecules of glucose 6-phosphate that enter the cycle, one is completely oxidized to CO_2 and H_2O and five are regenerated. In the limit, essentially all available glucose 6-phosphate would be completely oxidized to CO_2 and H_2O.

It is clear that glucose is not oxidized directly to CO_2 and H_2O. There are, in fact, only two oxidative reactions—the oxidation of glucose 6-phosphate to 6-phosphogluconolactone and the oxidative decarboxylation of 6-phosphogluconolactone to ribulose 6-phosphate, as shown in Eqs. (22) and (23).

Glucose 6-
phosphate   6-Phospho-
                             gluconolactone

$$(22)$$

$$
\begin{array}{ll}
\begin{array}{l}
\overset{O}{\underset{\|}{C}}- \\
HCOH \\
HOCH \\
HCOH \\
HC- \\
HCOPO_3H_2 \\
H
\end{array} O + TPN^+ &\longrightarrow
\begin{array}{l}
H \\
HC- \\
C=O \\
HCOH \\
HC- \\
HCOPO_3H_2 \\
H
\end{array} O + TPNH + CO_2 + H^+ \quad (23)
\end{array}
$$

6-Phospho- gluconolactone	Ribulose 5- phosphate

Ribulose 5-phosphate then embarks on a series of chemical inter-conversions, the net effect of which is to provide more glucose 6-phosphate for repeating oxidative steps.

Energy is derived from the pentose cycle by the oxidation of glucose 6-phosphate to 6-phosphogluconolactone [the reaction specified in Eq. (22)], and by the subsequent oxidative decarboxylation of 6-phosphogluconolactone to ribulose 5-phosphate [the reaction specified by Eq. (23)]. In each of these oxidations one molecule of TPN is converted to TPNH, which, as we shall see later, can be coupled to energy-requiring reactions. The rest of the pentose cycle involves reactions leading to the formation of fructose 6-phosphate and fructose 1,6-diphosphate, and ultimately to glucose 6-phosphate. Intermediates formed in these reactions may also be diverted for use in cellular metabolism. For example, the ribose required for synthesis of nucleic acid is provided by the pentose cycle.

Path of Carbon in Photosynthesis

In the green plant the synthesis of sugar is energized by ATP and TPNH and is initiated by the interaction of light with the chloroplast. The pentose cycle, and glycolysis carried out in reverse, provide the pathways by which CO_2 and H_2O are eventually transformed into sugar. Radiant energy, channeled by the chloroplast into ATP and TPNH, provides the driving force.

$$h\nu + H_2O + TPN^+ \xrightarrow{\text{chloroplasts}} TPNH + H^+ + \tfrac{1}{2}O_2$$

The starting point for the synthesis of carbohydrate from CO_2 and H_2O is ribulose diphosphate, formed from ribulose phosphate by interaction with ATP in presence of a specific enzyme, as shown in Eq. (24).

$$
\begin{array}{ccc}
\begin{array}{c}
H_2COH \\
| \\
C{=}O \\
| \\
HCOH \\
| \\
HCOH \\
| \\
H_2COP
\end{array}
&
\xrightarrow[\text{kinase}]{\text{ATP}}
&
\begin{array}{c}
H_2COP \\
| \\
C{=}O \\
| \\
HCOH \\
| \\
HCOH \\
| \\
H_2COP
\end{array}
\end{array}
\qquad (24)
$$

Ribulose 5-   Ribulose 1,5-
phosphate   diphosphate

Ribulose diphosphate interacts with CO_2 in presence of an enzyme known as epimerase. The product of carboxylation is unstable and breaks down into two molecules of phosphoglyceric acid, as shown in Eq. (25).

$$
\begin{array}{c}
H_2COP \\
| \quad OH \\
C \!\!\diagdown \\
\quad\;\; COOH \\
O{=}C \\
| \\
HCOH \\
| \\
H_2COP
\end{array}
+ H_2O \longrightarrow
\begin{array}{c}
H_2COP \\
| \\
HOCH \\
| \\
COOH \\
\\
+ \\
\\
COOH \\
| \\
HCOH \\
| \\
H_2COP
\end{array}
\qquad (25)
$$

Phosphoglycerate is phosphorylated to 1,3-diphosphoglyceric acid by ATP in presence of a kinase [Eq. (6)], and, in turn, 1,3-diphosphoglyceric acid can be reduced to triose phosphate by DPNH in presence of the triose phosphate dehydrogenase [Eq. (5)]. Triose phosphate gives rise to hexose phosphate by the aldolase reaction [Eq. (4)]. It is to be noted that three molecules of ATP and two molecules of DPNH (or TPNH) are required to carboxylate one molecule of ribulose phosphate to one molecule of hexose phosphate.

Thus far, reactions only of the glycolytic cycle have been implicated in the synthesis of carbohydrate from CO_2. It is in the regeneration of ribulose phosphate that the pentose cycle comes into play. If all the ribulose phosphate were converted to hexose phosphate, the synthesis of sugar would grind to a halt. The ribulose phosphate is, in a sense, a catalytic molecule and must therefore be regenerated. The triose phosphate formed subsequent to carboxylation of ribulose diphosphate undergoes two fates—part is converted to hexose phosphate and the rest is converted back to ribulose phosphate [by reversal of the reactions described by Eq. (17)–(19)]. It is to be noted that pentose phosphate includes three species, all in equilibrium—namely, xylulose 5-phosphate, ribose 5-phosphate, and ribulose 5-phosphate.

The synthesis of one molecular unit of starch $(C_6H_{10}O_5)$ from six molecules of CO_2 requires twelve molecules of TPNH, and the expenditure of eighteen high-energy bonds (see Figure 7.4). In

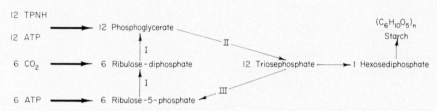

Fig. 7.4. Carbohydrate synthesis by isolated chloroplasts. Reactions I and III are parts of the pentose cycle; reaction II is part of the glycolytic cycle. *Net reaction:*
$$<6\ CO_2 + 12\ TPNH + 12\ H^+ + 18\ ATP \rightarrow [C_6H_{10}O_5] + 18\ ADP + 18\ P_i + 7\ H_2O>$$
Diagram is a modification of a slide shown in a lecture by D. Arnon.

this synthesis, the pentose and glycolytic cycles play a central role. It will be noted that one sugar molecule is synthesized for every ten molecules of triosephosphate that go through one cycle. Thirty of the thirty carbon atoms that enter a given cycle are regenerated; the extra six carbon atoms that end up as a starch unit are all derived from CO_2.

Energy Generation and Metabolism

The few essential oxidative reactions that lead to synthesis of ATP or to production of TPNH are buried, as it were, in a morass of ancillary reactions that have nothing to do directly with energy generation. Would it not have been simpler to segregate the energy-yielding processes from metabolism? There are, in fact, microorganisms that have achieved this simplicity. They can couple

ATP synthesis to the oxidation of some inorganic molecule, say hydrogen or thiosulfate, and in such microorganisms there is no mixing of these particular energy-coupling reactions with metabolism. However, this simplification of reaction categories is the exception and not the rule. It appears that Nature has built metabolic systems around the coupling reactions, and this would suggest that the metabolic pathways were later evolutionary developments than were the coupling reactions themselves.

Suggested Reading

Books

Bassham, J. A., and Calvin, M., "The Photosynthesis of Carbon Compounds," W. A. Benjamin, Inc., New York, 1962.

Bloch, K., ed., "Lipide Metabolism," John Wiley and Sons, New York, 1960: see chapter on fatty acid oxidation and synthesis.

Chance, B., ed., "Energy-Linked Functions of Mitochondria," Academic Press, New York, 1963.

Lehninger, A. L., "Bioenergetics," W. A. Benjamin, Inc., New York, 1965.

Special Articles

Arnon, D. I., *Proc. Fifth Intern. Congr. Biochem., Moscow, 1961,* Vol. VI, Pergamon Press, 1963: on photosynthetic phosphorylation and a unified concept of photosynthesis.

Axelrod, B., *in* "Metabolic Pathways" (D. M. Greenberg, ed.), 2nd ed., Vol. 1, Chapter 5, Academic Press, New York, 1960: on glycolysis.

Couri, D., and Racker, E., *Arch. Biochem. Biophys.* **83,** 195 (1959): on the oxidative pentose phosphate cycle V; complete oxidation of glucose-6-phosphate in a reconstructed system of the oxidative pentose phosphate cycle.

Green, D. E., and Fleischer, S., *in* "Metabolic Pathways" (D. M. Greenberg, ed.), 2nd ed., Vol. 1, Chapter 2, Academic Press, New York, 1960: on the mitochondrial system of enzymes.

Horecker, B. L., and Mehler, A. H., *Ann. Rev. Biochem.* **24,** 207 (1955): chapter on carbohydrate metabolism.

Karlson, P., *in* "Introduction to Modern Biochemistry," see Chapter XV, Academic Press, New York, 1963.

Krebs, H. A., *Harvey Lectures* Ser. 44, 165 (1948–49): on the tricarboxylic acid cycle.

Krebs, H. A., and Lowenstein, J. M., *in* "Metabolic Pathways" (D. M. Greenberg, ed.), 2nd ed., Vol. 1, Chapter 4, Academic Press, New York, 1960: on the tricarboxylic acid cycle.

Stadtman, E. R., *Federation Proc.* **15,** 360 (1956): on the *C. kluyveri* system for synthesis of fatty acids.

CHAPTER 8 _____

Energy-Requiring
Synthetic Processes

The formation of polysaccharides from monosaccharides, of complex lipids from fatty acids and other building blocks, of proteins from amino acids, and, in general, of large molecules from small molecules requires the outlay of chemical energy. In this chapter we shall be concerned with the form in which this chemical energy is made available and with the molecular tactics by which chemical energy powers the synthetic process.

Vehicles of Chemical Energy

ATP and the reduced forms of the pyridine nucleotides are the only primary vehicles of chemical energy involved in biosyntheses, which are common to all cells. ATP is generated in glycolysis and during oxidative and photosynthetic phosphorylation, whereas TPNH is generated in the pentose cycle. Since DPNH and TPNH are, in effect, in equilibrium with one another (there are enzymes that catalyze the transfer of hydrogen from the reduced form of one nucleotide to the oxidized form of the other), the generation of TPNH is essentially equivalent to the generation of DPNH. By the same token, the triphosphates of guanosine, cytidine, thymidine, and inosine are virtually equivalent to the triphosphate of adenosine since the mono- or diphosphate of any of the former quartet can be converted into the corresponding triphosphate merely by borrowing a phosphoryl or pyrophosphoryl group (enzymically) from the polyphosphate chain of ATP.

The cells of plants and photosynthetic bacteria have in ferredoxin a third vehicle of chemical energy. Ferredoxin is a protein of low molecular weight (6000–12,000) containing variable amounts of iron (2–8 atoms), linked to protein-bound sulfur in an acid-labile link. The oxidation-reduction potential of the ferredoxin system is the most negative of any known biological system, more reducing in fact than the hydrogen electrode. Ferredoxin is reduced by light during photosynthesis; the reduced form, thus generated, can energize various synthetic reactions as well as reduce TPN^+ to TPNH.

Reactions Mediated by Kinases

The many enzymic reactions in which the high-energy bonds of ATP (or of other purine and pyrimidine nucleoside triphosphates) are manipulated to energize synthetic processes are referred to as *kinase* (or *synthetase*) reactions; the enzymes that catalyze these reactions are called *kinases* (or *synthetases*). There are basically three types of kinase reactions. These are distinguished on the basis of the group in ATP (or ADP) which is transferred. This group could be phosphoryl, adenosinemonophosphoryl or adenosyl. If we represent ATP as ARPPP,* these group transfers in kinase reactions may be formulated as follows:

$$I. \quad ARPP \sim P + X \rightarrow ARPP + XP$$
or
$$ARP \sim P + X \rightarrow ARP + XP$$

$$II. \quad ARP \sim PP + X \rightarrow ARP \sim X + PP_i$$

$$III. \quad ARPPP + X \rightarrow ARX + PPP_i$$

In the first type of transfer reaction, ATP or ADP is cleaved between the terminal and second phosphate groups; the terminal group is transferred to some acceptor molecule. In the second type, ATP is cleaved into pyrophosphoryl and adenosinemonophosphoryl

---

* A for adenine, R for ribose, and P for phosphate.

moieties with transfer of the adenosinemonophosphoryl group. In the third type, ATP is cleaved into triphosphoryl and adenosyl moieties with transfer of the adenosyl group.

In terms of the molecular strategy of kinase reactions, there are essentially no distinctions among the three types. Let us consider an example of the second type of kinase reaction, the ATP-energized synthesis of acetyl-CoA. The overall reaction is given in Eq. (1).

$$CH_3COOH + CoASH \longrightarrow CH_3COSCoA + H_2O \tag{1}$$

Coenzyme A and acetic acid (really acetate) condense to form an acylthiol ester (acetyl-CoA). However, this esterification requires the outlay of a considerable amount of chemical energy—for which ATP foots the bill. Properly, the reaction should be expressed in the form shown in Eq. (2).

$$ATP + acetate + CoA \rightleftharpoons acetyl\text{-}CoA + AMP + PP_i \tag{2}$$

For each molecule of acetyl-CoA formed, one molecule of ATP is cleaved into one of adenosine monophosphate (AMP) and one of inorganic pyrophosphate (PP_i). The P—O—P link between the second and third phosphorus atoms* of the polyphosphate chain of ATP is ruptured and the "bond energy" thus released is conserved for driving the synthesis of acetyl-CoA.

FORMULATION OF THE ACETOKINASE REACTION

There is good experimental evidence for postulating that the enzyme (acetothiokinase) which catalyzes this ATP-energized synthesis of acetyl-CoA has four sites to which the reactants are bound:

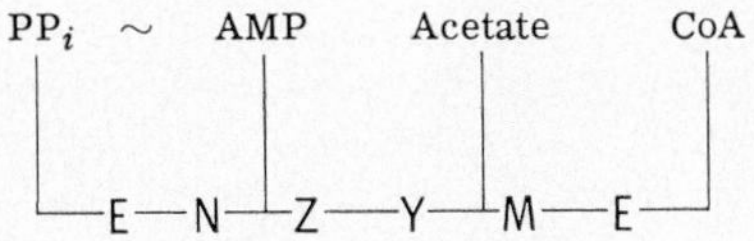

$$ATP = PP_i \sim AMP$$

* The convention is to refer to the terminal phosphate of ATP as the number-one group.

The synthesis would then involve the following sequence of reactions:

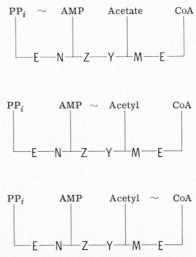

The "high-energy bond," represented by the symbol $\sim$, is moved along the chain from one set of partners to the next. This coupling process is an example of a reversible reaction in which the net free energy change is close to zero. The series of reactions can be thought of as a stepwise transfer of a high-energy bond from the primary energy source (ATP) to another pair of molecules or residues (acetate and coenzyme A), and this transfer leads to the formation of an acyl-coenzyme A ester. The "movement" of a bond between PP_i and AMP to a bond between AMP and an acetyl group, requires that AMP should be capable of reacting as readily with PP_i as with acetate. The same would apply to the next set of reactants; acetate should be capable of interacting as readily with AMP as with CoA.

ROLE OF MAGNESIUM IN THE BINDING OF ATP AND OTHER SUBSTRATE MOLECULES

All known kinases show an absolute requirement for magnesium ions (Mg^{2+}). This requirement is explicable largely in terms of the binding of ATP (or its parts) to the protein. The Mg^{2+} acts as a chelate* bridge between ATP and the kinase protein. The possibilities are not excluded that Mg^{2+} may chelate with substrates other than ATP in kinase reactions, and that Mg^{2+} chelation is part of the general strategy of aligning all the reacting substrates in appropriate slots in the enzyme protein and then anchoring those groups whose movement would interfere with the catalysis.

The factors which determine how ATP will be split are probably steric in nature. There is some reason to expect that the way in which ATP is chelated to Mg^{2+} is relevant to this determination. The proximity of the atom to which bond transfer will be made is another of the determinants of which bond in ATP will be cleaved.

FORMULATION OF THE GLUTAMINE SYNTHETASE REACTIONS

The ATP-energized synthesis of glutamine from NH_3 and glutamic acid is an example of the first mode of kinase reactions†:

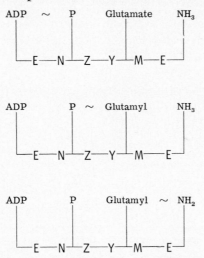

NUMBER OF REACTANTS IN KINASE REACTIONS

There is yet another basis for classifying kinase reactions. In some kinase reactions, as in the synthesis of acetyl-CoA or gluta-

---

* The term "chelate" implies two or more links between a metal atom and some molecule to which it is bonded by anhydride bonds.

† It is not essential to the argument that NH_3 precede glutamate in the sequence or vice versa.

mine, there are two reactants in addition to ATP. In others there is only one additional reactant. The ATP-energized phosphorylation of glycerol is an example of the latter type of reaction (as is the formation of the phosphodiester bond, energized by nucleoside diphosphates, in the synthesis of polynucleotides[*]):

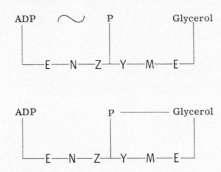

In this particular kinase reaction, involving the transfer of a phosphoryl group to glycerol, there is a considerable change in free energy during the oxidation. In the line diagram, the newly formed bond is represented by the symbol __, rather than by $\sim$. The fall in energy when the phosphoryl group is transferred from the first set of partners to the second is so great that reversal of the reaction is essentially excluded.

ATP-ENERGIZED KINASE REACTIONS

The variety of synthetic processes carried out by ATP-energized kinase reactions may be illustrated by Eqs. (3)–(9).

$$RCOOH + NH_3 \longrightarrow RCONH_2 + H_2O \tag{3}$$

Glutamic acid   Glutamine

$$RCOOH + CoASH \longrightarrow RCOSCoA + H_2O \tag{4}$$

Fatty acid   Acyl-CoA ester

---

[*] n nucleoside diphosphates $\underset{\text{phosphorylase}}{\overset{\text{polynucleotide}}{\rightleftarrows}}$ polynucleotide $+ n$ phosphate

$$ROH + P_i \longrightarrow \underset{\overset{|}{OH}}{RO\overset{\overset{O}{\|}}{P}OH} + H_2O \quad (5)$$

Glycerol   Phosphoglycerol

$$CH_3CO\overline{SCoA} + CO_2 \longrightarrow COOHCH_2CO\overline{SCoA} \quad (6)$$

Acetyl-CoA   Malonyl-CoA

$$NH_2COOH + P_i \longrightarrow HO\overset{\overset{O}{\|}}{\underset{\overset{|}{OH}}{P}}-O-\overset{\overset{}{\underset{\|}{O}}}{C}-NH_2 + H_2O \quad (7)$$

Carbamic acid   Carbamyl phosphate

$$RCOOH + \overline{R}NH_2 \longrightarrow RCON\overline{HR} + H_2O \quad (8)$$

Glutamate Cysteine   Glutamylcysteine

$$RSH + \overline{R}OH \longrightarrow RS\overline{R} \quad (9)$$

Methionine Adenosine   Adenosyl methionine

THE PROTEINS AND INTERMEDIATES OF KINASE REACTIONS

Each of the many kinase reactions investigated has been found to require the presence of a single protein molecule. No free intermediates are released into the medium, although enzyme-bound intermediates have been demonstrated in a few cases. It appears reasonable to postulate that there are multiple sites on the kinase, one for each of the reactants. The requirements for the transfer process are satisfied best by a zigzag, or triangular, arrangement of groups on the enzyme surface:

This is another way of saying that the fluctuating position of a bond in a chain of adjacent molecules that are fixed in position requires the formation of a ternary transition compound (I) in which the position of the bond can fluctuate between the possibilities (II, III):

$$\text{I. } PP_i \cdots\cdots AMP \cdots\cdots Acetate$$

$$\text{II. } PP_i \underline{\qquad} AMP \cdots\cdots Acetate$$

$$\text{III. } PP_i \cdots\cdots AMP \underline{\qquad} Acetate$$

REVERSIBILITY OF KINASE REACTIONS

Synthetic reactions catalyzed by kinases can proceed in either direction. For example, acetyl-CoA can drive the synthesis of ATP from AMP and PP_i as readily as ATP can drive the synthesis of acetyl-CoA from acetate and CoA. When the equilibrium constant is highly unfavorable, as it is in the ATP-dependent phosphorylation of glycerol, the *net* reaction appears to be unidirectional. However, it is possible to demonstrate, by experiments with labeled phosphorus atoms, that the phosphate group attached to glycerol can, in fact, be transferred to ADP to form ATP, despite the unfavorable equilibrium.

FORMATION OF REACTIVE MOLECULES IN KINASE REACTIONS

The conversions of fatty acids to fatty acyl-CoA esters, of amino acids to protein-bound aminoacyl derivatives, and of CO_2 to a biotinyl derivative are examples of yet another use to which kinase reactions are put (see Table 8.1). The acetokinase reaction discussed

Table 8.1
CONVERSION OF METABOLITES TO REACTIVE FORMS IN ATP-ENERGIZED KINASE REACTIONS

Original form of the reactant	Final form of the reactant	Metabolic process in which the reactive form participates
Amino acid	Aminoacyl RNA	Protein synthesis
Fatty acid	Fatty acyl-CoA ester	Fatty acid oxidation and synthesis, glyceride formation
Mevalonic acid	$\triangle$ 3-Isopentyl pyrophosphate	Steroid and isoprenoid synthesis
Glucose	Uridine diphosphoglucose	Glycogen synthesis
Phosphorylcholine	Cytidine diphosphocholine	Phospholipid synthesis
Glucose	Glucose 6-phosphate	Glycolysis
Ribose 5-phosphate	Phosphoribosyl pyrophosphate	Nucleotide synthesis

above is a faithful model for the enzymic activation both of fatty acids and of amino acids. The reactivity of fatty acids is enhanced by their esterification to coenzyme A; the reactivity of amino acids is enhanced by anhydride formation with some group in the kinase molecule. There is clearly a wide variety of devices (all kinase-mediated) for increasing reactivity. The introduction of a pyrophosphate moiety into a sugar molecule is a device of great importance in the biosynthesis of histidine, purine, and cholesterol. The conversion of formic acid into N-formyltetrahydrofolate is a key activation step in the metabolism of one-carbon compounds, as is the conversion of CO_2 to biotinyl-CO_2 or of carbamic acid to carbamyl phosphate. In the synthesis of glycogen the conversion of glucose to a diphosphorylated ester of uridine is the usual pathway, and this type of kinase-mediated substitution is quite general for synthesis of polysaccharides. The activation of molecules is an energy-requiring process, and it is thus not surprising that these are all mediated by kinases with ATP as the energizing source.

SYNTHESIS OF DINUCLEOTIDES IN KINASE REACTIONS

There is a special form of kinase reaction that merits notice. The synthesis of coenzymes having the dinucleotide form (DPN, TPN, flavin-adenin dinucleotide) and other closely related compounds (CoA, uridine diphosphoglucose, cytidine diphosphocholine) is a variation on the kinase theme. We shall consider the case of DPN synthesis from ATP and nicotinamide ribose phosphate (NRP). We may represent the kinase reaction as follows:

ATP = PP$_i$ ~ AMP
DPN = AMP ~ NRP

In effect, a bond is being shifted from a position between PP_i and AMP to a new position between AMP and NRP. With this shift, DPN is formed. It will be noted that a pyrophosphate bond is ruptured in the reactant and formed in the product. In dinucleotide synthesis by the kinase reaction, ATP is split and the AMP fragment is linked to another nucleotide by a P—O—P bond. Some of the variations in the kinase reactions for the synthesis of dinucleotide coenzymes are shown in Table 8.2.*

Table 8.2

THE NUCLEOTIDE POLYPHOSPHATES AND ACCEPTOR PHOSPHATE COMPOUNDS
REQUIRED FOR THE KINASE-CATALYZED SYNTHESIS OF VARIOUS COENZYMES
OF THE "DINUCLEOTIDE" GROUP

Coenzyme	Nucleotide polyphosphate required for synthesis	Acceptor phosphate compound
DPN+	ATP	Nicotinamide ribose phosphate
TPN+	ATP	Nicotinamide phosphoribose phosphate
CoA	ATP	Pantetheine phosphate
Uridine diphosphoglucose	UTP	Glucose 1-phosphate
Cytidine diphosphocholine	CTP	Choline phosphate

Implicit in our discussion of kinase reactions is the concept that each reactant is in a mobile equilibrium with the enzyme itself, in a constant flux of combination with, and dissociation from, the enzyme. It is only the internal transition complexes that are tightly bound to the enzyme. This accounts for the fact that none of the intermediates in a kinase reaction has ever been shown to be released into the medium, uncombined with enzyme.

STEPWISE PROCESSES IN KINASE REACTIONS

In the representation of kinase reactions we have considered only the concerted process, the process in which all the reactants are

* In this context we use the designation dinucleotide to indicate the product formed by the linkage of the phosphate ester group of one mononucleotide to the phosphate ester group of another mononucleotide (or similar molecule, for example, a sugar- or alcohol-phosphate ester).

present simultaneously. For many of the kinase reactions, it is possible to show that a stepwise, partial process can also proceed. For example, when ATP and acetate are added to the appropriate kinase in the absence of CoA (I), the same transition compound is formed as in the presence of acetyl CoA and AMP (II):

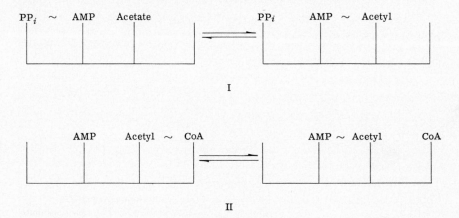

I

II

This stepwise formation of enzyme-bound intermediates may have important physiological implications.

INTERMEDIATES AND ACTIVE GROUPS IN KINASE REACTIONS

There are two distinct modalities for kinase-mediated phosphoryl transfers. In the first modality, the phosphoryl group of ATP is transferred directly to a phosphate acceptor which is a substrate of the enzyme. No phosphoryl intermediate of the enzyme is demonstrable. The glycerol kinase system discussed above appears to be of that type. In the second modality, the phosphoryl group of ATP is transferred to some phosphate acceptor on the enzyme— that is, an amino acid residue of the kinase. For instance, the kinase of Robert Beyer catalyzes the exchange between ADP and ATP, as shown in Eq. (10).

$$\text{ATP} + \text{kinase} \quad \text{ADP} + \text{kinase} \sim \text{P} \qquad (10)$$

The nature of the amino acid residue which is linked to the phosphoryl group is unknown. The nucleoside diphosphokinase of erythrocytes has been shown by R. E. Park to form a similar phosphorylated intermediate, as shown in Eq. (11).

$$ADP + kinase \rightleftarrows AMP + kinase \sim P \qquad (11)$$

The most thoroughly documented instance of such an intermediate is provided by the succinylthiokinase, as shown in Eq. (12).

$$GTP + kinase \qquad GDP + kinase \sim P \qquad (12)$$

Paul Boyer and his colleagues have implicated a histidine group in the kinase as the phosphate acceptor group

R is [CH$_2\cdot$ CHNH$_2\cdot$ COOH]

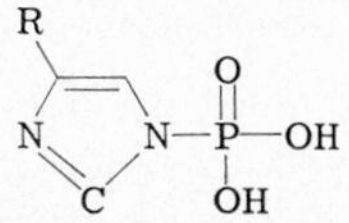

$$\underset{\text{Histidine phosphate}}{}$$

Histidine phosphate

In the activation of amino acids mediated by ATP and a specific kinase, the amino acid is converted into an aminoacyl derivative of the kinase, as shown in Eq. (13).

$$RCHNH_2COOH + kinase + ATP \rightarrow RCHNH_2\,C{-}O{-}kinase + AMP + PP_i \qquad (13)$$
$$\underset{O}{\overset{\parallel}{}}$$

This acyl derivative is in fact the end product of the reaction. The aminoacyl-kinase compound then serves as the substrate for a second kinase-mediated reaction in which the aminoacyl group is transferred to some group in transfer-RNA (cf. Chapter 11).

In the line diagrams for the acetokinase system shown earlier in the chapter, it is implicit that a bond between AMP and acetate is established prior to the formation of acetyl-CoA. While acetyl $\sim$ AMP is not demonstrable as a soluble intermediate in the sense that it leaves the kinase, nonetheless external acetyl $\sim$ AMP can interact with the kinase in presence of CoA to form acetyl-CoA, as shown in Eq. (14).

$$Acetyl \sim AMP + CoA \xrightarrow{\text{kinase}} acetyl \sim CoA + AMP \qquad (14)$$

This conversion *does not* require the presence of ATP or pyrophosphate. The fact of conversion confirms the postulate that enzyme-bound acetyl $\sim$ AMP must be formed as an intermediate in the

ATP-mediated synthesis of acetyl-CoA. The line diagrams shown below illustrate this point (the unoccupied slot in the diagram is for pyrophosphate):

Kinases in Substrate-Level and Oxidative Phosphorylation

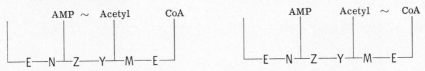

In the synthesis of ATP—whether in substrate-level or in oxidative phosphorylation, or in glycolysis—there are two clearly distinguishable series of events: (1) the formation of the first high-energy intermediate and (2) the utilization of the high-energy bond in this intermediate for the linking of ADP and P_i to form ATP. The second series of events involves exclusively kinase reactions. We shall consider the participation of kinase systems in each of these coupled phosphorylations. In glycolysis, ATP is synthesized in each of two separate kinase reactions, shown in Eqs. (15) and

$$\text{Diphosphoglycerate} + \text{ADP} \rightleftarrows \text{phosphoglycerate} + \text{ATP} \quad (15)$$

$$\text{Phosphoenolpyruvate} + \text{ADP} \rightleftarrows \text{pyruvate} + \text{ATP} \quad (16)$$

(16). In the substrate-level phosphorylation of the citric acid cycle, succinyl-CoA interacts with GDP and inorganic phosphate in a kinase reaction to form GTP, as shown in Eq. (17).

$$\text{Succinyl-CoA} + \text{GDP} + P_i \rightarrow \text{succinate} + \text{CoA} + \text{GTP} \quad (17)$$

This reaction is essentially the reverse of the acetokinase reaction (GTP replacing ATP and succinyl-CoA replacing acetyl-CoA).

In oxidative phosphorylation, at least two of the kinase systems which participate in ATP synthesis have been recognized. The first is the system of Robert Beyer, discussed above. The second is myokinase, an enzyme which catalyzes the transfer of a phosphoryl group from one molecule of ADP to a second molecule of ADP, as shown in Eq. (18).

$$\text{ADP} + \text{ADP} \rightleftarrows \text{AMP} + \text{ATP} \quad (18)$$

The particular myokinase we are referring to is a membrane-bound enzyme which acts on bound ADP. There are probably still other kinases implicated in the sequence of transfer reactions by which the bond in the first high-energy intermediate formed during oxidative phosphorylation, ends up as a bond between ADP and P_i.

An Atomic Model of the Mechanism of the Acetokinase Reaction

In the earlier part of this chapter we have dealt with the strategy of kinase-mediated synthetic reactions in general terms only. Specific chemical details were deliberately omitted. At the detailed chemical level, however, it is possible to recognize some remarkable features of kinase reactions; it is towards these chemical insights that the following discussion will be directed.

Biochemists often speak of Nature as a brilliant chemist. What they have in mind is not that Nature makes use of exotic chemical principles but, rather, that the *tactics* of exploiting well known chemical principles are ingenious. The study of living processes has yet to uncover a new chemical principle, but it has many times uncovered fantastic originality in the application of known chemical principles. These applications have required specialized macromolecules, such as enzymes, for their realization.

Although all the details of the mechanism of kinase reactions have not as yet been elucidated, available evidence coupled with deductions from this evidence and other chemical considerations, such as the known spatial relationship of atoms in molecules, allow us to make reasonable postulations of the mechanism. We shall consider only one kinase reaction as a model, namely, the acetokinase reaction [see Eq. (2)]. Figure 8.1 is a pictorial representation of the mechanism of the acetokinase reaction based on an atomic model devised by E. Frank Korman. It is presented here not as a final picture of the mechanism of a kinase but as a detailed illustration of how the *principle* of a kinase activity may be viewed at the level of the participating atoms. In Figure 8.1, the particular atoms relevant to the mechanism are shown and labeled. The rest of each of the two large molecules is represented as a sphere. The mechanism is shown as a sequence of steps, but this sequence is merely a pictorial device since the actual reaction is not a discontinuous process.

In Figure 8.1, Mg^{2+} is pictured as chelated (represented by dashed lines) to all three of the phosphate groups of ATP by oxygen atoms (four links in all) and to the nitrogen atom of the amino group on C-6 of the adenine ring.* The four oxygens and the one

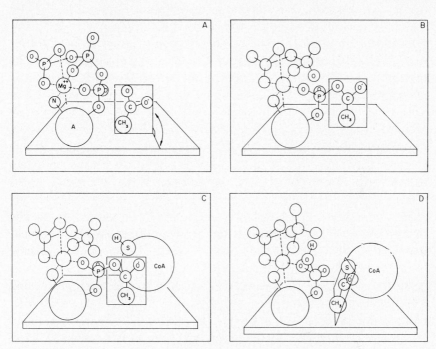

Fig. 8.1. An atomic model of the acetokinase reaction sequence.

nitrogen have taken up five of the six coordination positions available in Mg^{2+} and have fixed Mg^{2+} in a claw-like hold. Then, with all of the five ionizable groups of ATP engaged, the one as yet unoccupied position in Mg^{2+} is taken up by an atom in some group on the enzyme surface. In Figure 8.1 the enzyme surface is represented as flat and at right angles to the direction to which the remaining coordinating position of Mg^{2+} is pointing.

The fastening of Mg^{2+} by both the oxygen and nitrogen atoms

* Molecular models recently built have indicated that the chelation of Mg^{++} by ATP pictured here to be incorrect in some details, but the acetokinase mechanism suggested here is independent of the mode of Mg^{++} chelation by ATP.

can be viewed as an essential element in the device used by the enzyme to anchor the phosphate groups of ATP in place. Thus, the molecule of ATP is represented as being bound to the enzyme surface; its triphosphate group chelates Mg^{2+} in such a way that a molecule of acetate, also shown taking up a position on the enzyme surface (anchored through the methyl group), can attack the phosphorus atom of the innermost phosphate group of ATP (Figure 8.1A). This attack is initiated by the close approach of one of the two equivalent oxygen atoms of acetate toward the phosphorus atom (Figure 8.1B). When this happens, a bond begins to form between the "attacking" oxygen atom and the "attacked" phosphorus atom. At the same time, a bond begins to break between the same phosphorus atom and one of its original attached oxygen atoms. Experiments have shown the bond which is broken to be the one to the "bridge" oxygen, that is, the bond from the "attacked" phosphorus atom to the oxygen atom linking the innermost phosphorus atom to its adjacent phosphorus neighbor. The oxygen which has broken away in this reaction is indicated in Figure 8.1B. The oxygen is held, by virtue of the chelation of Mg^{2+} by pyrophosphate, in a position above the phosphorus atom from which it parted company. Its position is not rigidly fixed, since the phosphate moiety to which it is still bound can rotate about an axis defined by two of the other oxygen atoms of the same phosphate moiety, namely, the one chelating Mg^{2+} and the bridge atom to what was, in ATP, the outermost phosphate group. Nevertheless, despite the rotation (perhaps because of it), this "displaced oxygen" is restricted to a region above, and close to, the phosphorus atom from which it was displaced; it is thus in a perfect steric position to reestablish the original bond. This "return" would lead to the reformation of the original phosphorus-oxygen bond, concomitant with the cleavage of the phosphorus-oxygen bond to acetate. This alternation of making and breaking bonds accounts for the easy reversibility of the reaction shown in Eq. (19).

$$\text{ATP} + \text{acetate} \rightleftarrows \text{acetyl-AMP*} + \text{pyrophosphate} \qquad (19)$$

* Acetyl-AMP formed in the left to right direction is always enzyme-bound.

In Figure 8.1A acetate is represented in a "canted" position, going to an "upright" position when it is bound to AMP in acetyl-AMP as shown in Figure 8.1B. One can think of acetate as undergoing a "rocking" motion between these two positions.

As the acetate, bound to the enzyme surface by its methyl group (which acts as a pivot), rocks towards ATP, the attacking oxygen atom can come from below and from the right, closer and closer in line with the phosphorus atom; a bond between the two atoms begins to form. The oxygen atom which is leaving moves upward. Two of the original oxygens bonded to the attacked phosphorus atom are "fixed" and cannot move, but they act as an axis around which the phosphate moiety can rotate. This ability to rotate allows the phosphorus atom to move slightly to the left and downward. By the time the rocking motion of acetate has moved the attacking oxygen to the apogee of its arc, the bond to phosphorus is essentially formed, and the bond to the "bridge" oxygen is essentially broken. Of course the whole process occurs in one integrated "concerted" action. The rocking motion brings the acetate oxygen closer and closer to phosphorus and causes the phosphorus moiety to rotate on the axis of its two fixed oxygens and affords the departing oxygen the perfect steric path for withdrawal. This kind of "concerted" reaction is the essence of enzymic catalysis, and we shall find this a recurring theme in the discussion.

It was stated above that the sequence depicted in Figure 8.1 is only a device to make the events of the kinase reaction clearer. However, Eq. (19) above presents a "partial" reaction which can actually be carried out by the enzyme in the presence of ATP and acetate but in the absence of CoA. The mechanism given explains how this enzyme can synthesize acetyl-AMP from ATP and acetate. Also, the mechanism explains how the enzyme is capable of catalyzing the synthesis of ATP and acetate from acetyl-AMP and pyrophosphate in the reverse of Eq. (19).

In addition, this mechanism for the "partial" reaction accounts for the ATP-pyrophosphate "exchange" reaction that depends upon acetate. By exchange we mean that a pyrophosphate moiety of ATP can be split out and replaced by a different pyrophosphate moiety.

The exchange reaction can be demonstrated by the isolation of ATP after the incubation of the enzyme with nonlabeled ATP, acetate, and labeled pyrophosphate. The ATP isolated after the reaction will be labeled. This observation can be rationalized by considering Figure 8.1A and B. The ATP and acetate react as shown in parts A and B. Now, if the pyrophosphate moiety released by the reaction can "unchelate" and leave, and if a different (labeled) pyrophosphate moiety can take its place, reversal of the reaction will lead to incorporation of label into ATP. This exchange reaction depends upon the presence of acetate, since the production of "exchangeable" pyrophosphate requires the displacement of pyrophosphate from ATP by acetate. The mechanism presented here would lead to the prediction that the amount of acetate required for the "exchange" could be extremely small, since the acetate is acting catalytically.

In Figure 8.1, acetate is represented as lying on a flat plane—that is, the two oxygen atoms, the carbon atom to which the oxygens are linked, and the carbon of the methyl group all lie on a plane represented in the figure as perpendicular to the enzyme surface (this is parallel to the plane of the page). The acetyl group of acetyl-AMP is essentially in the same plane. In Figure 8.1C the CoASH molecule is positioned on the enzyme surface behind the plane of the acetyl group of acetyl-AMP. The sulfur atom is above and behind the carbon atom of the carboxyl group of acetyl-AMP. The attack on the carbonyl group is initiated by an approach of the sulfur atom. As this approach comes closer, the sulfur-carbon bond is formed, and, at the same time, the carbon-oxygen bond begins to break. In addition, as the sulfur approaches the carbon atom, the hydrogen atom bonded to sulfur is forced to approach the oxygen atom which is leaving. The sulfur-hydrogen bond breaks as the hydrogen simultaneously forms a bond to the oxygen being ejected. The most striking aspect of this reaction, however, is that the plane defined by the sulfur atom, the carbonyl carbon, the oxygen which is retained, and the methyl group carbon is no longer parallel to the original plane but is, essentially, at an angle of 90° to this plane (see Figure 8.1D). It can be said that the molecule has undergone a "flip" to a plane perpendicular to the original plane.

This most interesting "flip" in orientation can occur easily because there is free rotation about the carbon-carbon bond in the acetyl group. As a consequence of this "flip," the oxygen atom which was just ejected is in a perfect steric position to reestablish the original bond. It follows necessarily that the oxygen displaced by sulfur must be in the perfect steric position because such an attack is really only the reversal of its departure; that departure has taken the best possible path. Since the binding of the interacting molecules to the enzyme surface and the chelation of ATP to Mg^{2+} keep all the molecular parts essentially in place, the oxygen atom cannot be far removed from the most advantageous position for the reversal of the reaction. This situation is not unlike the one discussed above for the steric position of the bridge oxygen displaced from ATP by acetate.

In Figure 8.1D the phosphate group of AMP, formed as a result of the attack of sulfur, can rotate about an axis defined by its two fixed oxygens. This allows the hydroxyl group to approach closely to the carbonyl carbon. As this process continues, the plane of the acetyl group can undergo a reverse rotation, a "flip," with the sulfur atom now afforded the most advantageous path to depart. This, of course, is the reverse of the best possible route it took for the attack on the carbon atom, which led to the establishment of the carbon-sulfur bond and the ejection of oxygen. By analogy with the transfer we noted above of the hydrogen from sulfur to oxygen in the forward reaction, the reversal of the reaction occurs with the hydroxyl approaching carbon in such a way that the hydrogen is forced to come close to the sulfur atom. The bond between oxygen and hydrogen begins to break as the bond between sulfur and hydrogen begins to form.

This transfer of hydrogen from one atom to the next in both the forward and backward reactions facilitates the reaction greatly. The carbon that is being attacked is essentially a center of relatively positive electrical charge. It will, therefore, attract an attacking species that is oppositely charged. Any atom which is forced to leave by virtue of the attack of a second atom will best be able to depart as a positively charged, or at least neutral, species. Thus, in the reverse reaction which we are considering here, hydroxyl begins to attack. As it approaches, the hydrogen tends to move as a proton, with its positive charge, toward sulfur. This leaves oxygen with greater and greater negative charge. The closer the approach of oxygen to the carbon, the more the hydrogen moves toward sulfur, and the more negative the oxygen becomes. This buildup of the negative charge on oxygen makes it a better and better attacking species. On the other hand, sulfur, which is forced to leave in this reaction, would have to leave as a negatively charged species. However, the hydrogen which is coming closer and closer in this reaction sequence brings its positive charge and tends to make the sulfur less and less negatively charged. Thus, the sulfur becomes less and less tightly held by the relatively positive charge on the carbon. This proton transfer (the reverse of acetyl-CoA formation) is another excellent example of the "concerted" reaction. The ready reversibility of the reaction is one of the consequences of the concerted process.

By way of recapitulation, let us assume that all three molecules (ATP, acetate, and CoA) are locked in their slots on the enzyme surface simultaneously. Before reaction with ATP, acetate is capable of rotating freely about its carbon-carbon bond. Let us say that it is free to do so on the enzyme surface. This rotation is a rapid process, as is the "rocking" mentioned above. Therefore, it will not be long, after all three of the components of the reaction occupy their slots on the enzyme surface, before the acetate rotates and rocks into a position such that one of its oxygen atoms approaches and attacks the innermost phosphorus atom of ATP. Once this attack begins, and the oxygen of acetate is attracted and restricted to a region close to the phosphorus it is attacking, the acetate has assumed such a position in space that the plane defined by its flat carboxyl group is perfectly disposed for attack by the sulfur atom of CoA. The acetate "rocks" in its approach to phosphorus, and, at the instant when the attacking oxygen and the phosphorus have formed a bond, the carbon of the acetate carboxyl is in the most advantageous position for attack by sulfur. The newly formed oxygen-phosphorus bond is no sooner formed than the sulfur atom begins its attack, with the cleavage of the carbon-oxygen bond. In a sense, a bond never exists between acetate and AMP. Acetyl-AMP exists only for a fleeting instant in the smooth and continuous flow of the entire process. The sulfur atom approaches the carbon of the carboxyl group of acetate, with ejection of oxygen. As sulfur comes in closer and closer, the carboxyl group begins to rotate, or "flip." As the flip progresses, the sulfur atom can come in closer and closer, and the plane of the acetyl group comes closer and closer to the new position it will occupy when the 90° change is made. As the plane gets closer and closer to the new position toward which it is rotating, the oxygen that is leaving can move out more easily. The ease of this escape is enhanced by the transfer of hydrogen discussed above plus the steric factor (oxygen escapes most efficiently when the rotation is virtually complete).

This brilliant integration of the shape of molecules, of the binding of molecules so that the reactive portions are brought into virtually perfect juxtaposition, of the change of electrical charge, of the change in orientation from one plane to another, and of other factors which have not been dealt with here (and some which are still unrecognized) is Nature's exploitation of transition-state chemistry. Similar pictures can be formulated for other kinase reactions. In the midst of the impressive organization seen here, one cannot help but be struck at the same time by the simplicity of what is going on. There is no violent motion of the reacting molecules as occurs when reactions take place in solution. The molecules are essentially tied hand and foot; indeed, they are compelled to be introduced face to face, so to speak. The most drastic change in the whole process seems to be the rotation of a group from one plane to another at right angles. This is the genius of catalysis, of which the kinases represent so powerful an example.

TPNH as Energizer of Fatty Acid Synthesis

We have mentioned in Chapter 6 that TPNH can serve in an energizing capacity; in this respect it has to be classified with ATP. The synthesis of long-chain fatty acids is one of several synthetic processes in which TPNH plays this energizing role. Figures 8.2 and 8.3 provide a summary of the sequential reactions that lead to the synthesis of palmitic acid from acetyl-CoA and malonyl-CoA. Each of these starting acyl-CoA intermediates is converted to the corresponding acyl derivatives of a sulfhydryl-bearing protein (discovered by Roy Vagelos and named the acyl-carrier protein,

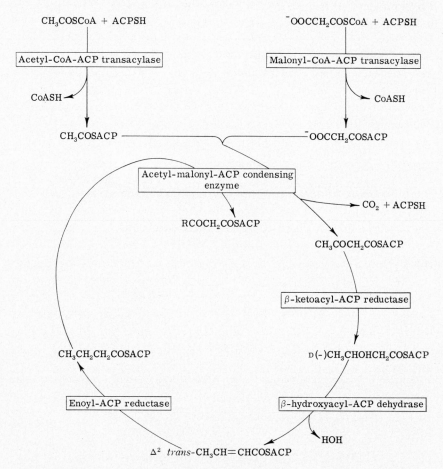

Fig. 8.2. The cycle for synthesis of fatty acids from acetyl-CoA and malonyl-CoA. The reactive form of the acyl-acceptor protein is represented as ACPSH. This figure was kindly provided by Dr. S. Wakil of Duke University.

abbreviated as ACP). The functional groups of the acyl-carrier protein are, in fact, identical with those of coenzyme A. The acyl-carrier protein may be looked upon as pantetheine phosphate bound to a protein of relatively small size (molecular weight of 6000).

The acetyl- and malonyl-ACP derivatives condense to form the β-keto butyryl-ACP which is then reduced in two stages, first to the β-hydroxyacyl-ACP and finally to the fatty acyl-ACP. Between the first and second reductive steps a rearrangement takes place—the

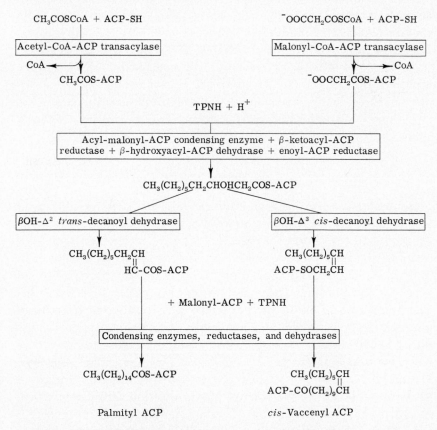

Fig. 8.3. A summary of the sequential steps and participating enzymes in the cycle for synthesis of palmitic acid and *cis*-vaccenic acid from acetyl-CoA and malonyl-CoA. This Figure was kindly provided by Dr. S. Wakil of Duke University.

elimination of water from the β-hydroxyacyl-ACP with formation of the enoyl-ACP derivative. This cycle of condensation (with malonyl-ACP) and reduction is repeated until the chain reaches the C_{18} stage, the chain growing in length by two carbon atoms in each cycle. At the C_{10} stage in the synthesis, the β-hydroxyacyl-ACP can be isomerized as usual to the *trans* 2-enoyl derivative, or in the presence of an additional enzyme to the corresponding *cis* 3-enoyl-ACP. Palmityl-ACP is eventually formed from the *trans* 2-enoyl decanoyl-ACP whereas the unsaturated *cis*-vaccenyl-ACP (a C_{18} unsaturated acid) can be formed from the *cis* 3-enoyl decanoyl-ACP.

The TPNH is the driving force in each of the two key reductive steps in the synthetic cycle. In a few organisms TPNH can be replaced by DPNH or the two can be equivalent. ATP is the driving force in the kinase-mediated carboxylation of acetyl-CoA to malonyl-CoA—the key reagent in the *de novo* synthesis of fatty acids.

Reversal of the Citric Cycle by Ferredoxin

In photosynthetic bacteria, the carbon chains for synthesis of amino acids are formed essentially by reversal of the citric cycle according to the studies of Daniel Arnon. Such bacteria contain a set of synthetases (also known as syntases) that respectively catalyze the reductive carboxylation of acetyl-CoA to pyruvate, of succinyl-CoA to α-ketoglutarate, and of α-ketoglutarate to isocitrate. The reductant in these three carboxylative reactions is reduced ferredoxin—generated photochemically during photosynthesis. Reduced ferredoxin is required for energizing only those carboxylative reactions which involve oxidoreduction. The nonoxidative carboxylation of pyruvate to oxalacetate is known from the studies of M. Utter to be an ATP-mediated kinase reaction. Thus, reversal of the citric cycle is achieved by a combination of ferredoxin-mediated reductive carboxylations, an ATP-mediated carboxylation, and finally the ATP-mediated conversion of acetate to acetyl-CoA. All the other steps in the reversal of the citric cycle are catalyzed by the same enzymes that operate in the forward direction.

The Themes for Biologic Syntheses

In our survey of the synthetic processes of the cell—whether synthesis of proteins, lipids, nucleic acids, purines, pyrimidines, or sugars—we have found only two themes—the theme of ATP as energizer for the kinases and the theme of the reduced coenzymes (TPNH, DPNH and ferredoxin) as energizers for synthetic reactions. The kinase theme is based on bond transfer from one pair of molecules to another; the reduced coenzyme theme is based on the reversal of energetically unfavorable reactions (the hallmark of synthetic reactions). It is of interest to note that the pentose cycle, which is the principal system for the generation of TPNH, requires the initial intervention of ATP for the conversion of glucose into glucose 6-phosphate. On closer examination, therefore, we come to recognize that the two categories of energizing synthetic processes are actually interdependent.

Suggested Reading

Books

Dixon, M., and Webb, E. C., "Enzymes," 2nd ed., Academic Press, New York, 1964.

Special Articles

Arnon, D. I., Tsujimoto, H. Y., and McSwain, B. D., Nature **207**, 1367 (1965); ferredoxin and photosynthetic phosphorylation.

Berg, P., *J. Biol. Chem.* **222**, 1015 (1956): acyl adenylates, an enzymatic mechanism of acetate activation.

Buchanan, J. M., Flaks, J. G., Hartman, S. C., Levenberg, B., Lukens, L. N., and Warren, L., *in* "Symposium on the Chemistry and Biology of Purines," Ciba Foundation, p. 233, 1957: the enzymatic synthesis of inosinic acid *de novo*.

Goldman, P., Alberts, A. W., and Vagelos, P. R., *J. Biol. Chem.* **27**, 1255 (1963): acyl protein coenzyme of fatty acid synthesis.

Huennekens, F. M., Whiteley, H. R., and Osborn, M. J., *in* "Symposium on Enzyme Reaction Mechanisms," Gatlinburg, April 1959: mechanisms of formylation and hydroxymethylation reactions.

Kornberg, A., *Advan. Enzymol.* **18**, 191 (1957): pyrophosphorylases and phosphorylases in biosynthetic reactions.

Lynen, J., *Federation Proc.* **20**, 941 (1961): biosynthesis of saturated fatty acids.

Majerus, P. W., and Vagelos, P. R., *Federation Proc.* **23**, 166 (1964).

Meister, A., *Proc. 1st Intern. Pharmacol. Meeting* **6**, 77 (1962): mechanisms of enzymatic acylation and peptide bond formation.

Meister, A., Krishnaswamy, P. R., and Pamiljans, V., *Federation Proc.* **21**, 1013 (1962): mechanism of glutamic acid activation and glutamine synthesis.

Mourad, N., and Parks, R. E., Jr., *Biochem. Biophys. Res. Communs.* **19**, 312 (1965): on a phosphoryl-protein intermediate in nucleoside diphosphokinase.

Wakil, S. J., Pugh, E. L., and Sauer, F., *Proc. Natl. Acad. Sci. U. S.* **52**, 1360 (1964): the mechanism of fatty acid synthesis.

CHAPTER 9 _____

Energy Transductions and Biochemical Machines

Primary Energy Transducing Systems vs. the Sensing Systems

In this chapter we shall be dealing with the properties and characteristics of the cellular devices which convert energy from one form into another. These devices may be classified under two headings: (1) the primary energy-transducing systems which either generate ATP or utilize ATP (or something derivable therefrom) for the performance of work, and (2) the "sensing" systems for energy transformation which translate some external stimulus such as sound, light, and pressure eventually into an electric impulse or into some other form which can influence the biochemical transactions of cells. The first set of devices is common to all cells. The tasks of generating ATP, moving ions against a gradient, and synthesizing proteins, carbohydrates, nucleic acids, and lipids must be accomplished by cells of all forms of life. The second set of devices is contained within cells that are specialized for sensing various external stimuli. These sensing devices often involve some mechanism for amplifying the original stimulus, and this amplification is likely to require the cooperation of the primary energy-transducing systems.

The Comparative Mechanisms of the Three Primary Energy-Transducing Systems

Our attention will be focused on the primary energy-transducing systems of the cell and particularly on the systems which convert

183

oxidative energy into the "bond" energy of ATP. There are, basically, only three systems that can carry out this conversion—the glycolytic, mitochondrial, and chloroplastic systems. The mitochondrion and chloroplast are first cousins, mechanistically speaking, and the two may be looked upon as variations on a single theme. These two ATP-generating systems stand in contrast, mechanistically, to the glycolytic system.

The details of the glycolytic process are almost invariant in animal and plant cells but not in bacterial cells. In bacterial cells one finds what appears to be enormous variability in the nature of the glycolytic process. If one looks beneath the surface, however, one may discern two principles that underlie all glycolytic systems. The essence of the glycolytic process is the splitting of a diphosphorylated keto hexose molecule into halves and the generation of ATP by coupling the anaerobic oxidation of the resultant halves to the esterification of inorganic phosphate. There are, in fact, anaerobic bacteria (such as *Clostridium sporogenes*) which contain systems for coupling the anaerobic oxidation of amino acids to the synthesis of ATP. The coupling process in this case, like that of the glycolytic system, does not involve an electron-transfer chain. The anaerobic coupled oxidation of acetaldehyde to acetylphosphate in *Clostridium kluyveri* is another example of this phenomenon which may be looked upon as a mechanistic variant of the glycolytic cycle, even though sugars are not involved.

The simple coupling mechanism of the glycolytic system is fundamentally different from that used by the mitochondrion* or chloroplast. In the latter two, the primary oxidation is many steps removed from the esterification of inorganic phosphate. Here, the coupling of oxidation to phosphorylation is carried out by an organized electron-transfer chain, whereas in the glycolytic cycle the same molecule that undergoes oxidation is the acceptor of inorganic phosphate.

---

* It is curious that in the mitochondrion there is one coupled oxidation carried out in the outer membrane (oxidation of α-ketoglutarate to succinyl-CoA) that follows the glycolytic mechanism, in the sense that the oxidation leads directly to the formation of a high-energy intermediate, namely, succinyl lipoate.

Biochemical Machines

It may be appropriate to consider first some general features of the devices in living cells that carry out energy transductions—devices which we shall describe as biochemical machines. In nature we never find one huge machine; rather, we find large numbers of identical machines strung together like beads in a necklace. For example, there are several hundred mitochondria in a single liver or muscle cell, and any given mitochondrion contains tens of thousands of repeating units, each of which is concerned in the linking of oxidation to the synthesis of ATP. In the inner ear there are thousands of repeating units involved in converting sound waves into nerve impulses. In the retinal rods and cones there are thousands of units specialized for absorbing photons and translating the resultant photochemical change into a nerve impulse.

All biochemical machines are subcellular—that is, they are contained within the precincts of the individual cell. This fact alone automatically excludes giant-sized machines. Indeed, the ultimate machines lie at the very limit of resolution of the light microscope; many of the fine details are beyond recognition even by the electron microscope. Cellular machines are molecular machines. That is to say, the actual transducing elements are individual molecules, and any description of how biochemical machines work has to be couched in terms of the behavior and performance of molecules specialized for transduction. These molecules are not freely moving; rather, they are fixed within a solid state, an organized matrix. Hence, the performance of these transducing molecules requires the contribution of other molecules that provide the structural scaffolding of the machine.

Transducing molecules are activated by energy in one form and converted to some other form with release of energy. During this transduction they undergo chemical or physical changes or both. In order to maintain function such molecules must return to their original states if they are to fulfill a cyclical role. Thus, all transducing molecules have the property of undergoing *reversible* changes.

Each different biochemical machine has its own special molecules which are uniquely suited for the particular transduction to be carried out. The green color of plants is due to chlorophylls—the key transducing molecules in the chloroplast machine. The cells of the retina of the eye have special pigments capable of converting light energy ultimately into electric energy. Muscle cells contain a protein complex, actomyosin, which is the molecular instrument for converting chemical energy into mechanical work. Our knowledge of the nature of the transducing molecules is still far from complete; these molecules are now the objects of intensive search and investigation. The biochemical machine may be looked upon as a device that has been evolved to facilitate the operation of the transducing molecules. The performance of the transducing molecules requires special conditions and arrangements. The structure of the machine has to be interpreted in terms of its adaptation to the cyclical performance of these working molecules.

Our most extensive knowledge of how a transducing machine operates comes from the study of the mitochondrion. Although each transducing machine has certain special equipment, many of the principles of structure and design are common to all such machines. We shall, therefore, turn our attention to the mitochondrion, which we may consider to be the prototype of all the energy-transducing machines of the cell.

The Mitochondrion

The energy transductions catalyzed by mitochondria involve the following component operations: (1) the generation of the electron donors for the electron-transfer chain (succinate and DPNH) either by the oxidations of the citric cycle and related processes or by the oxidation of metabolites such as β-hydroxybutyrate and choline; (2) the transfer of electrons through the chain, coupled to the formation of high-energy intermediates; (3) the utilization of the high-energy intermediates either for the synthesis of ATP or for the performance of work (translocation of ions across a membrane, transfer of hydrogen from DPNH to TPN^+, etc.). All but the first operation take place in the inner membrane of the mitochondrion.

The generation of the electron donors for the chain is carried out by a number of dehydrogenating systems localized in the outer mitochondrial membranes. These systems generate mainly DPNH. The α-ketoglutaric dehydrogenase system generates both DPNH and succinate and is, in fact, the only mitochondrial system known to generate succinate. DPNH and succinate are not the exclusive electron donors—in some types of mitochondria, α-glycerophosphate can also serve as direct electron donor for the chain. There is, however, no known system for generating α-glycerophosphate in the mitochondrion. This electron donor is delivered to the mitochondrion after it has been formed by an extramitochondrial system.

Although it is possible to dissociate the flow of electrons through the chain from the formation of a functionally detectable high-energy intermediate, this is not to say that the two events involve completely separate systems. Coupling requires a special *state* of the electron-transfer chain. Uncoupling may reflect an altered conformation of the chain which allows electron flow but does not permit the generation of high energy intermediates.

The work performances of the mitochondrion are processes that are energized by the high-energy intermediates formed by coupled electron flow. The systems and structures that implement these work performances (active transport of divalent ions is one of several such performances) are distinct from those of the electron-transfer chain. It is, however, one membrane (the inner membrane) that houses both the electron-transfer chain and the systems that perform work. The electron-transfer system for producing high-energy intermediates is thus situated *cheek by jowl* with the systems that have to be energized by high-energy intermediates.

Among the work performances of the mitochondrion we are including the synthesis of ATP from ADP and P_i. Strictly speaking, the synthesis of ATP involves conservation of high-energy intermediates whereas other work performances, such as active transport of ions, involve dissipation of high-energy intermediates. We shall classify all uses of high-energy intermediates as work performances whether they involve chemical syntheses or mechanochemical events.

The multiplicity of options for the disposition of the high-energy intermediates argues for the intervention of central mechanisms that decide which work performance will take place when more than one is possible at a given time. The nature of these controls will be discussed later when the work performances have been considered in some detail.

THE MITOCHONDRIAL ELECTRON-TRANSFER CHAIN

Some eighty molecules of protein make up one complete electron-transfer chain.* However, not all these molecules participate directly in the electron-transfer process. The oxidation-reduction catalysts that constitute the direct carriers of the electrons probably represent no more than one third of the total number of protein molecules. Thus, we have to distinguish between proteins that serve in a supporting role (fulfilling structural or coupling functions) and proteins that are the carriers in the electron-transfer process.

We shall for the moment confine our attention to the fifteen or more species of protein that are engaged directly in the electron-transfer process. Each is linked to some oxidation-reduction prosthetic group such as flavin, heme, nonheme iron, or copper. In Table 9.1 are listed the known species of these groups. There are twelve different known species of proteins with oxidation-reduction prosthetic groups. Within a single electron-transfer chain there may be more than one molecule of a given species. Thus, there are two molecules of cytochrome b per chain and at least three molecules of nonheme iron protein.

COMPLEXES OF THE ELECTRON-TRANSFER CHAIN

One complete electron-transfer chain is made up of four separable complexes (sectors) that are designated as complexes I, II, III, and IV. These complexes are the natural subdivisions of the chain—representing the smallest units still capable of integrated electron-transfer activity. The various known oxidation-reduction

---

* The data on the molecular aspects of the electron-transfer chain discussed here are derived from studies of beef heart mitochondria. There are, undoubtedly, variations in the molecular statistics between the chain of a mitochondrion from beef heart muscle and that of a mitochondrion from another source.

proteins are distributed among the four complexes as depicted in Figure 9.1. The molecular weight of each complex is about 300,000, of which 64% is contributed by protein and 36% by lipid. Only about half of the mass contributed by protein (192,000) represents catalytic proteins, that is, proteins that undergo oxidation-reduction. Thus, each complex contains no more than 4–5 molecules of catalytic protein (an average molecular weight of 20,000 for the individual proteins is assumed), and an equal number of molecules of noncatalytic protein.

Table 9.1

THE PROTEINS WITH OXIDATION-REDUCTION PROPERTIES KNOWN TO BE PRESENT IN THE MITOCHONDRIAL ELECTRON-TRANSFER CHAIN

Class of protein	Members of the class	Functional group(s)
Flavoproteins	Succinic dehydrogenase	Peptide linked "FAD"
	DPNH dehydrogenase	Flavin mononucleotide
Cytochromes	Cytochrome a	Heme a
	Cytochrome a_3	Heme a
	Cytochrome b	Protohemin
	Cytochrome c_1	Mesohemin
	Cytochrome c	Mesohemin
Nonheme iron proteins (with electron spin resonance signals)	A species in complex I	Iron linked to sulfur
	A species in complex II	Iron linked to sulfur
	A species in complex III	Iron linked to sulfur
Copper-bearing proteins	A species associated with cytochrome a	Copper
	A species associated with cytochrome a_3	Copper

The only nonheme iron protein in the chain that has been characterized by isolation is that of complex III. The monomeric unit of this isolated nonheme iron protein has two gram atoms of iron per 30,000 gm of protein. From electron spin resonance studies, Helmut Beinert has deduced the existence of a specific nonheme iron protein in both complexes I and II. There is four times as much bound iron in complexes I and II as would correspond to one molecule of nonheme iron protein per complex. On the basis of this excess iron, and on the assumption of two atoms of iron per molecule, we are postulating four molecules of nonheme iron protein in both complexes I and II. The exact number of catalytic molecules in these two complexes and the nature of these molecules have yet to be defined.

The number of catalytic proteins in complex IV is also undefined. This complex contains one molecule each of cytochrome a and a_3, and two atoms of copper. A copper protein can be isolated from complex IV and this would argue for the association of copper and

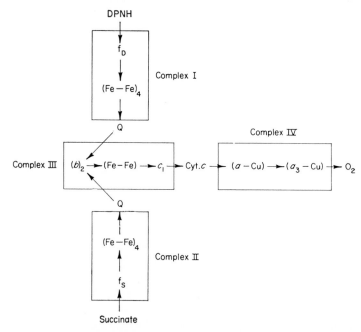

Fig. 9.1. Distribution of the oxidation-reduction proteins among the complexes of the electron-transfer chain. Fe–Fe represents nonheme iron; f_S, the succinic dehydrogenase; and f_D, the DPNH dehydrogenase.

heme with separate proteins. The alternative possibilities are either two catalytic species (a-Cu and a_3-Cu) or four catalytic species (a, a_3 and two different copper proteins). Half the copper of complex IV appears to be associated with cytochrome a; the rest with cytochrome a_3.

The overall reaction of the chain involves transfer of electrons from DPNH to molecular oxygen. However, this overall transfer is the result of three component transfer reactions: the transfer of electrons from DPNH to coenzyme Q (catalyzed by complex I); the transfer of electrons from reduced coenzyme Q to cytochrome *c* (catalyzed by complex III); and, finally, the transfer of electrons from reduced cytochrome *c* to molecular oxygen (catalyzed by complex IV) (cf. Figure 9.2). Coenzyme Q is the link which shuttles electrons between I and III, and between II and III, whereas cytochrome *c* is the link which shuttles electrons between III and

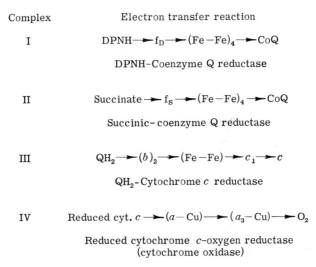

Complex	Electron transfer reaction
I	$DPNH \longrightarrow f_D \longrightarrow (Fe-Fe)_4 \longrightarrow CoQ$
	DPNH–Coenzyme Q reductase
II	$Succinate \longrightarrow f_S \longrightarrow (Fe-Fe)_4 \longrightarrow CoQ$
	Succinic–coenzyme Q reductase
III	$QH_2 \longrightarrow (b)_2 \longrightarrow (Fe-Fe) \longrightarrow c_1 \longrightarrow c$
	QH_2-Cytochrome *c* reductase
IV	$Reduced\ cyt.\ c \longrightarrow (a-Cu) \longrightarrow (a_3-Cu) \longrightarrow O_2$
	Reduced cytochrome *c*-oxygen reductase (cytochrome oxidase)

Fig. 9.2. The sequence of electron flow within the complexes of the electron-transfer chain.

IV. The mobile molecules which serve as connecting links between complexes (coenzyme Q and cytochrome *c*) are readily separable from the complexes; and they move freely within the lipid layer which extends over the entire membrane in which the complexes are localized. There are two entry points for electrons into the chain—one by way of DPNH and the other by way of succinate. Complex I is the entry point for electrons originating in DPNH, and complex II is the entry point for those originating in succinate. Electrons from DPNH, and those from succinate, traverse different paths until they reach complex III. Thereafter, the paths are identical.

Three of the complexes of the electron-transfer chain (I, III, and IV) are also the units for the coupling of electron flow to synthesis of ATP. That is to say, when a pair of electrons traverses any one of these three complexes, ATP is synthesized concomitantly with this movement. Thus, the arrangement of proteins within each complex is also related to the necessities of linking electron flow to synthesis of ATP.

Each complex is a composite of catalytic protein, noncatalytic protein and phospholipid. The proteins are linked one to the other by hydrophobic bonding predominantly; at least one hydrogen bond has been recognized in complex III (mediated by a sulfhydryl group). The positioning of the proteins within a complex is not random. On the contrary, the pattern for the arrangement of all the proteins, catalytic as well as noncatalytic, appears to be highly precise. This is to be expected in view of the necessities for sequential flow of the electrons within a complex. Phospholipid is bonded hydrophobically to the proteins of the complex. The distribution of bound phospholipid in the complex is not uniform. As we shall discuss in the next chapter, the pattern of localization of phospholipid in a complex is dictated by the necessities of membrane formation.

In the electron-transfer chain of beef heart mitochondria there is one each of complexes I, II, and III, and three of complex IV. The molecular proportions of the four complexes are highly variable depending on the source of the mitochondrion. This variability is evidence that the electron-transfer chain is an abstraction. The reality is, of course, the complex. The electron-transfer chain was formerly conceived of in terms of four complexes, positioned in a precise order, and in 1:1:1:1 stoichiometry. Not only is the notion of exact stoichiometry of the complexes to be abandoned but also that of precise positioning of complexes. When the mitochondrion is assembled, the proportions of the various complexes are determined by the hereditary apparatus, and not by specific interactions. Within a membrane continuum, electron flow between complexes depends on the shuttle role of the mobile components, and not on the positioning of complexes.

POTENTIAL DROP OVER THE ELECTRON-TRANSFER CHAIN

The oxidation of DPNH by molecular oxygen involves a drop in potential of about 1.2 volts (cf. Figure 9.3). This potential difference is the driving force for the coupling of electron flow to synthesis of ATP.* The overall potential drop is divided into three sectors, each about 0.4 volt, and these three sectors of potential drop correspond to three complexes of the chain.

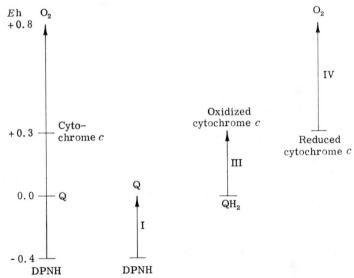

Fig. 9.3. The partition of the energy drop associated with the three complexes participating in oxidative phosphorylation. Eh represents the oxidation-reduction potential in volts.

As might be anticipated, the various oxidation-reduction proteins in each complex appear to be arranged in order of decreasing negative potential (or increasing positive potential). Thus, the total drop in potential of 0.4 volt within a complex is further subdivided into a set of smaller potential changes which are determined by the number of oxidation-reduction proteins within the complex in

---

* The free-energy change (ΔF) in an oxidative reaction is related to the oxidation-reduction potential by the formula $\Delta F = nEF$, where n is the number of equivalents, E is the standard potential, and F is the Faraday equivalent.

question. What is the rationale for the "even spacing" of oxidation-reduction proteins within a complex? Maximal coupling of oxidation to high-energy bond formation requires the reversibility of the coupling reaction. Reversibility, in turn, requires that the difference in potential between any two adjacent members in the electron-transfer chain should be relatively small. The greater the difference in potential, the greater the difficulty of reversal.

In the evolution of the electron-transfer chain, Nature was faced with the problem of spacing the component proteins of the chain fairly evenly over the span of potential between -0.4 volt and $+0.8$ volt. Flavoproteins are best suited for the region of negative potentials; copper proteins and the cytochromes for the region of positive potentials. Thus, considerations of potential determine the assignment of position for the oxidation-reduction groups in the electron-transfer chain. Each member of the chain fills one of the many slots that can be interposed between DPNH and oxygen. The nature of the protein and the mode of linkage of the protein to the coenzyme bearing the functional oxidation-reduction group are two other variables that affect oxidation-reduction potentials, and these variables have been exploited by Nature for the spacing of potential drops along the chain. Even spacing of the potentials of the oxidation-reduction proteins insures that the changes in oxidation-reduction potential between adjacent proteins in the chain are never large.

TRANSFER OF ELECTRONS WITHIN A COMPLEX

In each of the complexes there is a set of about five proteins with prosthetic groups capable of oxidation-reduction. This set of proteins has to be considered apart from the other proteins associated with each complex. They must be linked, one to the other, in a precise sequence since the electrons flow in a particular order from the first functional group to the last. The question arises: How are electrons transferred from one such group to another if the positions of the proteins within the complex are frozen?

Several hypotheses have been proposed to account for electron transfer within a "solid-state" macromolecular system. Britton Chance has invoked partial rotation of the protein; Richard Criddle and Robert Bock have postulated that the oxidation-reduction groups of the proteins are capable of movement by virtue of flexible amino acid side chains which attach the structures bearing the oxidation-reduction groups to the proteins, and that this fluctuating movement is sufficient for contact to be made between adjacent groups in the chain (cf. Figure 9.4). E. Frank Korman has recog-

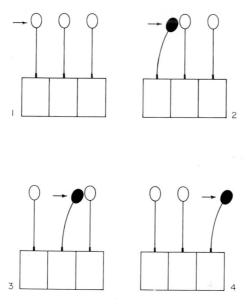

Fig. 9.4. Diagrammatic representation of the postulated mechanism of electron flow within a complex. The model shows a set of three oxidation-reduction proteins (represented as rectangles) linked one to the other, each with a flexible functional group (represented by a circle connected to the protein by a line). The successive states show how the electron entering from the left moves, *seriatim*, from one functional group to the next.

nized from studies on atom models, yet another device by which electron flow can be achieved within a system of positioned macromolecules (cf. Figure 9.5). The oxidation-reduction coenzymes of the chain such as DPN^+ and flavin are bonded to protein but this bonding does not exclude molecular rearrangement within the coenzymes or within the associated proteins. In the conversion of DPN^+ to DPNH, and of flavin to reduced flavin, there is a profound change in the angle which the ring system undergoing reduction subtends with respect to the rest of the molecule. This change comes close to 90° for DPN$^+$ and flavin. There are some grounds for postulating that conformational changes of a similar magnitude obtain for all other oxidation-reduction components of the mitochondrial electron-transfer chain. This picture of the electron-transfer process involves a wave of conformational change sweeping through the chain. The "flip" which a component makes during oxidation is synchronized with a complementary "flip" accom-

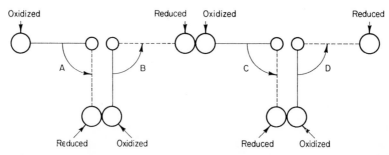

Fig. 9.5. Electron transfer by synchronized "making" and "breaking" of contact induced by conformational changes during oxidoreduction of the functional groups (○) of the electron-transfer chain. A, B, C, and D represent oxidation-reduction groups in the sequence of the chain.

panying the reduction of the next component in line. Thus, when A is reduced, it flips into a position touching B, and the stage is set for the interaction between A and B. After interaction takes place, A (now in the oxidized form) flips back to the original position and B (now in reduced form) flips to the position where it can react with the next component in line.

ROLE OF LIPID IN THE ELECTRON-TRANSFER PROCESS

About 30% of the dry weight of the electron-transfer chain is made up of lipid, largely in the form of phospholipid. When lipid is removed from the electron-transfer chain, integrated electron-transfer activity is lost. With reinsertion of lipid into the chain, this activity is restored. The essentiality of lipid for the electron-transfer function appears not to be related to considerations of conformation. As we shall discuss more fully in the next chapter, phospholipid is a major determinant of membrane formation. It is in terms of the necessities of membrane formation that the essentiality of lipid has to be rationalized.

APOLAR CHARACTER OF THE CHAIN

The nature of the bonds by which lipid and protein are linked to one another is now clearly established; they are predominantly hydrophobic bonds.* The bonds which link one protein to another are also predominantly hydrophobic. From this we may infer that there are extensive nonpolar regions in the complexes from which water is essentially excluded. The oxidation-reduction groups of the chain also have a nonpolar character. For example, coenzyme Q, by virtue of its hydrocarbon chain of fifty carbon atoms, is completely insoluble in water. The fact that coenzyme Q is a mobile molecule (shuttling electrons between complexes I and III, and II and III) can be explained in terms of its localization within a lipid area. The ring systems of flavin and heme are hydrophobic sectors of their respective coenzymes; it is, after all, the character of the functional group in which electron flow takes place that is critical. We cannot at present evaluate the possible hydrophobic character of the functional groups of the nonheme iron proteins and the copper proteins, for lack of information about their structures. Granted that the functional oxidation-reduction groups of the chain could be buried in the hydrophobic sectors of phospholipids or of proteins, what particular advantage does this lend? A reasonable explanation is that the intermediates in the coupling process are more stable in a nonaqueous environment than in water. Such an environment is provided within the interior of the complexes.

THE MITOCHONDRIAL COUPLING SYSTEM

When electrons flow through any of the three complexes of the chain, the primary high-energy intermediate, characteristic of the

---

* A notable exception is the electrostatic binding between cytochrome *c* and phospholipid. However, this interaction makes a relatively minor contribution to the overall interaction between protein and phospholipid.

complex, is invariably formed. This formation is an intrinsic part of the electron-transfer process. In isolated particles which are functionally well preserved, the intermediate is relatively stable, and can be converted to other intermediates by the associated kinase systems. If the particles become functionally damaged during isolation from mitochondria, the primary high-energy intermediates may have very transient existence and break down spontaneously. It is, therefore, not easy to distinguish between nonformation and transitory lifetime of intermediates. The difficulty may be one of demonstration, rather than of formation.

There are several reagents, such as 2,4-dinitrophenol, that can uncouple electron flow from the *formation* of *stable* and *measurable* high-energy intermediates. Probably there is no such thing as uncoupling in the sense that *no* intermediate, however transient, is formed during electron flow. Uncouplers may only so augment the instability of the intermediate that its lifetime is too short for utilization in subsequent reactions. Also, uncouplers can act at various points, not only at the level of the primary high-energy intermediate. Each of the various high-energy intermediates has unique chemical properties and its own specific "uncoupling" agent. Dinitrophenol acts specifically on the first high-energy intermediate, and arsenate on a phosphorylated form of the intermediate.

Granted the thesis that coupling is a process intrinsic to electron flow, the question arises: How can electron flow lead to high-energy bond formation? A good working hypothesis, as noted above, is that electron flow is accompanied by a wave of conformational change in all the participating proteins of a given complex; this conformational change, in turn, is translated* into a high-energy bond between a pair of molecules, or residues, which is associated with that particular sector of the electron-transfer chain. The coupling system would then be identified with the structure that undergoes the conformational change leading to the formation of the high-energy intermediate. The identity and nature of the first high-energy intermediates are still problematic, but educated guesses can be made.

---

* The accumulated energy could also be electrostatic; when a critical density of charge has accumulated, the conformational change could be triggered.

NATURE OF THE COUPLING SYSTEM

According to the interpretation given above, the coupling system may be conceived of in terms of an "elastic" system that can be held in a stretched form by some restraining force. When the restraining force is released the system snaps back to the original shape. The restraining force in the case of the electron-transfer chain is the high-energy bond formed during electron flow. Once the bond is disposed of by transfer of one of the molecules in the pair joined by that bond, the chain returns to its original position. The conformational change in the chain leads to the close approach of two groups that are initially separated in space, and this proximity facilitates bond formation. Conformational energy would thus be applied to overcoming the repulsive forces which act as barriers to the interaction of molecules.

CONFORMATIONAL CHANGES IN THE MITOCHONDRION

The most direct evidence for conformational changes in the repeating units of the mitochondrion comes from electron microscopy. The conditions which lead to the formation of high-energy intermediates or to the utilization of high-energy intermediates for ion translocation have been found to lead to striking modifications of the membrane ultrastructure. The light scattering studies of L. Packer also point to a correlation between changes in the state of the membrane and the production of high-energy intermediates. It is not easy to decide which is cause and which is effect. Our own interpretation is that conformational change in the membrane is the causation of high energy bond formation. H. Baum and J. Rieske have observed profound changes in the properties of complex III in the transition from the oxidized to the reduced form. Sulfhydryl groups that are readily titratable in the oxidized form of the complex are not available for titration in the reduced form of the complex. The pattern of the susceptibility of the complex to digestion by trypsin is also profoundly altered by reduction.

GENERATION OF HIGH-ENERGY INTERMEDIATES VIA ATP

The oxidative generation of high-energy intermediates and the utilization of this bond energy for the synthesis of ATP are known as oxidative phosphorylation. This is, in fact, the physiological direction of the energy transduction. However, it is of value to recognize that the formation of intermediates having high-energy bonds can be energized experimentally in two ways—either by electron flow or from preformed ATP. ATP-mediated formation of intermediates does not involve the electron-transfer chain directly, as indicated by the fact that it is not affected by inhibitors of electron flow (such as antimycin A). However ATP-mediated formation of high-energy intermediates is inhibited by oligomycin—a reagent which has no effect on the process by which high-energy intermediates are formed during electron flow. The fact that ATP may be used to generate a high-energy intermediate indicates, once again, that the energy levels of the ATP and the intermediate must be of comparable magnitudes.

UNITIZATION OF THE CHAIN

All but one of the four complexes of the chain (I, III, and IV) are also coupling sites. Thus, the structural unit of electron transfer may be identified with the structural unit of coupling. In three of the four primary electron-transfer complexes, high-energy intermediates can be generated, and in turn, high-energy intermediates can be utilized for ATP synthesis, ion translocation, or transhydrogenation. This clearly indicates that each complex of the chain is associated with the entire set of catalytic molecules required not only for coupling but also for ion translocation and transhydrogenation.

THE NATURE OF THE MOLECULES JOINED BY THE
HIGH-ENERGY BOND

If high-energy intermediates were generated in each of the three coupling sites of the electron-transfer chain, then perforce the pair of molecules or residues joined by the high-energy bond would be different at each site. A difference in the electron-transfer process at each site would dictate such a difference in at least one of the partners participating in the high-energy bond. There is some evidence for implicating the mobile carriers of the electron-transfer chain in high-energy bond formation. Thus, one of the partners forming the high-energy intermediate generated at each site[*] may be DPN at Site I, coenzyme Q at Site II, and cytochrome c at Site III. The nature of the other partner at each site is still unknown.

As of 1966 no detailed scheme of the mechanism of high-energy bond formation can be deduced from the available data. However, the general form of the solution is now recognizable, albeit dimly. It is probable that each of the mobile components of the electron transfer chain provides one of the pair of molecules joined by a high-energy bond. G. Pinchot and D. E. Griffiths have provided such data for DPN$^+$; A. Brodie for vitamin K; and J. Penniston for cytochrome c. The studies of P. Boyer on the loss of ^{18}O from labeled phosphate provide impressive evidence for the anhydride nature of the first high-energy intermediate, and point to a carboxyl group or its functional equivalent as the second of the pair of molecules. AMP, P_i, and arsenate can replace one or other of the partner molecules which form the bond. If we can assume that the replacing molecules resemble the replaced molecules in respect to functionality, then another line of evidence in favor of an anhydride character can be invoked. These observations are the basis for the following interpretation of the mechanism of oxidative phosphorylation. Each of the complexes that carries out coupled electron transfer is assumed to contain a bound carboxyl group. Electron flow leads to the "acylation" of the oxidized form of the reductant for each of the complexes:

$$DPNH + [I_{ox}]—COOH \rightarrow [I_{red}]—\underset{\underset{O}{\|}}{C} \sim DPN + H_2O$$

$$QH_2 + [III_{ox}]—COOH \rightarrow [III_{red}]—\underset{\underset{O}{\|}}{C} \sim Q + H_2O$$

$$Reduced\ cyt.\ c + [IV_{ox}]—COOH \rightarrow [IV_{red}]—\underset{\underset{O}{\|}}{C} \sim cyt\ c + H_2O$$

[*] The phosphorylation sites are designated as follows: Site I (DPNH to Q), Site II (QH$_2$ to cytochrome c), and Site III (reduced cytochrome c to oxygen).

We are assuming that DPN, Q, and cytochrome c can react like alcohols to form acyl derivatives with the carboxyl function. In this connection it is significant that a phosphorylated derivative of DPN has been isolated by David Griffiths; the phosphoryl group of this derivative can be transferred to ADP with formation of ATP. In the Griffiths compound, DPN has the character of an alcohol.

The synthesis of external ATP from the first "acylated" high-energy intermediate would involve two substitution reactions (by AMP and P_i respectively), and a transfer reaction.

$$[I_{red}]—C \sim DPN + AMP \rightarrow [I_{red}]—C \sim AMP + DPN$$
$$\| \qquad\qquad\qquad\qquad \|$$
$$O \qquad\qquad\qquad\qquad O$$

$$[I_{red}]—C \sim AMP + P_i \rightarrow [I_{red}]—COOH + AMP \sim P_i$$
$$\|$$
$$O$$

$$2 \; AMP \sim P_i \rightarrow ADP \sim P_i + AMP$$

Myokinase catalyzes the transfer of a phosphoryl group from one molecule of ADP to another molecule of the same species. The adenine nucleotide that participates in the interaction with the first high-energy intermediate, is bound to the complex. The synthesis of external ATP requires the transfer of a phosphoryl group from internal bound ADP or ATP to external AMP. Enzymes capable of catalyzing transmembrane, phosphoryl transfers would have to be postulated.

The above formulation applies to complex I but exactly the same sequence of substitution and transfer reactions would be involved in the formation of ATP from the first high-energy intermediates formed by complexes III and IV respectively. It should be noted that the reduced complex can undergo reoxidation by the oxidant for the complex (coenzyme Q, cytochrome c, or oxygen) as soon as the oxidation-reduction group is released from the high-energy intermediate.

An important distinction has to be made between adenine nucleotides bound to the inner mitochondrial membrane (these participate directly in ATP *formation*) and adenine nucleotides free in the external suspending medium. The outer membrane prevents the movement of adenine nucleotide in and out of the mitochondrion. Special enzymic devices are needed to make possible the transmembrane transfer of phosphoryl groups from inside the mitochondrion where these are generated to the acceptor adenine nucleotides external to the mitochondrion. Bound AMP is the first phosphoryl acceptor in the inner membrane; AMP is also the form of the adenine nucleotide which accepts transferred phosphoryl groups on the outside of the mitochondrion. Transmembrane transfers of acyl groups also take place in the mitochondrion.

Work Performances of the Mitochondrion

The high-energy intermediates generated by electron flow energize four different work performances. Each of these needs to be defined before we can develop a generalized interpretation of mitochondrial transductions (cf. Figure 9.6).

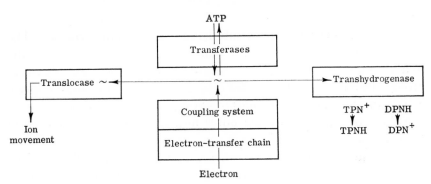

Fig. 9.6. The interrelationship of the systems which generate high-energy intermediates ($\sim$) and the work-performing systems which utilize the high-energy intermediates.

OXIDATIVE PHOSPHORYLATION

The esterification of AMP by inorganic phosphate (leading to the formation of ADP) or of ADP by inorganic phosphate (leading to the formation of ATP) is defined as oxidative phosphorylation when the esterification is energized by the primary high-energy intermediate formed during coupled electron flow. The postulated sequence of reactions by which the synthesis of bound ATP or ADP is achieved has been discussed above. There is a set of kinases which transfer a phosphoryl group from bound ADP or ATP to free AMP or ADP.

ION TRANSLOCATION

A high-energy intermediate, as yet unspecified, energizes the translocation of certain divalent metal ions (Mg^{++}, Ca^{++}, Mn^{++}, Sr^{++}, but not Fe^{++} or Cd^{++}). Two ions are translocated per high-energy intermediate. The translocated ions are transferred from the space exterior to the inner membrane (between outer and inner membranes) to the space in the interior of the inner membrane. The translocation can be effected at each of the three coupling sites, that is, complexes I, III, and IV.

The mitochondrial translocation of divalent metal ions is always accompanied by the release of protons into the *external* medium. There are grounds for postulating that the energized entry of divalent metal ions into the inner membrane is accompanied by proton release as a consequence of interaction of the ions with binding groups of the translocating system. Energized translocation leads to a *net* movement of divalent metal ions, hence to a *net* release of protons into the external medium. In this way, events in the interior can determine external changes in hydrogen ion concentration.

Anions penetrate both the outer and inner membranes via the phospholipid. This penetration requires that the anion be in its undissociated form (cf. Figure 9.7). The net movement of anions across the mitochondrial membrane leads to disappearance of protons from the external medium, and release of protons into the internal medium. Energized translocation involves the energized movement of the cation, and the synchronized passive movement of the anion. If an anion such as chloride does not readily penetrate the mitochondrion, translocation of the cation is exceedingly slow. If an ion such as acetate readily penetrates the mitochondrion, translocation of the cation can be very rapid. Thus, there is an interplay between movement of anions and cations even though these are independent processes.

The amount of divalent metal ion that can be translocated per unit amount of mitochondria is fixed. When this level is reached, no further accumulation of metal ion can take place. This upper limit is set by the total number of phospholipid binding sites with which metal ions can interact. The limit can be exceeded when phosphate is used as the anion. Virtually unlimited translocation of divalent cations can proceed when phosphate is the counterion. The insolubility of metal phosphates such as $Mg_3(PO_4)_2$ and $Ca_3(PO_4)_2$ leads to the displacement of the complexed metal ion from the phospholipid to the aqueous medium in the internal space. Under these

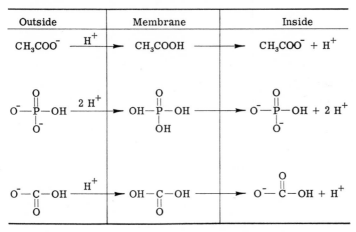

Fig. 9.7. Movement of anions through the phospholipid interior of a membrane.

conditions the limited number of phospholipid binding sites in the inner mitochondrial membrane is no longer an obstacle to unrestricted translocation.

The deposition of $Ca_3(PO_4)_2$ or $Mg_3(PO_4)_2$ in the aqueous medium of the interior space points up another aspect of translocation. The metal ion is bound to phospholipid during translocation (cf. Figure 9.8). The movement of the metal ion from one molecule of phospholipid to another, or from the phospholipid to the aqueous medium in the interior space, requires protons; this requirement can be filled only by the anions, the movement of which is geared to the movement of cations. If the protons are not available, the translocating system cannot discharge the metal ions, and the continuity of translocation is interrupted.

In the energized translocation of calcium ions carried out in presence of phosphate ions, two protons are released into the medium for each three Mg^{++} ions translocated. This net release is the balance between the release of six protons accompanying the entry of three Mg^{++} ions and the uptake of four protons accompanying the entry of two phosphate ions (HPO_4^{2-}).

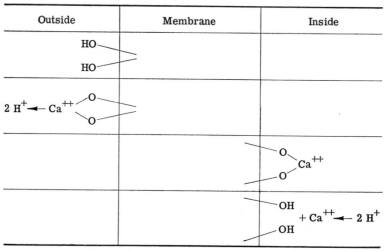

Fig. 9.8. Energized movement of a cation through the mitochondrial membrane.

SWELLING OF THE MITOCHONDRION

Monovalent cations such as K^+ and Na^+, in the presence of substrate and appropriate anions (imidazole, acetate), can penetrate into the interior space of the mitochondrion by a passive process. The net movement of monovalent ions into the mitochondrial interior is accompanied by an increase in the volume of water in the mitochondrion. Substrate probably alters the permeability of the inner membrane to monovalent cations—the membrane being more permeable when the chain is in the reduced form.

Specific reagents are known, such as gramicidin and valinomycin, which facilitate the passive penetration of monovalent ions into the mitochondrion. These reagents at the same time depress energized mitochondrial work performances. For example, both gramicidin and valinomycin are potent inhibitors of oxidative phosphorylation.

The penetration of monovalent ions through the outer and inner membranes successively and finally into the interior space, leads inevitably to swelling of the mitochondrion. The collapsed inner membrane (the form with cristae) blows up into an expanded vesicular form. The water volume enclosed by the expanded vesicular form of this membrane is many times that of the collapsed form. The immediate cause of swelling is a change in the shape of the repeating units, induced by monovalent ions or other reagents. During extensive swelling, the outer mitochondrial membrane perforates.

REVERSED ELECTRON FLOW

In reversed electron flow, electrons originating in succinate or in reduced cytochrome c can reduce DPN^+ to DPNH. This thermodynamically unfavorable oxidoreduction has to be energized. In other words, energy has to be introduced into the system to make possible this "uphill" oxidoreduction. There are several ways in which this could be accomplished. If DPN^+ could be transformed into some phosphorylated derivative with a sufficiently positive oxidation-reduction potential, the interaction with succinate would no longer be thermodynamically unfavorable. A second possibility would be the modification of DPN^+ by some group other than phosphoryl; this could lead to the same equalization of potentials between the reducing and oxidizing systems.

ENERGIZED TRANSHYDROGENATION

Mitochondria contain a flavoprotein enzyme which catalyzes the transfer of a hydride ion from DPNH to TPN^+. There is a difference of about 80 millivolts between the respective potentials of the TPN^+-TPNH and the DPN^+-DPNH systems; because of this differential the only thermodynamically permissible direction of hydride transfer is from TPNH to DPN^+. However, it is possible to achieve the transfer of a hydride ion from DPNH to TPN^+ when the transhydrogenation is energized by some high-energy intermediate. Again, the question has to be raised: How can energy be utilized to drive a thermodynamically unfavorable reaction? Again two categories of explanations are possible—one involving modifications of the hydride ion donor (DPNH) and the other involving modifications of the hydride ion acceptor. Both types of modification would involve interaction with some high-energy intermediate. It is of interest that David Griffiths has isolated a highly unstable phosphorylated derivative of DPNH under conditions of reversed electron flow. This may be the form of DPNH that is concerned in transhydrogenation.

LOSS OF WORK PERFORMANCES DURING COMMINUTION OF MITOCHONDRIA

When mitochondria are fragmented, the capacity for one of the work performances disappears completely while the capacities for the remaining three can be fully preserved. The capacity for translocation of both divalent and monovalent ions is the vulnerable work performance. Oxidative phosphorylation, reversed electron flow, and energized transhydrogenation are the work performances which are unaffected by the comminution of mitochondria. This dropout of one category of work performances and not of another is not a simple matter of variable lability; the explanation has a more profound basis. Ion translocation requires the directional alignment of the translocating system within the membrane. The movement of ions is only one way—from the exterior space to the interior space. When mitochondria are comminuted by sonic irradiation or other means, the membrane is in fact turned inside out, and the directionality is reversed. This inversion may account for the complete loss of the translocating capability in comminuted mitochondria.

PHYSIOLOGICAL SIGNIFICANCE OF THE WORK PERFORMANCES

The utilization of high-energy intermediates for the synthesis of ATP is the raison d'être of the mitochondrion; the physiological meaning of this particular work performance is obvious. However, it is not possible to rationalize satisfactorily the other work performances of the mitochondrion. Our concern in this chapter has been centered on the mechanisms by which high-energy intermediates are utilized for carrying out work performances. Whether some of the work performances are laboratory curiosities or biologically meaningful processes is still an unanswered question.

The Translocase Hypothesis

The operational unit which implements the energized translocation of divalent cations and phosphate through the inner membrane into the otherwise impenetrable chamber of the mitochondrion will be called the *translocase*. This system translocates certain divalent metal ions (e.g., Ca^{++}, Mg^{++}, Mn^{++}, Sr^{++}) but has no action on monovalent cations such as K^+. The translocase is capable of undergoing a profound conformational change when triggered by an appropriate high-energy intermediate. It is the mitochondrial equivalent of the actomyosin system of muscle. In the actomyosin system the conformational change leads to an approximation of the particles in the fiber (shortening of the fiber); in the analogous mitochondrial system the conformational change leads to an inversion of position so that a face originally directed outward is finally directed inward,

$$\varepsilon + \sim \longrightarrow 3$$

where the sign ε is the translocase unit and the conformational change is represented by the $180°$ rotation of the letter ε. As the equation suggests, this conformational change is triggered by some high-energy intermediate. One cycle of change probably requires the expenditure of one high-energy intermediate.

THE CONFORMATIONAL CHANGE OF THE TRANSLOCASE

When the translocase is actuated by the high-energy intermediate, the divalent metal ions that combined with sites originally on the exterior of the inner membrane now are exposed to the interior of the inner membrane (see Figure 9.9). In effect, energized translocation has brought these divalent metal ions across the membrane into the interior space where they may then be unloaded. The unloading could be due to a mass action effect, or to lowered binding affinity. The unloaded divalent ion eventually bends to charged groups on the phospholipid coat of the membrane.

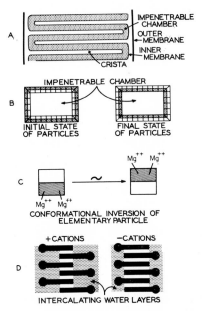

Fig. 9.9. The essential assumptions of the translocase hypothesis are represented graphically in the four-part figure. A: the whereabouts of the impenetrable chamber within the membranes of the mitochondrions. B: The change in conformation of the repeating particles abutting on the chamber. C: A representation of the 180° twist of a single repeating unit induced by the action of the high-energy intermediate on the "loaded" particle. D: The change in the water volume of a phospholipid micelle induced by ion binding. The change in the dimensions of a bimolecular phospholipid micelle is illustrative of a comparable change induced by metal ions in the phospholipid molecules bonded hydrophobically to the complex.

Some Properties of the Translocase System

In the intact mitochondrion, the operation of the translocase is limited by the accessibility of divalent metal ions to the inner membrane. Calcium ions even at low concentrations readily penetrate the outer membrane (the penetration, in fact, involves the damaging or modification of the membrane) whereas magnesium ions penetrate relatively slowly. The slow translocation rate for magnesium ions is an expression of this permeability barrier. Ions such as Zn^{++} and Cd^{++} can facilitate the translocation of Mg^{++} by damaging the outer membrane and rendering it permeable to Mg^{++}. Thus, unless the outer membrane permits the permeation of a divalent ion, the translocase system will be inoperative. The relative rates of translocation of different divalent ions reflect largely the respective rates of permeation of the outer membrane by these ions. The change in the properties of the outer membrane induced by metal ions such as Ca^{++} is reversible only at relatively low concentrations of the ions.

The net energized movement of ions (any divalent ion) into the mitochondrial interior invariably leads to swelling. This swelling is a secondary phenomenon—a consequence of ion translocation. When the sites in the phospholipid of the inner membrane are occupied with metal ions brought in by energized translocation, the inner membrane undergoes a rearrangement from a tubular to a vesicular form. This rearrangement leads to an augmented interior space which becomes filled with water. Metal ions are not the only devices for achieving this rearrangement. Lipid peroxidation can induce a similar rearrangement. The metal-induced rearrangement is reversible whereas that induced by lipid peroxidation is irreversible. The addition of EDTA or ATP can reverse metal-induced swelling. This reversal is achieved by tight chelation of divalent metal ions resulting in the "pulling out" of metal ions from the mitochondrial interior into the external medium.

When divalent metal ions are translocated in presence of inorganic phosphate, the mitochondrion shrinks. This shrinkage is a consequence of the disengagement of metal ions from the phospholipid of the inner membrane. These ions are released into the internal aqueous medium and precipitated as the highly insoluble metallophosphates. The membrane tends to assume a more condensed form when the phospholipid is metal-free; the interior water volume is smaller when the membrane is in the condensed form. The net result is the shrinkage of the mitochondrion.

RESPIRATORY CONTROL

Mitochondria, but not submitochondrial particles, shut off respiration (electron transfer) when the supply of ADP or P_i is exhausted. This phenomenon is known as respiratory control. It can be accounted for in terms of high-energy intermediates which cannot be "unloaded" for lack of either phosphate or ADP or both.

The accumulation of the primary high-energy intermediates brings the electron-transfer process to a halt because these intermediates involve a carrier as one of the pair of combining molecules. Unless the intermediate can undergo substitution reactions, the electron-transfer carrier trapped in this intermediate cannot undergo oxidation, with consequent paralysis of electron transfer. Submitochondrial particles show no evidence of respiratory control, which may indicate that the high-energy intermediates are less stable in these particles than in mitochondria.

Respiratory control is never complete since, even in the protected sealed chamber of the intact mitochondrion, the high-energy intermediates have a limited lifetime. Eventually, they undergo spontaneous hydrolysis.

THE EFFICIENCY OF COUPLING

The accepted limiting value for the experimentally determined P:O ratio is three; that is, the passage of one pair of electrons, traversing the chain from DPNH to oxygen, is coupled to the generation of three molecules of high-energy intermediates, or to the synthesis of three molecules of ATP. The same ratio is found to apply whether the high-energy intermediate is used to synthesize ATP or to translocate ions. However, the studies of Lynn have reopened the question of the maximally attainable ratio. He has found conditions under which ratios in excess of 3 and approaching 6 can be consistently measured. Lynn's interpretation is that a large proportion of the high-energy intermediates is lost or siphoned off under the usual conditions of measurement of P/O ratios. The true coupling efficiency is, according to Lynn, twice as high as has been reported previously. The issue has yet to be satisfactory resolved.

TRANSDUCING SYSTEMS AND MEMBRANES

The energy-transducing systems of the cell have a membranous character. The converse appears to be equally true; namely, all membranes* are engaged in some form of energy transduction. This

---

* By *membrane* we are referring to a vesicular or tubular system, the structured rim of which is made up of fused repeating units, such as those we have been discussing in the context of the mitochondrion.

generalization leads to an enormous simplification of the problems of transducing systems, since the general features of design are constant. Transducing systems contain a set of characteristic molecules arranged in a characteristic pattern. Variation in some of the molecules and in certain aspects of the arrangements of these molecules differentiate one membranous transducing system from another. Although the general architecture of membranes appears to be invariant, the size, shape, and number of component parts in the repeating units are characteristic of each transducing system.

A distinction has to be made between the systems that generate high-energy intermediates, and the systems that utilize high-energy intermediates for some work performance. The only membranes which contain systems for generating high-energy intermediates are those few which contain an electron-transfer chain or the glycolytic system. However, all membranes contain systems for implementing some energized work performance, be it ion translocation, active transport of molecules, or biosynthesis. Thus, it is the capacity to do some form of biochemical work that is common to membranes.

The mitochondrial translocase may serve as a tentative model for all devices in membranes which are concerned with active transport. It provides a mechanism for the energized translocation of an ion or molecule from the exterior surface of a membrane into an interior space. Specificity of transport is determined by the nature of the binding sites of the macromolecules which comprise the translocating apparatus.

The Chloroplast

There is now available an extensive body of evidence for the fundamental similarity between the mitochondrion and the chloroplast. The ultrastructural patterns of the two systems correspond very closely indeed. The elementary particle of the inner mitochondrial membrane has its counterpart in the quantasome of the chloroplast. The outer mitochondrial membrane, with its subunits of ancillary enzymes, probably corresponds in the chloroplast to the enzymes of the pentose and the glycolytic cycles, which appear to be localized in the membrane enclosing the chlorophyll-containing lamellae. The amounts of structural protein and lipid in the two transducing systems are approximately equal. The electron-transfer chain of the chloroplast contains oxidation-reduction components which have their counterparts in the mitochondrial chain.* These components are plastoquinone (similar to coenzyme Q), at least two cytochromes (b and f), and a pyridine nucleotide (TPN). In both organelles, electron flow is coupled to the synthesis of ATP via one or more high-energy intermediates, and this flow is Antimycin sensitive. Uncoupling agents, such as dinitrophenol and dicumarol, act equally well in both systems. The work capacities of the mitochondrion and the chloroplast are virtually identical. Both can catalyze the energized translocation of ions. Both show energized shrinking and swelling. This formidable list of basic similarities between the operational characteristics of these respective systems provides the most unambiguous evidence for the common architectural and molecular principles of the two organelles, and suggests that membranes, generally, may be constructed according to a common blueprint.

D. Arnon finds in green plants two types of photophosphorylating systems—cyclic and noncyclic. These are separate systems, probably localized in separate membranes of the chloroplast. In many respects the noncyclic system resembles the mitochondrial system for substrate level phosphorylation (in the outer mitochondrial membrane) whereas the cyclic system has close analogies with the system that implements oxidative phosphorylation (in the inner mitochondrial membrane). The noncyclic photophosphorylation system evolves molecular oxygen and generates TPNH and reduced ferredoxin in addition to generating ATP. It is insensitive to antimycin A and desaspidin, but sensitive to p-chlorophenyl-1,1-dimethylurea (CMU). The cyclic photophosphorylation system evolves no oxygen, does not generate TPNH or reduced ferredoxin externally, and is sensitive to antimycin A and desaspidin, but not to CMU. The electrons are expended in each turnover of the photochemical sequence of the noncyclic system, and cycled in the cyclic

---

* The fundamental difference lies in the nature of the ultimate electron donor—this being DPNH for mitochondria and reduced ferredoxin for chloroplasts.

system. The two points of community between the two systems are the participation of chlorophyll and the production of ATP. The active species of chlorophyll is different in the two systems. The cyclic system has an electron-transfer chain with oxidation-reduction components covering the span of potential from ferredoxin to molecular oxygen whereas the noncyclic system is an oxidation-reduction system covering a much more restricted span of potential (from reduced ferredoxin to TPN$^+$). The resemblance of the noncyclic system to the α-ketoglutaric dehydrogenase complex is striking.

Muscular Contraction

The complete contractile process in red skeletal muscle involves the collaboration of four major systems: (1) the elements of nerve cells which inervate the muscle fibers; (2) the sarcoplasmic reticulum which radiates in the form of channels through the muscle fiber; (3) the mitochondria which are imbedded at regular intervals within the matrix of muscle; and (4) the actomyosin system of filaments. The nerve elements trigger the release of Ca^{2+} ions from the sarcoplasmic reticulum. The mitochondria generate the ATP required for energizing the contractile process. The actomyosin network undergoes its cycle of contraction when actuated by ATP in presence of Ca^{2+} ions. Thus, the nerve elements and the sarcoplasmic reticulum regulate the triggered delivery and withdrawal of Ca^{2+} ions—the ion species which determines whether contraction will or will not take place. Presumably, the concentration of ATP also goes through high and low cycles paralleling the cycles of contraction and relaxation.

It is not ATP as such which directly energizes muscular contraction. Myosin, one of the two proteins in actomyosin, is phosphorylated by ATP, and the phosphoryl myosin thus formed is the *de facto* energy source for all the endergonic reactions that follow. The formation of phosphoryl myosin requires the presence of Ca^{2+} ions. We have to distinguish between the ATPase activity of myosin and the contractile sequence initiated by ATP and leading *eventually* to the release of inorganic phosphate and ADP. The two

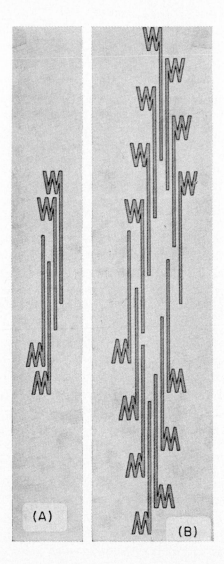

Fig. 9.10. The chemical properties of the myosin molecule. Molecular structure of myosin makes it aggregate as shown. Head of molecule is schematically represented by zigzag molecule, tail by straight line. Tails join in center; heads extend as projections at ends, oppositely pointed at each end. Figure taken from the *Scientific American* **231**, 21 (1965) in the article by H. E. Huxley on the "Mechanism of Muscular Contraction."

processes are not necessarily identical. In both cases phosphoryl myosin is formed. But the energy released when phosphoryl myosin is hydrolyzed may be utilized in driving the contractile process or dissipated in the form of heat.

In the working muscle the high-energy intermediate is used for actuating the sliding of myosin filaments across actin filaments. The chemistry of this sliding phenomenon is not understood at present. It is as if the myosin filament successively makes and breaks connections with actin. Each "make" and "break" leads to a movement of the actin filament in a direction opposite to that of the myosin filament. The "making" of a cross connection probably involves the formation of a covalent bond between the two filaments; the "breaking" would then involve the rupture of the bond. It is postulated by H. E. Huxley *et al.* and independently by A. F. Huxley *et al.* that there are multiple sites on each actin filament where bonds with myosin filaments can be formed.

Electron microscopy has proved to be a decisive tool in uncovering the fine details of the interrelations of the actin-myosin filaments. The individual myosin molecule resembles a sperm cell. It is a linear molecule with a bulbous head. Mysosin molecules align with one another in a staggered fashion to form linear aggregates that have the appearance of double-headed arrows (see Figure 9.10). Thus there is always a sector in a myosin filament that is less dense than either end. This sector lies between the two "arrow heads." The actin filament appears to be a double helix (see Figure 9.11)

Fig. 9.11. Double helical form of actin filament.

made up of two strands that wind around one another in helical fashion. It is postulated that contact between the actin and myosin filaments is achieved through the bulbous heads of the individual myosin molecules (see Figure 9.12).

Information about the physical events in muscular contraction is far more detailed than information about the enzymic and chemical

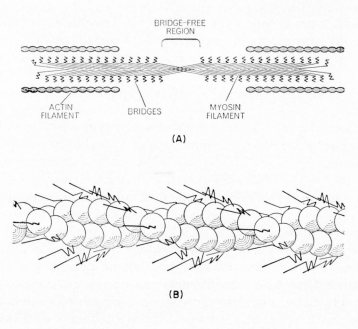

(A)

(B)

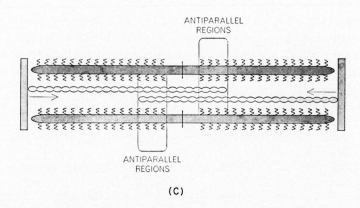

(C)

Fig. 9.12. The relationship between actin and myosin filaments. A: The heads of the myosin molecules are represented as zigzags; the two way directionality of each filament is pointed up by the opposed direction of the zigzags. The zigzag head is assumed to be the bridge between the actin and myosin filaments. The middle of the myosin filaments shows the bridge-free region. B: A representation of the postulated interactions between the helical actin filament and the zigzag heads of the myosin filament. C: Some further relationships between actin and myosin filaments. The antiparallel regions represent sectors of maximal electron density by virtue of

events. In that respect the opposite is true for the mitochondrial system. We know a great deal about the enzymic events but relatively little about the physical events.

A Concluding Thought

In this chapter we have examined the mitochondrial and muscular apparatus for energy transformations, and, although some details are still blurred, the broad picture seems remarkably clear. Biological energy transformations depend upon conformational changes, and these changes take place within macromolecular, membrane-bound systems. The machines which effect the transformations are molecular machines. The ability of protein or lipoprotein systems to undergo major, reversible conformational changes appears to be the key property exploited by Nature for accomplishing energy transformations. In skeletal and cardiac muscle an ATP-energized conformational change leads to shortening of muscle; in the mitochondrion conformational changes lead to synthesis of high-energy intermediates, to ion translocation and to movement of water; in the outer segments of the retinal rods conformational changes are eventually translated into flow of current in a neural membrane. The chemistry of conformational changes within lipoprotein macromolecular systems is becoming the focus of studies on energy transformations.

Suggested Reading

Books

    Chance, B., ed., "Energy-Linked Functions of Mitochondria," Academic Press, New York, 1963.

    Gest, H., San Pietro, A., and Vernon, L. P., eds., "Bacterial Photosynthesis," The Antioch Press, Yellow Springs, Ohio, 1963.

---

the complete overlap of the two filaments. In (A) the myosin filament is shown flanked by two actin filaments: in (C), each of the two parallel myosin filaments is shown flanked by only one of the two actin filaments.

    Figure and legend taken from the article by H. E. Huxley, Mechanism of muscular contraction, *Sci. Am.* **231**, 21 (1965).

Hill, R., and Wittingham, C. P., "Photosynthesis," Methuen and Co., Ltd., London, 1957.

Kamen, M. D., "Primary Processes in Photosynthesis," Academic Press, New York, 1963.

King, T. E., Mason, A. S., and Morrison, M., eds., "Oxidases and Related Redox Systems," John Wiley and Sons, New York, 1965.

Lehninger, A. L., "The Mitochondrion," John Wiley and Sons, Inc., New York, 1964.

Lehninger, A. L., "Energy of the Living Cell: Molecular Basis of Energy Transformations in the Cell," Benjamin, Inc., New York, 1965.

Morton, R. A., ed., "Biochemistry of Quinones," Academic Press, New York, 1965.

"Quinones in Electron Transport," Ciba Foundation Symposium, Churchill, London, 1961.

Rabinowitsch, E. I., "Photosynthesis," Vol. I, Interscience Press, Inc., New York, 1945.

Special Articles

Arnon, D. I., in "The Photochemical Apparatus, Its Structure and Function," Brookhaven National Laboratory, Upton, New York, 1959: on chloroplasts and photosynthesis.

Arnon, D. I., Tsujimoto, H. Y., and McSwain, B. D., Nature 207, 1367 (1965): on cyclic versus noncyclic photophosphorylation.

Boyer, P. D., Falcone, A. B., and Harrison, W. H., Nature 174, 401 (1954): on the mechanism of phosphoryl transfer in oxidative phosphorylation.

Boyer, P. D., Proc. Intern. Symp. Enzyme Chem., Tokyo and Kyoto, 1957, p. 301: on the nature of oxidative phosphorylation.

Brierley, G. P., Bachmann, E., and Green, D. E., Proc. Natl. Acad. Sci. U.S. 48, 1928 (1962): on the active transport of inorganic phosphate and magnesium ions by beef heart mitochondria.

Chance, B., and Williams, G. R., Advan. Enzymology 17, 65 (1956): on the respiratory chain and oxidative phosphorylation.

Conn, E. E., in "Comparative Biochemistry" (M. Florkin and H. Mason, eds.), Vol. I, Chapter 10, Academic Press, New York, 1960: on comparative biochemistry of electron transport and oxidative phosphorylation.

Criddle, R. S., Bock, R. M., Green, D. E., and Tisdale, H., Biochemistry 1, 827 (1962): on the physical characteristics of proteins of the electron transfer system and interpretation of the structure of the mitochondrion.

Davies, R. E., in "Essays in Biochemistry, Vol. I" (P. N. Campbell and G. D. Greville, eds.) Vol. I, Academic Press, New York, 1965: on the mechanism of muscular contraction.

Elliott, G. F., Lowy, J., and Millman, B. M., Nature 206, 1357 (1965): on the x-ray diffraction of living muscle during contraction.

"Energy Transfer with Special Reference to Biological Systems," Discussions Faraday Soc. 27, 1959.

Green, D. E., Comp. Biochem. Physiol. 4, 81 (1962): on the structure and function of subcellular particles.

Green, D. E., and Fleischer, S. in "Horizons in Biochemistry" (M. Kasha and B. Pullman, ed.), p. 381, Academic Press, New York, 1962: on the molecular organization of biological transducing systems.

Hanson, J. and Lowy, J. *J. Mol. Biol.* **6**, 46 (1963): on the structure of F-action and actin filaments.

Hill, R., *in* "Essays in Biochemistry" (P. N. Campbell and G. D. Greville, eds.), Vol. I, Academic Press, New York, 1965: see chapter on the photosynthetic electron transfer chain.

Huxley, H. E., *J. Mol. Biol.* **7**, 281 (1963): on electron microscopy of natural synthetic protein filaments from striated muscle.

Keilin, D., *Proc. Roy. Soc.* **B98**, 312 (1925): on cytochromes and the respiratory Pigments.

Lynn, W. S., and Brown, R. H., *Biochim. Biophys. Acta* **105**, 15 (1965): efficiency of energy conservation in oxidative phosphorylation.

Nisman, B., *Bacteriol. Rev.* **18**, 16 (1954): on the Stickland reaction.

Ozawa, T., *Arch. Biochem. Biophys.*, in press (1966): on AMP as the terminal phosphoryl acceptor in oxidative phosphorylation.

Packer, L., and Marchant, R. H., *J. Biol. Chem.* **234**, 2061 (1964): on the action of adenosine triphosphate on chloroplast structure.

Page, S. C., and Huxley, H. E., *J. Cell Biol.* **19**, 369: on filament lengths in striated muscle.

Slater, E. C., *Australian J. Exptl. Biol. Med. Sci.* **36**, S1 (1958): on oxidative phosphorylation.

Tonomura, Y., and Kanazawa, T., *J. Biol. Chem.* **240**, P4111 (1965): on the formation of a reactive myosin-phosphate complex and its role in muscle contraction.

CHAPTER 10 _____

The Membranes of the Cell

Until the 1960's, the membranes of the cell were generally be-yond the reach of the full range of biochemical analysis. Four de-velopments were crucial in clearing the way to this objective. The first was the perfection of the electron microscope; second, the discovery of radically new methods for the fixing, staining, and ex-amination of specimens; third, the refinement of the techniques for isolating and purifying particulate systems with retention of enzy-mic activity; and finally, the correlation of electron-microscopic ex-amination with biochemical isolation and analysis.

The fundamental concepts of membrane biochemistry are still in process of formulation, and the tentative character of the writing of this chapter reflects the comparative youth of the field. Membrane biochemistry is now one of the frontier areas. Changes inevitably are rapid as new data pour in. Every well defined area of bio-chemical investigation has gone through such a transition period. There is much to be learned from watching the developments in a field in transition since a new field provides the most stringent test-ing ground for experimental strategies.

Definition of a Membrane

All known membranes may be defined in terms of the following set of properties: (1) closed vesicular or tubular systems with a structured rim and a fluid interior; (2) a structured rim, a mosaic of nesting repeating particles, one-layer-thick, and lipoprotein in nature; and (3) the presence of structural protein as a major, in-trinsic component of the repeating units. It is implicit in this defini-tion that there are no structured elements in the membrane other than the repeating units and the subunits thereof.

VESICULAR OR TUBULAR CHARACTER OF MEMBRANES

One of the most important features of a membrane is that it is a closed system. On chemical grounds it would be predictable that there are no open ends in membranes except at the instant of fracture, and then only for an extremely short period before the fracture is sealed. In fact, fracture and sealing may be simultaneous processes.

The closed system may be tubular (like a pipe), vesicular (like a hollow ball), bulbar (like a light bulb), or disc-shaped (like a flattened duct). The plasma membrane which encloses all cells is an example of a wide vesicular, or spherical, membrane; the interior of the cell is, in fact, enclosed by the plasma membrane. The invaginations of the inner mitochondrial membrane (cristae) are examples of tubular membranes. Motion picture studies by phase-contrast light microscopy clearly establish that interiors of tubular membranes *in vivo* are filled with fluid, as shown by the jerky and continuous movement of particles suspended within this fluid. Membrane systems generally are highly plastic and can undergo extensive swelling and shrinking.

REPEATING UNITS AND SUBUNITS OF MEMBRANES

The structured layer of membranes (the outer rim of the vesicles or tubules) is a composite of nesting repeating units (cf. Figure 10.1). We can liken the membrane continuum to a brick wall, and the repeating units to the individual bricks. Hydrophobic forces would symbolize mortar that holds the bricks together in the wall.

To minimize possible confusion as to the meaning of the terms used to designate parts of membranes, we shall define at the start of our discussion some concepts which underlie the description of repeating units and their subunit parts. All membranes appear to be made up of composite particles. In any one membrane these particles are identical in respect to shape and size. These are the repeating units of membranes first described by H. Fernández-Morán in his study of the elementary particles of the mitochondrial cristae.

Repeating units are composites of two or more parts (sectors);

we shall refer to these constituent parts of a repeating unit as sub-units. Composite repeating units are made up of a base piece and a projecting knob (cf. Figure 10.2). The base pieces are the membrane-forming subunits (sectors), whereas the projecting knobs do not form an integral part of the membrane continuum since they are attached to the base pieces only at one end. When the project-ing subunits are detached, the residue is still a membrane. When

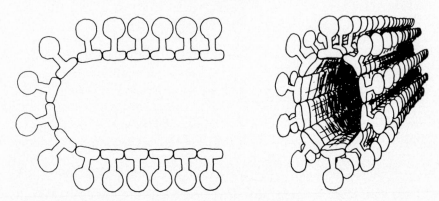

Fig. 10.1. Diagrammatic representation of the membrane as a fusion of repeating units. These particular repeating units are the elementary particles of the mitochon-drial inner membrane.

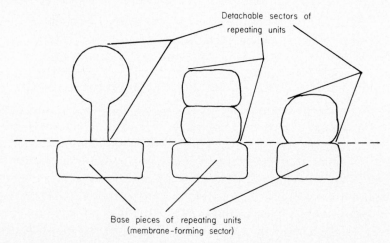

Fig. 10.2. Diagrammatic representation of various kinds of repeating units, and of the two sectors of each such repeating unit.

the base piece continuum is disrupted, however, all membranous structure disappears. Base pieces, separated from their projecting knobs, retain the capacity to form membranous structures, whereas the detachable subunits or knobs, once separated from the base pieces, cannot form such structures (cf. Figure 10.3).

Each membrane has its own distinctive type of repeating unit—distinctive with respect to size and shape. The elementary particle of the mitochondrial inner membrane, shown diagrammatically in

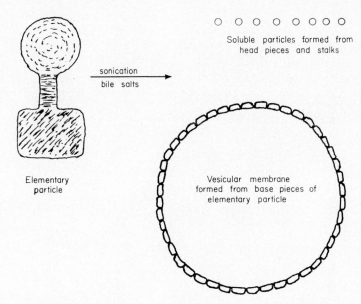

Soluble particles formed from head pieces and stalks

sonication
bile salts

Elementary particle

Vesicular membrane formed from base pieces of elementary particle

Fig. 10.3. Resolution of repeating units into the membrane-forming base pieces and the detachable knobs. The diagram is intended to convey the notion that the elementary particle *as a repeating unit of the inner mitochondrial membrane* undergoes the changes described.

Figure 10.1, is only one type of repeating unit, albeit the type that appears to have broad distribution among membranes. Similar repeating units are found in the outer membrane layer of the chloroplast and in the plasma membrane of liver cells. The elementary particle of the plasma membrane of intestinal epithelial cells (microvilli) has a tripartite structure in which each of the three subunits is of comparable size (see Figure 10.4).

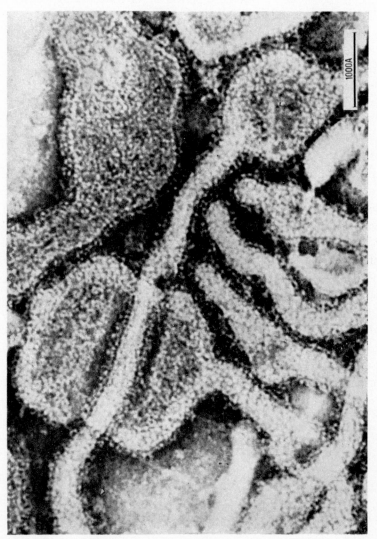

Fig. 10.4. Electron micrograph of isolated preparations of the microvilli of rat intestinal epithelial cells. The repeating units are clearly seen on edges of the tubules. Specimen stained with phosphotungstate. Photograph provided by Takuzo Oda of Osaka University.

1000A

The base piece, or membrane-forming sector, of the repeating units has a roughly rectangular shape which facilitates close nesting with adjacent base pieces. The conditions of mounting and staining specimens can lead to the swelling and rounding of base pieces seen in electron micrographs, but this is probably a distortion of the native arrangement.

The parts of a repeating unit are bound together by relatively weak forces; the links between these sectors may be readily ruptured by sonic irradiation or by bile salts. These treatments lead to the detachment of the projecting knobs, which may become water-soluble, whereas the residue retains its ordered membranous properties. It is of interest that, after detachment of the projecting knobs, the membrane often loses its tubular character and assumes a vesicular arrangement. Whether there is a causal relation between these two phenomena is still an unanswered question.

The various subunits of a repeating unit are chemically and functionally distinct. Each contains different proteins, and the patterns in which the component proteins are arranged are distinctive for each subunit.

Although the repeating units of a given membrane appear to be identical in respect to form and size, this is not to say that these are all identical chemically. In the few cases in which this has been studied, it has been found that there are multiple species of repeating units in a given membrane. Each species has a characteristic complement of proteins and spectrum of enzymic activity. A good analogy for this state of affairs would be afforded by the gamma globulins—a group of proteins which appear to be identical in respect to size, shape, and internal construction, but different in respect to antibody capabilities. The different species of repeating units in a given membrane share the same geometrical form and are outwardly indistinguishable one from the other.

THE INTERPRETATION OF ELECTRON MICROGRAPHS OF NEGATIVELY STAINED SPECIMENS

We shall have to digress to consider the interpretation of electron micrographs and to clear up a difficulty which can puzzle the non-expert. The repeating units of membranes have to be seen on edge to be visualized fully. This particular point is explained pictorially in the diagrams of Figures 10.5 and 10.6. In negatively stained specimens, the tubular or vesicular membranes are flattened on the grid, and it is only at the edges that the profiles of the individual particles are fully exposed. It should be stressed that the uniform

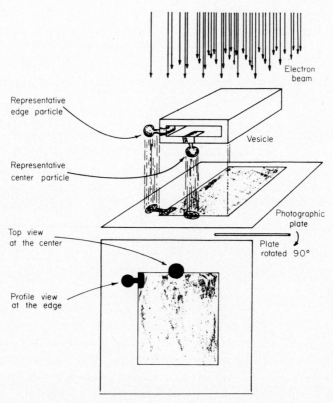

Fig. 10.5. An interpretive diagram showing why particles are more clearly visualized at the edge of a vesicle or tube than in the center.

orientation of all the repeating units in a membrane facilitates the visualization of the structural patterns. A row of identical particles all lined up aids the eye in recognizing shape and size. The same particles randomly oriented would be much more difficult to assess in respect to pattern and dimensions.

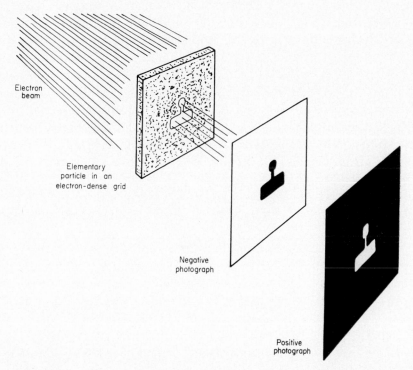

Fig. 10.6. An interpretive diagram illustrating the principle of the negative staining technique.

MEMBRANES AS EXPRESSIONS OF THE STRUCTURE AND FUNCTION OF REPEATING UNITS

A membrane system is nothing more than a particular geometric form which a system of repeating units must assume to satisfy the principle of minimal free energy of conformation, just as the phospholipid micelle is nothing more than the geometric form which a collection of phospholipid molecules must assume to achieve stability. That is, the structure assumed by a membrane is the one in which the sum total of interlocking parts is most stable under physiological conditions. The function of a membrane is the integration of the functions of the individual, oriented, repeating units which make up the membrane. The essence of all membranes is the repeating units, and the geometry assumed by the oriented arrays of these units. Thus, all aspects of membrane function can be reduced to the properties of the individual units.

Phospholipids in Membrane Systems

Lipid in the form of phospholipid, sulfolipid, or glycolipid is an intrinsic part of all membranes that have been studied and analyzed; it accounts for at least 30% of the total dry weight of the membrane. The chemical links joining protein to lipids in membranes are predominantly hydrophobic in nature. This means that the hydrocarbon chains of phospholipids penetrate deeply into hydrophobic faces of proteins while the polar sectors of these phospholipid molecules confer water solubility and charge on these faces.

It cannot be overly stressed that the lipoprotein motif is the very essence of membrane systems in the sense that the properties of membrane systems are expressions of the particular way in which lipids and proteins are packed together. When phospholipids are removed from the membrane by solvent extraction, essentially all the characteristic functional properties of the intact membrane system are lost, although some of these properties can be restored by reintroducing micellar phospholipid into the lipid-free proteins.

The lipids of membranes should not be conceived of in terms of individual molecules of phospholipid; rather, they should be pictured in terms of micellar groups, or clusters, of oriented phospholipid molecules. There is mounting evidence of a continuity among all the phospholipid molecules in a membrane. Thus, a lipid-soluble molecule may move in any direction through the entire membrane continuum without leaving the phospholipid phase.

Obviously, the proteins of membrane systems are endowed with the capacity to interact with lipid. A diagnostic feature of this capacity is the tendency of proteins in the membrane to form polymers whenever lipid is removed; proteins having this property are often referred to as hydrophobic proteins.

Each membrane has its own characteristic pattern of phospholipid. Thus, mitochondrial membranes contain three types of phospholipid—cardiolipin, phosphatidyl ethanolamine, and lecithin.

Cardiolipin is not found, however, in the endoplasmic reticulum. The fatty acid residues of mitochondrial phospholipids are, in general, highly unsaturated, whereas the phospholipids of bacterial membranes are not. The particular form of phospholipid found in a membrane may be a happenstance in the sense that other phospholipids or bimodal* molecules, such as sulfalipids or galactolipids, could fulfill the same function. What is probably the critical and indispensable property of phospholipid molecules is their bimodal character. Membrane structure may require the interpenetration of protein by bimodal molecules. The highly plastic character of membranes at the microscopic level may be an expression of this architecture at the molecular level.

In several membrane systems the lipid fraction contains substantial amounts of neutral lipid in addition to phospholipid. The weight ratio of protein to phospholipid (or its equivalent) is fairly constant from membrane to membrane, but the corresponding ratio for neutral lipid is highly variable. Neutral lipid appears to be dissolved within the phospholipid micelle, and apparently is not directly involved in the formation of bonds between protein and lipid. By modifying the composition of the hydrophobic sector of the phospholipid micelle, however, neutral lipid may indirectly influence the bonding of the micelle to protein.

Phospholipid is not distributed randomly within a repeating unit. The available evidence suggests that the bulk of the phospholipid is associated with the base pieces, and that its distribution within each base piece is asymmetric. The lipid-free base pieces polymerize to form three-dimensional conglomerates which are water-insoluble bulk phases, the enzymic activity of which is not measurable for lack of contact with the solute molecules of the solvent (cf. Figure 10.7). Apparently there are no restrictions to the way in which lipid-free, cuboid base pieces can combine one with another. The reintroduction of phospholipid into the base pieces dramatically alters the combining modalities (cf. Figure 10.8). The faces of the cuboid base piece, which are covered with phospholipid, no longer are capable of interaction with the combining faces of other

---

* The term bimodal refers to the hydrophobic fatty acid residues in one sector of the molecule and the polar or charged residues in the other sector.

base pieces. When phospholipid covers the "top" and "bottom" faces of the repeating units, the restrictions to combinations at these faces inevitably lead to membrane formation. Whenever cuboid repeating units are restricted to "side to side" interactions, three-dimensional stacking is prohibited; two-dimensional nesting is the essential condition for membrane formation. The side to side interactions of base pieces are basically hydrophobic in character. According to this interpretation, phospholipid is essential for membrane formation by virtue of the restrictions which it imposes on

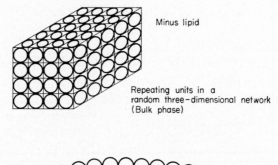

Minus lipid

Repeating units in a
random three-dimensional network
(Bulk phase)

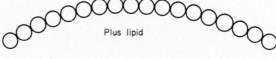

Plus lipid

Repeating units in an oriented membrane
(Unimolecular layer)

Fig. 10.7. The behavior of repeating units in absence and presence of lipid.

three-dimensional stacking. Implicit in this hypothesis of restriction, is the assumption that all the faces of the cuboidal repeating units are predominantly hydrophobic, and that lipid binds selectively to the top and bottom faces of the repeating units. The links between repeating units are accordingly protein to protein links. Lipid plays no part in the lateral binding of repeating units.

The essentiality of lipid for the enzymic functions of repeating units is a second order essentiality. Lipid is required for membrane formation, and the membranous state is one in which enzymic activity is measurable and demonstrable. A membrane is a mono-macromolecular layer in which each repeating unit is in direct contact with the solvent. It is this "molecularization" of the repeating units by membrane formation that underlies lipid essentiality, and not a chemical effect of lipid on the conformation of the enzymes in repeating units.

Membrane formation is not the only means of molecularizing repeating units. Bile salts can disaggregate the repeating units of a membrane into micellized complexes. Such complexes are also molecularized; indeed, the full enzymic activity of a repeating unit

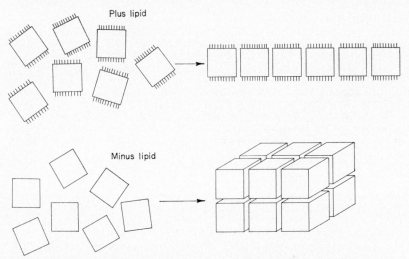

Fig. 10.8. Role of lipid in restricting the combining modes of repeating units. The repeating units are arbitrarily assigned a cuboidal form. Phospholipid is represented by vertical bars at right angles to the face of the repeating unit.

may be demonstrated (in absence of added lipid) in such micellar complexes. Whenever lipid is required for molecularization of the enzymic activity of a repeating unit by membrane formation, a lipid requirement for enzymic activity will apply unless other means are available for molecularizing the lipid-free repeating units.

STRUCTURAL PROTEIN OF MEMBRANE SYSTEMS

Some 50% of the total protein of membrane systems thus far examined is in the form of a protein known as the *structural protein*. Strictly speaking, structural protein is a class of proteins.

We may provisionally assume that the structural protein of a given organism is distinctive, although structural proteins, regardless of the membrane or organism, share the following properties: (1) the tendency to form insoluble polymers in aqueous media; (2) the capacity to bind phospholipid hydrophobically; (3) the capacity to interact with other membrane proteins to form water-soluble complexes; (4) the capacity to bind small molecules such as inorganic phosphate, ATP, and DPN$^+$; (5) the tendency of the polymeric form to disaggregate when exposed to dodecyl sulfate, 66% acetic acid, and dilute alkali.

Richard S. Criddle, who has made an intensive study of one of the structural proteins of mitochondria, has shown that this is a single species, with a molecular weight of 22,500. The C-terminal amino acid is leucine, and the N-terminal amino acid is acetylserine. Each monomeric unit carries one free —SH group which can participate in dimerization by formation of a disulfide link. The protein is relatively basic with an isoionic point of about pH 10.5.

Mitochondrial structural protein forms water-soluble complexes by hydrophobic interaction with myoglobin, cytochrome a, cytochrome b, and cytochrome c_1; it also forms a water-soluble complex by electrostatic interaction with cytochrome c. The molecular ratio of structural protein : heme protein can be 1 : 1, 1 : 2, and 1 : 3 in the complexes formed by hydrophobic interactions; but the ratio is fixed at 1 : 1 in the electrostatic interaction.

In the mitochondrion, approximately a 1 : 1 ratio by weight of catalytic and structural proteins has been demonstrated for each of the sectors of the repeating units of inner and outer membrane. The structural protein of the base pieces of the inner membrane appears to be different from the structural protein present in the head pieces of stalks (the protein characterized by R. S. Criddle). This 1 : 1 ratio of structural and catalytic proteins has wide applicability to all membranes tested, and may be a token of the way in which all membranes are assembled physiologically.

VESICLE FORMATION BY REPEATING UNITS

Repeating units of membranes which have been disaggregated have the capability to realign spontaneously to form a vesicular membrane structure. Figure 10.9 is a diagrammatic interpretation of the vesicularization phenomenon; the electron-micrographic evidence for this interpretation is shown in Figure 10.10(A–D). In this particular set of experiments, the repeating units have already been stripped of their projecting knobs, and it is only the base pieces which are being studied. The tendency of the base pieces to form

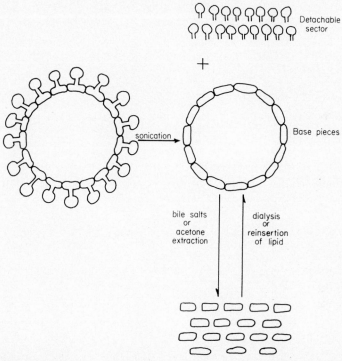

Fig. 10.9. Diagrammatic description of the vesicularization phenomenon. Strictly speaking the lipid-free repeating units are not disaggregated at all. On the contrary, they form disordered conglomerates.

a membrane continuum can be suppressed by detergents and bile salts. Removal of bile salts by dialysis and washing leads to restoration of the capability to form vesicles. Similarly, the reintroduction of lipid into lipid-depleted particles restores the original capability. Phospholipid alone forms ordered micellar structures but not vesicles.

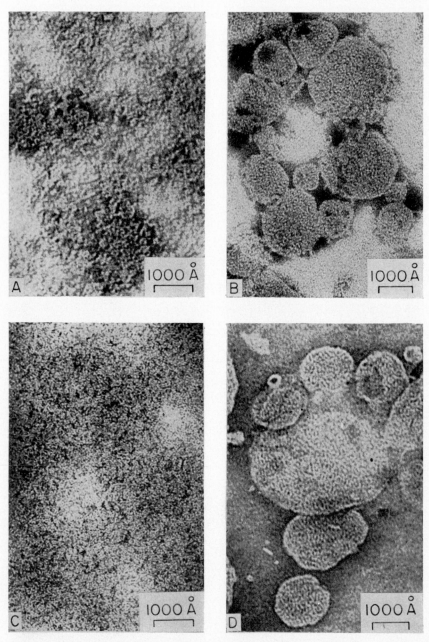

Fig. 10.10. Electron micrographs of cytochrome oxidase (a base piece of one of the repeating units of the inner mitochondrial membrane). A: After exposure to bile salts. B: After removal of bile salts by dialysis and washing. C: After removal of lipid by extraction with 90% acetone–10% water. D: After reintroduction of lipid. Photographs supplied by David McConnell of Ohio State University.

This tendency to vesicularize appears to be a general property of the repeating units of all membranes, and specifically of the base pieces of these repeating units. Thus, the assembly of a membrane from the individual repeating units is, in the proper environment, a spontaneous process which does not require the participation of external "informational" molecules.

It is to be noted that the base pieces form vesicular, but not tubular, structures. This could be a consequence of the removal of the detachable sectors. It is impossible at present to evaluate the role of the detachable sectors of repeating units in tubularization because the conditions necessary for disaggregating the repeating units (sonication or bile salts) also lead to the detachment of the projecting knobs.

The disaggregated monomeric species of the coat protein of the virus spontaneously form a tubular structure into which viral nucleic acid can be imbedded. Caspar and Klug have shown that tubularization involves a tendency of the coat protein to form a helix, whereas vesicularization involves a dodecahedral* or icosahedral pattern of symmetry for the alignment of the monomers (see Figures 10.11 and 10.12). The same theoretical considerations may apply to the formation of tubules and vesicles by membrane repeating units.

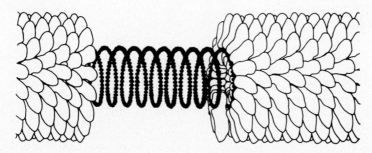

Fig. 10.11. Helical arrangement of repeating coat protein in a tubular virus. A portion of the coat protein has been "cut away" to expose the inner helix of DNA. From D. L. Caspar and A. Klug, *Cold Spring Harbor Symp. Quant. Biol.* **27,** 1 (1962).

* There are twenty faces in a icosahedron and twelve in a dodecahedron.

SYSTEMS OF MEMBRANES

The mitochondrion is not a single membrane; rather, it is a system of membranes which differ both chemically and functionally. The same multiplicity of membrane layers has been shown to apply to the endoplasmic reticulum, to the plasma membrane of intestinal epithelial cells, to the chloroplast, and to the outer segments of the retinal rods. It is probable that the multimembraned system is the rule and the system with the single membrane is the exception.

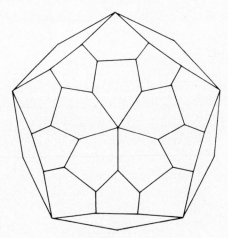

Fig. 10.12. Icosahedral arrangement of repeating units in a spherical virus. From D. L. Caspar and A. Klug, *Cold Spring Harbor Symp. Quant. Biol.* **27**, 1 (1962).

The mitochondrion is a composite of two separate and separable membrane layers. The arrangement of the two membranes shown in Figure 10.13 is an interpretation that is based on electron-micrographic evidence and is consistent with many biochemical observations. There is general agreement that the inner membrane system (with cristae) is distinct from the outer membrane layer that envelops the mitochondrion. The repeating particles in the outer membrane layer are different in form and function from those that make up the inner membrane layers.

The inner membrane can be visualized as a vesicular membrane with infoldings, or invaginations, called *cristae*. The interior of the inner membrane is a space that can be entered only by movement through the elementary particles. This space was referred to in Chapter 9 as the "impenetrable" interior space. Between the outer and inner membranes is a fluid-filled space that extends into the cristae.

The electron micrographs of the plasma membrane of intestinal epithelial cells from various mammalian sources suggest a pattern which follows closely the mitochondrial blueprint; that is, a regular pattern of tubules originating from a spherical membrane. The microvilli of intestinal epithelium could be looked upon as the struc-

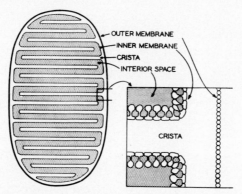

Fig. 10.13. Diagrammatic representation of the membranes of the mitochondrion. The form of the repeating units in the outer membrane has been *deliberately* simplified for purposes of contrast. The correct form is not very different from that of the inner membrane repeating units.

tural analogues of the cristae, except in reverse. The microvilli would be evaginations into the exterior rather than invaginations into the interior. The two-membrane module and the pattern of tubular extensions of an inner membrane appear to be the hallmark of energy-transducing organelles (mitochondria, chloroplasts, outer segments of retinal rods, etc.).

The mitochondrion is known to be a compartmentalized system. There is an area into which the entry of certain small molecules is interdicted. All signs point to the interdicted area as the space in the interior of the inner membrane; this space is sealed off completely from the environment external to the mitochondrion by a continuous membranous envelope. It appears to be this inner space into which ions are translocated (cf. Chapter 9).

MULTIPLE SPECIES OF REPEATING UNITS WITHIN A MEMBRANE

A given membrane has a characteristic spectrum of enzymic activities, and these activities could be many or few. Each of the repeating units does not necessarily contain all the species of the enzymes in the membrane. The enzymic activities are usually parceled out in blocs to different species of repeating units. For example, the electron-transfer function of the inner mitochondrial membrane is known to be implemented by a set of four different species of repeating units—each such species being responsible for one segment of the electron-transfer chain. Within any one species of repeating unit is localized a set of catalytic proteins, invariant in respect to sequence, composition, and stoichiometry. Thus, metabolic events carried out by membranes are implemented by sets of repeating units, all similar in form and size, but different in respect to composition and catalytic activity. The strategy for the parceling of the component enzymes of a metabolic sequence into different species of repeating units has been studied only in the two mitochondrial membranes. At present, no general set of rules for this phenomenon can be specified. The complete description of any metabolic process will eventually have to include the roster of all the enzymes in each species of repeating units that carry out this process, as well as the organization of these enzymes within each species of repeating unit.

LOCALIZATION OF ENZYMIC ACTIVITIES IN MEMBRANES

The distribution of enzymic activities within a given membrane system is not random. For example, the inner mitochondrial membrane contains the repeating units concerned exclusively with the electron-transfer process and with the generation and utilization of high-energy intermediates. The outer membrane contains all of the enzymes concerned with the citric acid, and fatty acid, oxidation cycles, with substrate-level phosphorylation, and with oxidation of β-hydroxybutyrate (cf. Table 10.1). This segregation of enzymic activities into different membranes is an expression of a master plan—albeit a plan that is not yet completely understood.

The citric cycle and related enzymes in the mitochondrion fall into two categories: (1) the readily solubilizable enzymes such as aconitase, fumarase, isocitric dehydrogenase, malic dehydrogenase, as well as the system of enzymes for elongation of fatty acids; (2) the dehydrogenase complexes of high molecular weight such as the pyruvic, the α-ketoglutaric, and the β-hydroxybutyric dehydrogenases, and the fatty acid-dehydrogenating complex.

In order to specify the localization of any membrane-bound enzymes, three questions have to be answered: in which membrane;

Table 10.1

A LIST OF ENZYMES KNOWN TO BE LOCALIZED IN THE OUTER MEMBRANE OF BEEF HEART MITOCHONDRIA

Citric cycle enzymes
  Pyruvic dehydrogenase complex (set of four enzymes)
  α-Ketoglutaric dehydrogenase complex (set of four enzymes)
  Malic dehydrogenase
  Isocitric dehydrogenase
  Acetyl-CoA-oxaloacetate condensing enzyme
  Aconitase
  Fumarase
Ancillary enzymes
  Fatty acid dehydrogenating complex (set of six to eight enzymes)
  Fatty acid elongation system (set of six to eight enzymes)
  Hexokinase
  β-Hydroxybutyric dehydrogenase
  Succinic thiokinase
  GTP-ADP kinase

in which sector of a repeating unit; and in how many species of repeating units? The localization of the electron-transfer chain can now be specified with respect to membrane (inner), with respect to the sector of the repeating unit (base piece of the elementary particle), and with respect to the total number of species of repeating units (four). However, the electron-transfer system is the only system that has been localized with this degree of definition.

The entire citric cycle is carried out by a set of enzymes spread over the two membranes of the mitochondrion (the localization of the succinic dehydrogenase in the inner membrane must be re-

called). The set of enzymes responsible for synthesis of phospholipid from long-chain fatty acids, glycerol, and a nitrogenous base
is also distributed between the two membranes of the mitochondrion. Such a disposition of the enzymes of a metabolic sequence
means that diffusion of metabolites from one membrane layer to
another within a system of membranes has to be invoked; this diffusion-controlled step may be very relevant to the regulation of metabolic sequences in membrane systems.

We have already discussed the distribution of the proteins of the
electron-transfer chain among multiple species of repeating units
within the inner membrane. This type of segmentation also appears
to hold for other metabolic sequences localized in the mitochondrial
membranes (the citric cycle and fatty acid oxidations). The exact
number of species of repeating units in these respective sequences
is still unknown, but there is little doubt that more than one is
involved. The electron-transfer process is divisible into four sectors,
or complexes, and these four functional sectors correspond to four
base pieces (one base piece per complex). The citric cycle involves
five separate oxidative steps, four of which take place in the repeating units of the outer mitochondrial membrane. In addition, the
cycle involves two hydrase reactions (fumarase and aconitase being
the catalysts) and one kinase reaction (synthesis of ATP energized
by succinyl-CoA). The enzymes responsible for two of the oxidative
steps can be isolated in the form of complexes of high molecular
weight. Each of these complexes would correspond to one or more
species of repeating unit. How the other enzymes of the citric cycle
are organized, particularly the readily solubilizable enzymes such
as aconitase and fumarase, remains to be determined.

E. Racker and his group have made important progress in the
identification of the headpieces of the inner mitochondrial membrane with an enzyme complex that has the properties of an
ATPase. Whether all headpieces can be so identified is still an open
question.

The enzymes of the glycolytic cycle, which number about eleven
in all, have been shown to be localized in the plasma membrane
both of red blood corpuscles and of brewer's yeast cells. Some of
the glycolytic enzymes are readily detachable from the membrane

whereas others are not. Aldolase, hexokinase, and triosephosphoric dehydrogenase are among the tightly associated enzymes; lactic dehydrogenase and phosphohexose isomerase, the enzyme that isomerizes glucose 6-phosphate and fructose 6-phosphate, are among those of the readily dissociable group. Observations of this kind strongly suggest the association of the glycolytic enzymes with multiple species of repeating units—each species with its own characteristic stability in respect to attachment to other repeating units of the membrane.

There is yet another facet of the localization problem, best illustrated by the studies of Takuzo Oda on the enzymic functions of isolated microvilli. The repeating unit of microvilli is a tripartite structure (see Figure 10.4). When the membranes are digested with the proteolytic enzyme papain, the detachable sectors (two of the three sectors) are split off. The dipeptidase and carbohydrase activities of the microvilli are likewise detached from the membrane by proteolytic digestion (these activities are found to be associated with the released soluble enzymes) whereas ATPase and alkaline phosphatase activities remain within the stripped membranes. From such evidence it may be concluded that the base pieces of the repeating units of the microvilli contain ATPase and alkaline phosphatase activities, whereas the detachable sectors of the same repeating units carry the enzymes with dipeptidase and carbohydrase activities.

RESOLUTION OF REPEATING UNITS

The separation of the repeating units of membranes can be accomplished either by the use of suitable detergents such as cholate, deoxycholate, and dodecyl sulfate, or by exposure of the membrane to dilute alkali (pH 11–12) or to 66% acetic acid. These are drastic conditions for fragmentation. Enzymic activity is not preserved when the repeating units are exposed to most of the reagents known to effect separation. Bile salts and tertiary amyl alcohol are among the few reagents available which can achieve separation of repeating units and still conserve some or all of the enzymic activity. The separation of repeating units involves the fracture of protein-protein hydrophobic bonds. The more drastic reagents affect not only the protein-protein bonds *between* repeating units but also the protein-protein bonds within a single repeating unit.

The detachment of the knobs from their base pieces may take place readily under the same conditions which lead to the separation of repeating units. Thus, bile salts not only detach one species of repeating unit from other species but may also strip the resolved repeating units of their detachable sectors. This would suggest that the component sectors of many repeating units are held together by the same kind of weak bonds that bind neighboring repeating units together in a membrane. In fact, under certain conditions it is easier to strip repeating units of their detachable sectors than to separate one repeating unit from another. The detachable sectors of the repeating units of the inner mitochondrial membrane can be detached by prolonged sonication, whereas sonication is ineffectual in separating the different repeating units of this membrane from each other.

The technical problem of isolating membranes without stripping off the detachable units during the isolation procedure is formidable for membranes such as the plasma membrane of the red blood cell. Evidently, the tactics presently used for rupturing the cell are still incompatible with full preservation of all membrane-associated enzymes.

RECONSTITUTION OF ELECTRON-TRANSFER ACTIVITY IN
RELATION TO ALIGNMENT OF REPEATING UNITS

Y. Hatefi *et al.* discovered the phenomenon of reconstitution of electron-transfer activity—a phenomenon which has been interpreted in terms of the exact alignment of the complexes of the electron-transfer chain within the mitochondrial membrane. Reconstitution requires the prior mixing of the complexes under conditions in which each complex is disaggregated into individual repeating units (cf. Figure 10.14). If this disaggregating step is omitted, no reconstitution can take place. The explanation of reconstitution in terms of membrane phenomena is now well established experimentally. When complexes I and III are mixed together at high dilutions, the mixture does not catalyze the oxidation of DPNH by cytochrome *c*. When the complexes are mixed in concentrated solution and then diluted, the "reconstituted" mixture does readily catalyze this oxidation. Complexes I and III at high dilutions exist as vesicular membranes. When mixed as membranes, the complexes cannot interact one with another since these are in separate membranes. Electron flow between membranes cannot take place since the mobile molecule (coenzyme Q) that shuttles electrons from complex I to complex III operates exclusively *within* a membrane and not *between* membranes. When the two complexes are first disaggregated by bile salts and then the mixture is diluted out, the vesicular membranes thus formed contain both complexes. Within

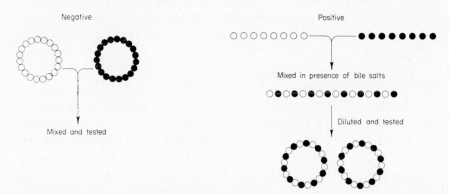

Fig. 10.14. Conditions for reconstitution. Empty circles represent repeating units of one complex and filled circles repeating units of a second complex. Negative means no reconstitution; positive means reconstitution.

the same vesicular membranes, the shuttling of electrons from complex I to III by coenzyme Q underlies the reconstitution of DPNH-cytochrome c reductase activity. It was not originally appreciated that reconstitution involved the formation of mixed vesicular membranes each of which contained the two or more complexes that had to be linked by mobile molecules. Once it became clear that reconstitution of electron-transfer activity did not depend upon direct chemical interaction between complexes, i.e., on the exact alignment of the interacting complexes, then the door was opened to a radically different interpretation not only of reconstitution but also of the nature of the electron-transfer chain.

The interaction of the four complexes of the chain depends upon the shuttling of electrons by lipid-soluble mobile components (co-enzyme Q and cytochrome c) within the continuous lipid layer of the membrane continuum. This movement is so rapid that efficient electron transfer can take place regardless of the relative positions of the component complexes, and regardless of the molecular proportions of the four complexes. In mitochondria from different sources, the molecular proportions of the complexes do, in fact, vary rather widely. Such variation does not seriously affect the electron-transfer process since electron transfer does not depend on the exact positioning of the complexes. Interactions between repeating units of membranes via lipid-soluble mobile components makes understandable why gross variations in the molecular proportions of repeating units does not present mechanistic difficulties.

MOLECULAR STATISTICS OF REPEATING UNITS

The elementary particle of the inner mitochondrial membrane is estimated to have a mass of 1.3×10^6 on the basis of the measured dimensions (see Figure 10.15). The particle exists either in the expanded tripartite form or in the compact spherical form. From the diameter of the spherical form (150 Å) and an assumed value of 1.25 for the density, the mass of the elementary particle can be estimated.

Each repeating unit contains about thirty molecules of protein (average molecular weight, 25,000) and about six hundred molecules of phospholipid (molecular weight about 800). If we assume that the base pieces constitute 40% of the mass of the repeating unit, then each base piece would contain about twelve molecules of protein and two hundred and forty molecules of phospholipid. The ratio of structural protein to total protein in the base piece of the inner mitochondrial membrane is 1 : 2. Thus, it is estimated that there are about six molecules of structural protein and six molecules of catalytic protein in each base piece.

Since the size of repeating units will vary from membrane to membrane, the molecular statistics for repeating units will vary correspondingly. The lower limit for the number of protein molecules per repeating unit has yet to be determined.

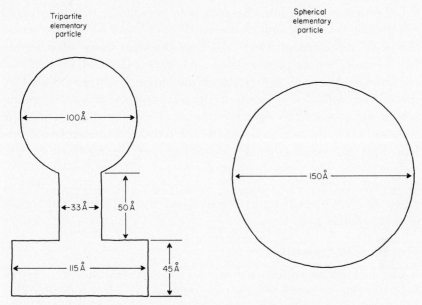

Fig. 10.15. The dimensions of the elementary particle of the inner mitochondrial membrane in its tripartite and spherical forms (beef heart).

Categories of Membrane Systems

The cells of multicellular organisms have both general and specialized membrane systems—the former in all cells, the latter in specialized cells. Unicellular protozoa or plants have multiple membrane systems, both general and specialized, all within one cell. The bacteria, however, have essentially one membrane system which is a composite of almost all the membrane systems found in the more complex forms of life. The important consideration is not the number of membrane systems but the full roster of repeating units and the functions fulfilled by these repeating units. If we could dissect out the various segments of the bacterial membrane we might well find extensive variation in respect to repeating units and functions. Thus, we come full circle to the recognition that the essential functions can be implemented either by multiple systems of membranes or by one composite membrane system. The difference between the two alternative arrangements is not fundamental.

Cells that approximate the metabolic simplicity of the minimal cell contain relatively few recognizable membrane systems, whereas the most highly specialized cells (for example those of mammalian liver or of intestinal epithelium) have extensive networks of membranes. Many of the special or metabolic functions fulfilled by specialized cells have required the elaboration of special membranes, or at least the modification of already existing membrane systems. Thus, there is some merit in discussing the membrane systems that are common to all cells before considering those of specialized cells. The pioneer electron-micrographic studies of Palade, Sjostrand, Porter, Fawcett, and others have provided us with a great deal of precise information about the principal membrane systems of the cell.

The Plasma Membrane

The membrane which encloses a cell, and delimits the internal from the external environments, is common to all forms of life. This membrane is usually referred to as the plasma membrane, and should not be confused with the cell wall which is an inert, non-membranous, protective layer enveloping some plant and bacterial cells. The plasma membrane fulfills several major functions. It regulates the movement of ions and molecules into and out of the cell by selective permeability and by energized translocation. In some cells it houses the glycolytic system of enzymes. In addition, it houses many other enzymes and proteins that are specifically adapted to the special needs of the cell from which the plasma membrane is derived.

The first two properties are probably common to all plasma membranes (selective permeability and energized translocation of ions and molecules). The last property (locale for specialized enzymes) is variable in nature and depends upon the particular type of cell in question. In cells of the intestinal epithelium, this membrane contains a set of enzymes essential for the final stages in the hydrolytic degradation of proteins and carbohydrates; in the epithelial cells lining the lumen of the kidney tubule, the membrane is specialized for secretory processes; in the nerve cell, it contains enzymes needed for the transmission of a nerve impulse.

The electron-microscopic examination of the plasma membrane of the intestinal epithelium clearly shows that this membrane is not merely a continuous wrapper around the cell. There appears to be a system of tubules which evaginate from the peripheral outer membrane(s), reminiscent of the relation of the cristae to the outer membrane in the mitochondrion, only in reverse (cf. Figure 10.16).

ENDOPLASMIC RETICULUM

The cells of higher organisms contain an extensive, and apparently continuous, network of tubules—the endoplasmic reticulum—radiating through a large segment of the interior of the cell (cf. Figure 10.17). Morphologically, this network is recognizable by its association with particles containing RNA (the ribosomes). Biochemical studies have shown that this is the seat of many important processes, such as the synthesis of proteins, fatty acids, steroids, and phospholipids, as well as the locus for the hydroxylation of steroids, and for a whole spectrum of the so-called detoxication processes. The repeating units derived from this network contain an electron-transfer chain, the known components of which are a flavoprotein, cytochrome b_5, and a heme pigment capable of reacting with carbon monoxide.

The endoplasmic reticulum is usually regarded as a single membrane system, but there is increasing biochemical evidence that it is not uniform in respect either to composition or to function within the single cell.* The analogy of the digestive tract may be helpful in making the point. The digestive tract is one continuous system from the oral to the anal end, yet the various subdivisions of the tract are manifestly different in composition and function. Very likely, there is an analogous differentiation of the segments of the endoplasmic reticulum in respect to function.

The endoplasmic reticulum points up some special difficulties of interpretation and localization. In a liver cell, for example, the endoplasmic reticulum fulfills a variety of functions covering the

* The set of particles which sediment together after removal of mitochondria from a homogenate of broken cells are often referred to as microsomes. There is, of course, no such unique particle or particulate system in the cell. The so-called microsomal fraction is probably a mixture of particles from several membrane systems.

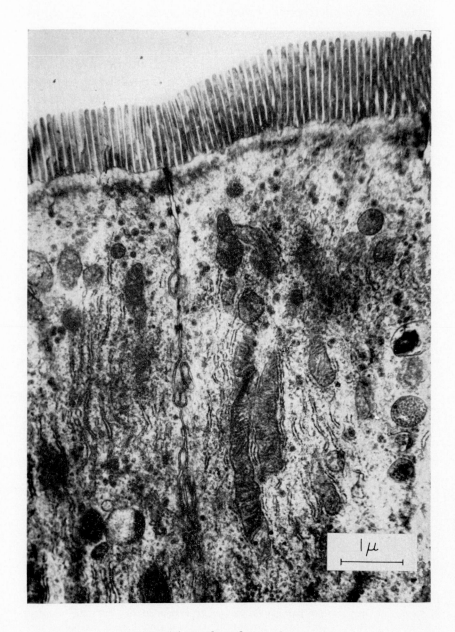

Fig. 10.16(A). For legend see opposite page.

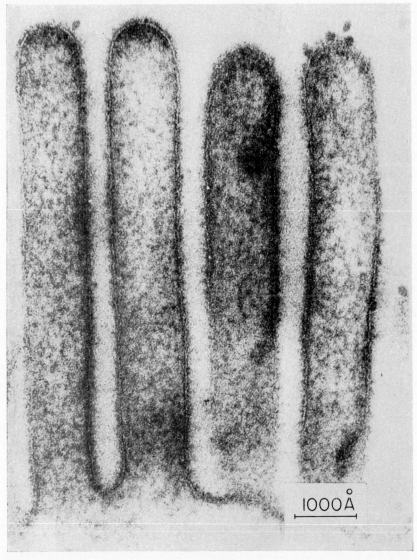

Fig. 10.16(B).

Fig. 10.16. Membrane layer systems of the plasma membrane of rat intestinal epithelial cells. Specimen stained with osmium tetroxide. A shows at low magnification the brush border region of the epithelium with the microvilli (at the top of the figure) extending to the exterior of the plasma membrane; B shows at high magnification a set of four microvilli. The connection of the microvilli with the plasma membrane (at the bottom of the figure) is clearly shown. Photograph supplied by Takuzo Oda of the University of Okayama.

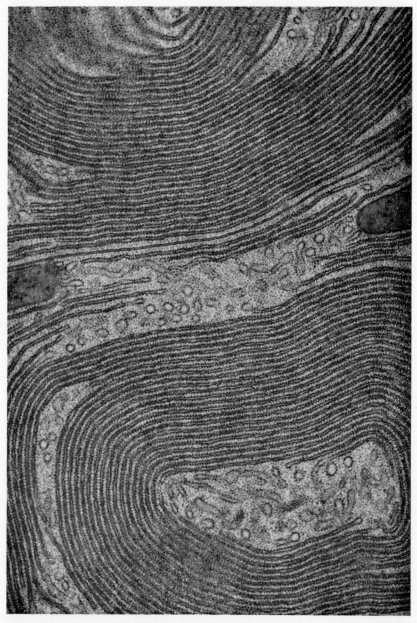

Fig. 10.17. Electron micrograph of the granular endoplasmic reticulum of the acinar cells of the bat. Photograph supplied by Don W. Fawcett of Harvard University.

gamut from RNA-mediated protein synthesis to ion translocation and detoxication. All cells carry out RNA-mediated protein synthesis, but the form and locale of the membrane that accomplishes this synthesis is not necessarily the same in all cells. This particular difficulty of assigning function and localization does not apply to the plasma membrane which is always the membrane enveloping the cell, and always implements the same general functions (glycolysis, ion translocation, selective permeability) regardless of any specific functions carried out in addition. What is invariant in cells is the capacity to carry out certain integrated metabolic pathways according to a universal blueprint. What may be variable is the membrane system in which these integrated capacities are localized. For example, protein synthesis in bacteria appears to be localized in membranous spurs originating from the plasma membrane; this localization is in sharp contrast to the association of the protein-synthesizing system in animal and plant cells with the endoplasmic reticulum. Clearly, the association between a universal function (protein synthesis) and a particular membrane (endoplasmic reticulum) may be valid for the plant and animal kingdom but may not necessarily be valid for all cells. Eventually, the complete description of the membranes of all cells will include information as to where in each cell certain essential synthetic processes are proceeding, and which parts of which membrane systems are concerned with each of these processes.

Nuclear Membrane

In animal and plant cells the chromosomal DNA is housed within an organelle, the nucleus, which is enclosed by a membrane referred to as the nuclear membrane (Figure 10.18). In bacteria the chromosomes are not contained within a membrane-limited organelle. This morphological distinction between bacteria and the cells of plants and animals may not be fundamental since chromosomes are released from the nucleus into the interior of the cell during cell division. After the liberation of the chromosomes from the nuclear envelope, a membranous coat may persist which envelops each chromosome. It is possible that the difference between bacterial and other cells in respect to organization of the nuclear apparatus reduces to the difference between containment of all chromosomes

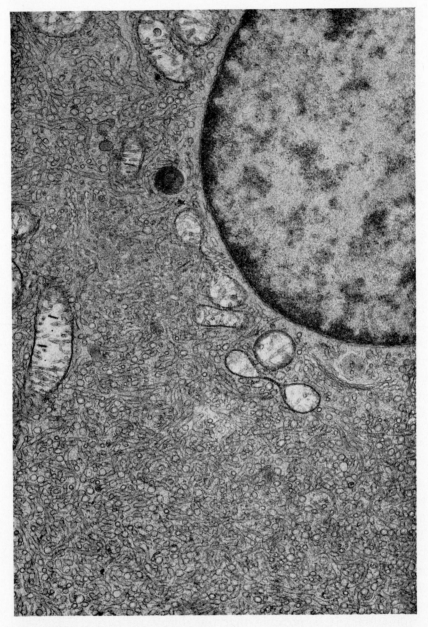

Fig. 10.18. Electron micrograph of the nuclear membrane and adjacent cytoplasm of an interstitial cell of a testis of opposum. The nucleus is in the upper right corner. Photograph supplied by Don W. Fawcett of Harvard University.

within one membrane and containment of each chromosome within its own membrane.

THE MITOCHONDRION AND THE CHLOROPLAST

These two membrane systems are extremely similar in morphological organization; both are subcellular organelles with energy-transducing functions. The mitochondrion (cf. Figure 10.19) and the chloroplast (cf. Figure 10.20) both contain the units which transform oxidative energy into the bond energy of ATP. In the chloroplast, the electrons destined to traverse the electron-transfer chain are generated by the interaction of radiant energy with chlorophyll; in the mitochondrion the electrons that traverse the chain are generated by the oxidations of the citric cycle. The actual energy transductions take place within the inner membrane systems of these two organelles—in the cristae of the mitochondrion and in the granae of the chloroplast. Both organelles are delimited by an outer membrane which is functionally and structurally distinguishable from the inner membrane.

In most unicellular organisms examined thus far, no mitochondria or chloroplasts are found, although a functional equivalent is clearly present. In such cells, extensions from the plasma membrane appear to be the locale of the subunits which carry out energy transductions.

Time-lapse cinematography of the fluid interior of animal and plant cells has revealed the fact that the size and number of mitochondria and chloroplasts are continually changing. At any one moment the organelle could be large or small. Some organelles are seen breaking up into smaller framents while other fragments are coalescing to form larger units. Clearly, the size of the organelle, at least in the fluid part of the cell, can be expressed only statistically. This phenomenon of fragmentation and fusion is a token of the plasticity of the membranes of these two organelles and suggests that the unit of mitochondrial and chloroplastic function is not the organelle but the subunits thereof.

MEMBRANES OF SPECIALIZED CELLS

In specialized cells the plasma membrane undergoes modification. For example, it may serve for purposes relating to digestion and

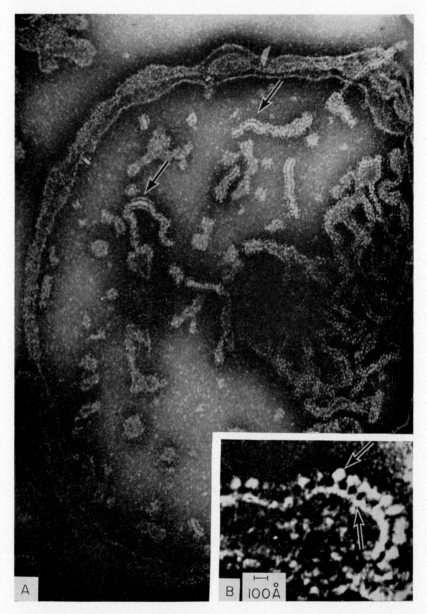

Fig. 10.19. Electron micrograph of a whole mitochondrion isolated from beef heart muscle (shown in A). Arrows point to arrays of tripartite repeating units. The orderly arrays of cristae are not seen in the electron micrograph since the mito-

absorption (microvilli of intestinal epithelium), for transmission of an electric impulse (nerve cells), and for secretion and selective absorption (cells lining the proximal tubules of the kidney). Only the smallest beginnings have been made in specifying the biochemical properties of the plasma membranes of specialized cells such as erythrocytes.

In skeletal muscle the endoplasmic reticulum, together with a transverse tubular system, takes the form of a membranous network specialized for the task of regulating the contractile function. This network is capable of the energized translocation of Ca^{2+} ions. It is postulated that the ions are involved in the control of the contraction-relaxation cycle. There are also grounds for postulating that the delivery of ATP to the contractile elements is yet another function of this membranous network. The cells of heart muscle contain a different membranous network which is less elaborate than that of skeletal muscle; this may be correlated with the fact that heart muscle cells are rich in mitochondria, whereas skeletal muscle cells are not.

The cells of sensory organs contain structures that are specialized for transforming a stimulus such as light, sound, pressure, temperature, or odor into an electric impulse, ultimately to be delivered to the central nervous system. The outer segments of the rods of the retina are organelles indistinguishable in gross appearance from mitochondria; it is clear that these are constructed according to a similar polymolecular blueprint (cf. Figure 10.21). The repeating units of this organelle contain the visual pigments which absorb the incident light. How the light signal is ultimately transformed into an electric impulse in the adjacent nerve element is still unknown.

An interesting cycle is observed in the phenomenon of *pinocytosis,* which involves the engulfing of fluid droplets outside the cell

---

chondrion has been allowed to age and undergo swelling. The electron micrograph shown in B is a higher magnification of a row of tripartite repeating units. Arrows point to a headpiece and basepiece, respectively. Stained with phosphotungstate. Photograph supplied by Humberto Fernández-Morán of the University of Chicago.

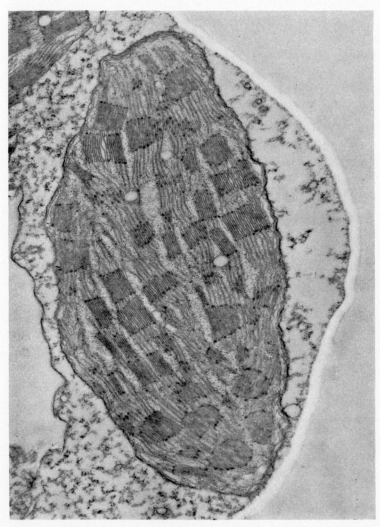

Fig. 10.20(A). For legend see opposite page.

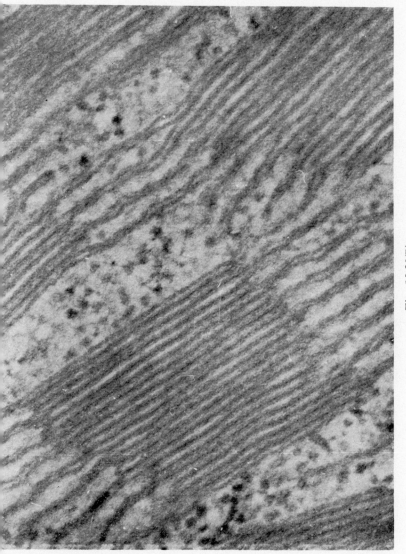

Fig. 10.20(B).

Fig. 10.20. Electron micrographs of the chloroplast in a sectioned mesophile cell of corn, stained with osmium tetroxide. A, Magnification: × 37,000; B, Magnification: × 165,000. Photograph kindly provided by Dr. A. E. Vatter, University of Colorado Medical Center.

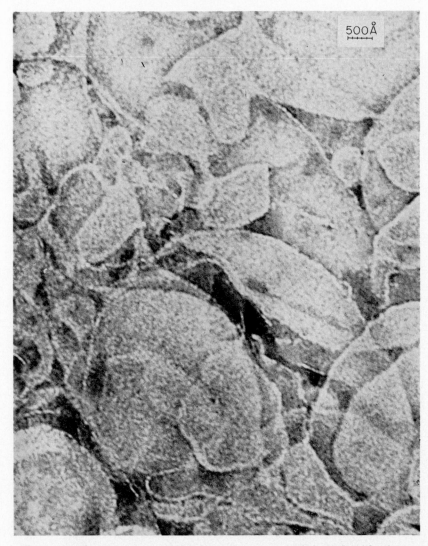

500Å

Fig. 10.21. Electron micrograph of the outer segments of the rods of beef retina. Stained with phosphotungstate. Photograph supplied by David McConnell of Ohio State University.

by a pinching off of the plasma membrane. The membrane-enclosed vesicles are constantly introduced into certain cells; the plasma membrane is constantly being pinched off in segments for this engulfing process. Whether or not the pinched off membrane is eventually reincorporated into the plasma membrane is still unknown.

The Golgi apparatus, a membranous network found in secretory cells of multicellular organisms, is made up of tubules which expand into sacs at regular intervals (Figure 10.22). This network is specialized to concentrate, package, and deliver secretory products elaborated by a cell to the exterior of the cell. Some physical connection between the Golgi apparatus and the plasma membrane must exist to make possible this delivery of secreted material to the outside of the cell.

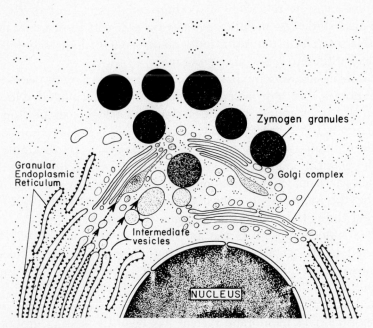

Fig. 10.22. Schematic representation of the postulated mode of transfer of secretory products from the granular endoplasmic reticulum to the Golgi complex of membranes. Diagram supplied by Don W. Fawcett of Harvard University.

The products elaborated by the endoplasmic reticulum (tubular network shown on the bottom left of the figure) are channelled into the Golgi apparatus (tubular network shown in the center of the figure). The tubules of the Golgi apparatus are continuous with extended vesicles that become filled with the secretory products. These vesicles eventually are detached from the network and at that stage show up as zymogen granules.

Some General Aspects of Membrane Systems

SOURCES OF INFORMATION RELEVANT TO MEMBRANE SYSTEMS

The field of membrane biochemistry is still so new that mention should be made of the available sources of experimental evidence. Relatively few membrane systems have been prepared in sufficiently homogeneous state, or in sufficient quantity, to make systematic biochemical studies possible. A contemporary list of "preparable membranes" would include the chloroplast, the mitochondrion, and the microvilli of the intestinal epithelium; it would also include the plasma membrane of the red blood corpuscle and of yeast, and the endoplasmic reticulum of certain cell types. Most of the biochemical studies on membranes have been directed toward members of this set. The list is admittedly sparse, but it does include some widely different types of membranes.

Electron microscopy has been extended to a wide variety of membranes, but morphological data alone, uncorrelated with biochemical information, provide a slender base for comparison and evaluation. Biochemical studies on membrane systems require quantities of material sufficient to permit isolation, purification, and both chemical and enzymic analysis. Only those membrane systems which can meet the requirements of quantity and purity* are likely to be the subjects of intensive study of ultrastructure, at least during the initial phase of membrane biochemistry.

The mitochondrion is the membrane system which has been studied in the greatest depth by both biochemical and electron-microscopic techniques; the chloroplast is second in this respect. In our general treatment of membrane biochemistry we have drawn heavily on the experience gained through studies on the mitochondrion. This membrane system has been the testing ground for the correlation of biochemical function with ultrastructure.

STABILITY OF MEMBRANE SYSTEMS

The correlation of the biochemical properties of membranes with their morphology requires the isolation of these membranes from

---

* Purity in the sense of the absence of contamination by fragments of other membranes.

the cell and their separation from other membranes without modification of structure. Experimentally, it is a question of balancing the rigors of the isolation procedure against the inherent instability of the membrane to be isolated. In very few instances has this balance been achieved. The procedures for isolation of membranes are still too rough; the isolated membranes are, therefore, more or less deficient in some of the membrane-associated enzymes.

The experimental conditions that have been found to effect a separation of the outer from the inner mitochondrial membranes inevitably lead to the detachment of some enzymes from both membranes. Thus, while clean separation of the two membranes can be achieved, the separated membranes are not complete in respect to their normal complement of enzymes.

It is this very fragility of membranes that deceived two generations of biochemists into thinking that the glycolytic complex of enzymes was not membrane-associated. In general, the dissociable parts of membrane systems are not held together by covalent bonds; the links are relatively weak hydrophobic and electrostatic bonds. A wide variety of experimental conditions further weaken these bonds, and lead inevitably to the dissociation of certain of the components from the membrane. The experimental art lies in the tactic of using extremely mild conditions both for rupturing cells and for separating the various membrane systems. Some of the difficulties are illustrated by the results obtained in the isolation of the plasma membrane of the red blood corpuscle. Under the best available conditions, variable proportions of the glycolytic enzymes are lost. Some enzymes, such as triosephosphoric dehydrogenase, are fully retained, whereas other enzymes, such as fructose 6-phosphate isomerase, are largely extracted during the isolation procedure.

The membrane of the red blood corpuscle is relatively stable as long as the erythrocyte is suspended in physiological saline solution. Nevertheless, the isolated membrane is rapidly stripped of most of the glycolytic enzymes when exposed to the same saline solution. What accounts for this discrepancy in properties? An intriguing possibility is that the repeating units of the erythrocyte membrane are exposed on their interior side to a "liquid crystalline" (possibly hydrophobic) medium, such as an array of oriented hemoglobin molecules. According to this interpretation, the interior facets of these repeating units normally do not come into contact with an aqueous medium; the screening of the repeating unit from the salt in the surrounding medium accounts for the stability of the membrane *in vivo*. It may, therefore, be extremely difficult to reproduce *in vitro* the special molecular environment of the intact cell which is so essential for the protection of fragile membranes. However, this difficulty will have to be overcome if the preservation of the full complement of membrane-bound enzymes is to be accomplished.

No problem in biochemistry illustrates more clearly than does the problem of membranes the necessity for approaching the structure and function of a whole system, and of isolated parts of the system, at the same time. Investigations of one, to the exclusion of the other, lead inevitably to misconceptions. It is only through a constant meshing of the two approaches that a meaningful and accurate picture of membranes can emerge.

MEMBRANE SYSTEMS AND CONTROL MECHANISMS

Some of the important control mechanisms of cells are operative at the level of membrane systems. Insulin, by a direct effect, enhances the permeability of the plasma membrane of muscle cells, but not liver cells, to glucose; hence it stimulates the metabolism of glucose in muscle. Acetylcholine initiates rapid permeability changes in regions of the plasma membrane of certain nerve cells; these changes lead to the initiation of an electric impulse. These examples demonstrate the relevance of the state of the membrane to physiological controls and to drug sensitivity. The conformation which an enzyme assumes in a membrane may not be identical with the conformation of the same enzyme after extraction from the membrane. A change in protein conformation of the extracted enzyme may well obliterate the effects of certain agents which react dramatically with the counterpart enzyme in the membrane. Atractyloside has a profound effect on fatty acid oxidation in intact mitochondria but far less effect on partial reactions carried out in solution. Similarly, drugs may exert powerful effects on particular enzymes within a membrane, but may have no demonstrable effect on the same enzymes after these have been extracted from the membrane.

MAINTENANCE OF MEMBRANE SYSTEMS

Membranes are not static systems; the integrity of the membrane requires the constant input of energy to counterbalance environmental changes (such as osmotic changes) which would otherwise lead to the deterioration of the membrane system. Energy is also required for the performance of work by the membrane, be it translocation of ions, ATP-driven syntheses, or generation of an electric current. These requirements for continuous expenditure of energy make it necessary for membranes to contain catalytic systems either to generate ATP or to convert it into the high-energy intermediates that power the work of the membrane.

THE VECTORIAL CHARACTER OF MEMBRANE SYSTEMS

There is a characteristic difference in electrochemical potential between a membrane system and the surrounding fluid in which it is bathed that is related to the difference in the concentrations of particular ions in the internal fluid and in the fluid external to the membrane. Such differences in concentrations are largely the consequence of the energized translocation of particular ions in one direction only, usually from the outside of the membrane into the interior.* This directionality of membranes depends upon the orientation of the translocating systems in the repeating units. The invariance of the orientation ensures that the energized movement of ions or molecules can proceed in one direction only.

THE PERMEABILITY OF MEMBRANE SYSTEMS

The molecular structure determines the permeability of a membrane to ions and polar molecules. In turn, tightness of fit between one repeating unit and its nesting neighbors is determined by the structure of the repeating unit. There is wide variation among membranes in respect to permeability. The outer mitochondrial membrane is in general more permeable to ions and polar molecules

---

* In red blood corpuscles the ATPase activity can be activated either by raising the level of Na^+ inside the cell or the level of K^+ outside the cell.

than is the inner membrane. Most membranes contain a set of translocases which permit the selective, energized flow of soluble molecules across the membrane barrier.

The nature and relative composition of the lipid moiety of repeating units appear to be among the determinants of the permeability of the red cell membrane to small molecules and ions. However, this cannot account for the gross differences in permeability between the outer and inner mitochondrial membranes which have essentially identical lipid compositions. The architecture of the repeating units and their mode of packing may, at least in the case of the mitochondrial membranes, be among the crucial determinants of membrane permeability.

MEMBRANES AND METABOLIC SEQUENCES

The association of certain major metabolic processes with membranes is so general that we may well consider this association to be a universal attribute of cells. The apparent invariability of the chemistry of these major metabolic sequences would have its root in this link to membranes since membrane association requires organization within the framework of repeating units and subunits. Such a framework imposes rigid requirements on the three-dimensional fit of enzymes and coenzymes participating in the sequence, and it severely limits the degree of permissible change and innovation. Equally important, the fact of membrane association introduces yet another category into the complete description of a metabolic sequence—namely, how this sequence is fitted into the architecture of a membrane and how, in turn, this architecture influences the control and regulation of this sequence.

MODIFICATION OF THE FORM OF COMPLEXES DURING ISOLATION FROM MEMBRANES

The α-ketoglutaric and pyruvic dehydrogenase complexes have been isolated and characterized in great detail by Lester Reed and his colleagues. These are both complexes of high molecular weight $(2–4 \times 10^6)$; a single molecule of either complex contains multiple molecules of four different component enzymes. The arrangement of these component enzymes within the complex is highly precise, as illustrated in the model of Figure 10.23. The size of the isolated complex (diameter of 200 Å or more) is larger than that of the repeating units in the outer mitochondrial membrane (diameters of less than 100 Å)—the membrane in which the respective isolated complexes originate. This discrepancy suggests that during isolation,

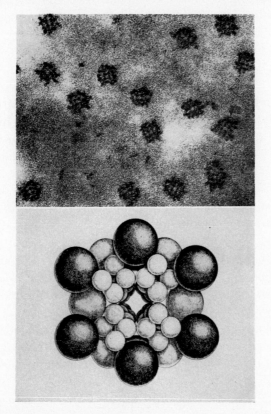

Fig. 10.23. The upper half of the figure is an electron micrograph of the pyruvate dehydrogenase complex of *Escherichia coli,* negatively stained with 0.25% potassium phosphotungstate, pH 7.0. Magnification: × 200,000. Photograph kindly supplied by Lester J. Reed.

The lower half of the figure is a model of the *Escherichia coli* pyruvate dehydrogenase complex, proposed by Lester J. Reed. The model consists of twelve molecules of pyruvate decarboxylase (large spheres) and six molecules of dehydrolipoyl dehydrogenase (medium-sized spheres) disposed in an orderly arrangement around the twenty-four (or forty-eight) subunits comprising the lipoyl reductase—transacetylase aggregate (small spheres).

and as a consequence of the isolation procedure, the repeating units associated with a given activity may polymerize to form much larger aggregates. In the membrane the pyruvic and α-ketoglutaric dehydrogenases are linked to other repeating units and to phospholipid. When separated from these associated repeating units and lipid, the repeating units of the respective complexes polymerize to form high-molecular-weight units of the type described in Figure 10.23.

A Concluding Comment

Within a relatively few years, membrane biochemistry has become one of the most dynamic areas in molecular biology. The concept that a membrane system is nothing more than the integration of the repeating units and of their pattern of organization has helped to sweep aside the mumbo-jumbo of membrane lore. Precise biochemical data can now be used to specify the composition of membrane systems. There is no chemical evidence that membranes contain structured elements other than the repeating units and their subunit parts.

The solutions to the problems of membrane design and of membrane function now have to be found in the molecular structure and function of the repeating units—in their form and nesting geometry, in the ways in which lipids and proteins are bonded together, and in the ways in which the proteins are arranged within the subunits. The problems are basically chemical in nature; their solutions will require the most powerful biochemical methodology.

Suggested Reading

Books

De Robertis, E. D. P., Nowinski, W. W., and Saez, F. A., "General Cytology," Saunders Co., Philadelphia, Pennsylvania, 1960.

Engström, A., and Finean, J. B., "Biological Ultrastructure," Academic Press, New York, 1958.

Finean, J. B. "Chemical Ultrastructure in Living Tissues," C. C. Thomas, Springfield, Illinois, 1962.

Hayashi, T., ed., "Subcellular Particles," Ronald Press Company, New York, 1959.

Heidenreich, R. D., "Fundamentals of Transmission Electron Microscopy," Interscience Publishing Co., New York, 1964.

Locke, M., ed., "Cellular Membranes in Development," Academic Press, New York, 1964.

Loewenstein, W. R., ed., "Biological Membranes: Recent Progress," *Ann. N. Y. Acad. Sci.* 137, Article 2 (1966).

Loewy, A. G., and Siekevitz, P., "Cell Structure and Function," Holt, Rinehart, and Winston, New York, 1963.

Nachmansohn, D., "Chemical and Molecular Basis of Nerve Activity," Academic Press, Inc., New York, 1959.

Seno, S., and Cowdry, E. V., eds., "Intracellular Membraneous Structure," Japan Soc. Cell Biology, Okayama, Japan, 1965.

Special Articles

Allmann, D. W., Bachmann, E., Perdue, J. F., and Green, D. E., *Arch. Biochem. Biophys.* 114, 153 (1966); 114, 165 (1966); 114, 172 (1966): on the enzymes of the outer mitochondrial membrane.

Benedetti, E. L., and Emmelot, P., *J. Cell Biol.* 26, 299 (1965): on subunits of liver plasma membrane.

Bronchard, M. R., *Compt. Rend. Acad. Sci.* 260, 4564 (1965): on subunits of chloroplasts.

Caspar, D. L. D., and Klug, A., *Cold Spring Harbor Symp. Quant. Biol.* 27, 1 (1962): on the structure of virus particles.

Criddle, R. S., Edwards, D. L., and Peterson, T. G., *Biochemistry* 5, 578 (1966): on the homogeneity of mitochondrial structural protein.

Fernández-Morán, H., Oda, T., Blair, P. V., and Green, D. E., *J. Cell Biol.* 22, 63 (1964): on the elementary particle of the mitochondrion.

Fernández-Morán, H., Reed, L. J., Koike, M., and Willms, C. R., *Science* 145, 930 (1964): on the α-keto acid dehydrogenase complex.

Fleischer, S., Klouwen, H., and Brierley, G. P., *J. Biol. Chem.* 236, 2936 (1961): on the lipids of mitochondria.

Goldberger, R. F., Pumphrey, A., and Smith, A., *Biochim. Biophys. Acta* 58, 307 (1962): on the modification of the oxidation-reduction potential of a hemoprotein by interaction with a structural protein.

Green, D. E., Murer, E., Hultin, H. O., Richardson, S. H., Salmon, B., Brierley, G. P. and Baum, H., *Arch. Biochem. Biophys.* 112, 635 (1965): on the association of the glycolytic system with the plasma membrane.

Green, D. E., and Perdue, J. F., *Proc. Natl. Acad. U. S.* 55, 1205 (1966): on membranes as expressions of repeating units.

Green, D. E., and Fleischer, S., *in* "Metabolism and Physiological Significance of Lipids" (R. M. C. Dawson, and D. N. Rhodes, eds.), p. 581. John Wiley and Sons Ltd., London and New York, 1963: on the role of lipid in mitochondrial function.

Hatefi, Y., Haavik, A. G., Fowler, L. R., and Griffiths, D. E., *J. Biol. Chem.* 237, 2661 (1962): studies on the reconstitution of the electron transfer system.

Holter, H., *Intern. Rev. Cytol.* 8, 481 (1959): on pinocytosis.

Kagawa, Y., and Racker, E., *J. Biol. Chem.* **241**, 2475 (1966): on the identification of the headpieces of inner membrane repeating units with a macromolecular ATPase.

Koike, M., Reed, L. J., and Carroll, William R., *J. Biol Chem.* **238**, 30 (1963): on α-keto acid dehydrogenation complexes.

McConnell, D., MacLennan, D., Tzagoloff, A., and Green, D. E., *J. Biol. Chem.* **241**, 2373 (1966): on membrane formation by a repeating unit.

Palade, G. E., *J. Histochem. Cytochem.* **1**, 88 (1953): on membrane systems.

Palade, G. E., *in* "Enzymes: Units of Biological Structure and Function" (O. H. Gaebler, ed.), p. 185, Academic Press, New York, 1956: on electron microscopy of mitochondria and other cytoplasmic structures.

Palade, G. E., *in* "The Scientific Endeavor," The Rockefeller Institute Press, New York, 1965: on the organization of living matter.

Richardson, S. H., Hultin, H. O., and Green, D. E., *Proc. Natl. Acad. Sci. U. S.* **50**, 82 (1963): on the structural proteins of different membrane systems.

Robertson, J. D., *Prog. Biophys. Biophys. Chem.* **10**, 343 (1960): on the molecular structure and contact relationships of cell membranes.

Sjöstrand, F. S., and Rhodin, J., *Exptl. Cell Res.* **6**, 426 (1953): on membrane systems.

Woodward, D. O., and Munkres, D. K., *Proc. Natl. Acad. Sci. U. S.* **55**, 872 (1966): on the alteration of structural protein in respiratory-deficient strains of *Neurospora*.

CHAPTER 11

DNA, RNA, and Protein Synthesis

Cellular reproduction is one of the most elegant, and most complex, processes of living organisms. Every cell arises from a precursor, or parent, cell. In multicellular organisms, the two cells which arise by division of the parent remain attached and go on to divide again, so as to produce four cells. The progression goes on geometrically, at least in the early stages, and then differentiation begins; some cells become destined for one part of the organism and others for another part. The various groups of cells go on dividing at different rates and for different periods of time, and finally a whole organism is formed. It is obvious that the mechanism of cellular reproduction must be precisely controlled so that mistakes may be avoided. Each error would be multiplied by the number of cells destined to arise from the abnormal one. Perhaps the most remarkable feature of the process is, in fact, the exactness with which the cell duplicates; after each division, both daughter cells are essentially identical copies of the parent.

Form and function are determined by the characteristic proteins of a cell more than by any other single type of molecule. One might expect, therefore, that cell division would involve the duplication of proteins, but this is not so. The only structures of a cell which must be copied prior to division are the chromosomes, the intranuclear bodies that contain the genes.* The morphology of cell division forms a complete story in itself, and there are many varia-

* Other structures that are duplicated during cell division appear to be required only to ensure duplication of the chromosomes or the process of division itself.

271

tions of the process to be seen in cells from different organisms. For the present purpose, however, we shall give only a brief description of some of the basic elements of cell division at the morphologic level. A simple schematic illustration of the process is shown in Figure 11.1. When one watches a cell divide under a microscope, the first thing one notes is the appearance of the mitotic apparatus—the centrioles, which divide and gravitate toward opposite poles of the cell, and a system of fibers known as the spindle (Figure 11.1, A and B). In the meantime, the chromosomes have been duplicated and now appear across the center of the cell (Figure 11.1, C and

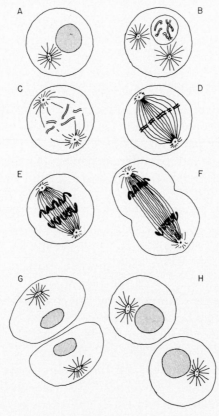

Fig. 11.1. Major stages in the process of cell division, as seen with the light microscope. The process is described in the text. Redrawn from figure of Daniel Mazia, *Sci. Am.* **189**, 53 (1953).

D). One of each pair of chromosomes then migrates to one of the two poles, appearing to be "pulled" by the fibers of the spindle (Figure 11.1, E and F). Next, the cell pinches off and the wall closes at the point of constriction (Figure 11.1, G and H). Two daughter cells are formed, each with a complete set of chromosomes. It is a striking fact that, although the chromosomes are the only structures duplicated and equally apportioned between the daughter cells (aside from parts of the mitotic apparatus), the daughter cells are in all respects identical with the parent. What of the thousands of other specific structures and molecules? What of the characteristic set of protein molecules? The answer is that, with the correct chromosomes, the cell can make essentially everything else needed for its own formation. The chromosomes are the "blueprints" for building a functional cell, and the small amount of cytoplasm (with its subcellular organelles) which is divided between the daughter cells at the time of division is sufficient to carry out the instructions contained in these blueprints.

Nucleic Acids and Genes

IDENTIFICATION OF DNA AS THE GENETIC MATERIAL

For many years deoxyribonucleic acid (DNA) has been thought to be closely related to genes, perhaps to be the very chemical substance of which genes are made. It has taken a great deal of work, however, to verify this idea and to dispel the previous notion that the genetic material was protein. Among the simplest criteria to be met for any substance that functions as a gene are the following: localization within the nucleus of the cell, where the chromosomes (containing the genes) are known to be; invariance of the amount present in any given cell, since cells neither acquire nor lose genetic material (except under highly unusual specialized conditions); sensitivity to chemical and physical agents that cause genes to undergo mutations; and increase in mass during cell division, when chromosomes are known to be duplicated. DNA meets all these criteria; thus, it would seem to be a good contender for the title *genetic material*.

Another line of evidence for the genetic function of DNA is even more compelling than those cited above: *bacterial transformation.* Certain *virulent* strains of the microorganism *Diplococcus pneumoniae* cause pneumonia when given to animals, whereas other *nonvirulent* strains do not. When a virulent strain is killed by heat before introduction into animals, the animals, as expected, do not develop pneumonia. However, when the test animals are given a mixture of the heat-killed, virulent strain and the living, nonvirulent strain (neither of which alone induces pneumonia), they do develop pneumonia. Upon isolation from the animals so treated, the organism causing the disease can be identified as the virulent strain. Thus, a transformation of the nonvirulent strain has been effected by the heat-killed, virulent strain. This phenomenon is called *bacterial transformation.* The fact that after isolation the transformed organism retains its virulence, generation after generation, indicates that the transformation is heritable and therefore has affected the genetic material. Somehow, a substance from the dead, virulent strain of bacteria manages to penetrate the living, nonvirulent strain and to confer virulence upon it. The pioneering efforts of Oswald Avery in his study of this phenomenon provided the first breakthrough in the understanding of the chemical nature of the genetic material. By careful fractionation, he was able to isolate from the heat-killed, virulent strain of bacteria the active transforming principle. It was DNA, not protein. Destruction of the chemical integrity of this macromolecule by enzymic or chemical means destroyed its transforming ability. Since this first experiment, other transforming principles have been isolated from a variety of bacteria, and they have all been identified as species of DNA. Further investigations have shown that one, or several, specific genetic traits—such as resistance to a particular antibiotic, requirement for a particular vitamin, or certain morphological characteristics—can be transferred to recipient bacteria by "infecting" them with transforming DNA from an appropriate source.

CHEMISTRY OF NUCLEIC ACIDS

The study of nucleic acids began in the second half of the nineteenth century, when DNA was isolated from cell nuclei. Since that time a great deal has been learned about this strongly acidic molecule and about a closely related molecule—namely, ribonucleic acid (RNA). Some of the elementary facets of the chemistry of nucleic acids were discussed in Chapter 3. For the present purpose, the following summary will suffice.

Essentially, DNA and RNA are both linear polymers of four different nucleotides. Aside from the fact that the sugar moiety of the nucleotides in RNA is ribose and in DNA is deoxyribose, the major distinguishing feature of each type of nucleic acid is the nonidentity of one of the bases, respectively, out of each set of four major component nucleotides. In DNA the nucleotides are d-adenylic acid (A), d-guanylic acid (G), d-cytidylic acid (C), and thymidylic acid (T). The first three of these nucleotides (but with ribose as the sugar moiety) also appear in RNA, but as its fourth nucleotide RNA contains uridylic acid (U) instead of thymidylic acid. Thus, whereas DNA is composed of A, G, C, and T, RNA is composed of A, G, C, and U. The individual nucleotides of both DNA and RNA are joined together through their phosphate and sugar groups, as shown in Figure 11.2. The number of nucleotide residues in a single molecule of nucleic acid varies from about eighty to over a million. Thus, nucleic acids are polynucleotides—long molecules, in which a single strand is composed of nucleotides joined together in a linear array.

THE STRUCTURE OF DNA

By the use of partition chromatography and ion-exchange chromatography it has been shown that the absolute amounts (per unit mass of nucleic acid) of the four nucleotides of DNA (A, T, C, and G) vary over a wide range, depending upon the biological source. However, the ratios of A to T, and of G to C, are always close to one. With this information, together with X-ray diffraction patterns, titration data, and brilliant imagination, James Watson and Francis Crick deduced a chemical structure for DNA involving a highly organized three-dimensional conformation. They proposed that in DNA two independent linear strands of polynucleotides are held together by means of hydrogen bonds and that this double-stranded structure is coiled, like the threads of a screw, in helical form (Figure 11.3). The hydrogen bonds are formed between pairs of bases

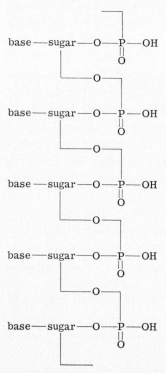

Fig. 11.2. Linkage of nucleotides to form a polynucleotide. The sugar residue of each nucleotide is bound to the phosphate group of the next nucleotide; thus, a linear polymer is formed.

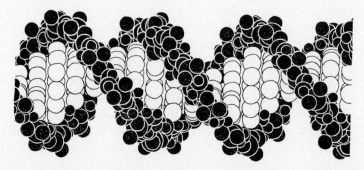

Fig. 11.3. Space-filling model of a portion of a DNA double helix. The atoms of the bases are shown as open circles, whereas those of the phosphate and sugar residues are shown as dark circles.

which are opposite one another in the two different strands. The chemical structures and sizes of the bases allow hydrogen bonds only between A and T and between C and G, as shown in Figure 11.4. The sugar-phosphate residues, forming the backbone of the strands, are on the outside of the helix, and the bases are on the inside, as shown in Figure 11.5. The uniqueness of this structure resides in the arrangement of the bases; they are perpendicular to the axis of the double helix and are bonded in specific pairs. Be-

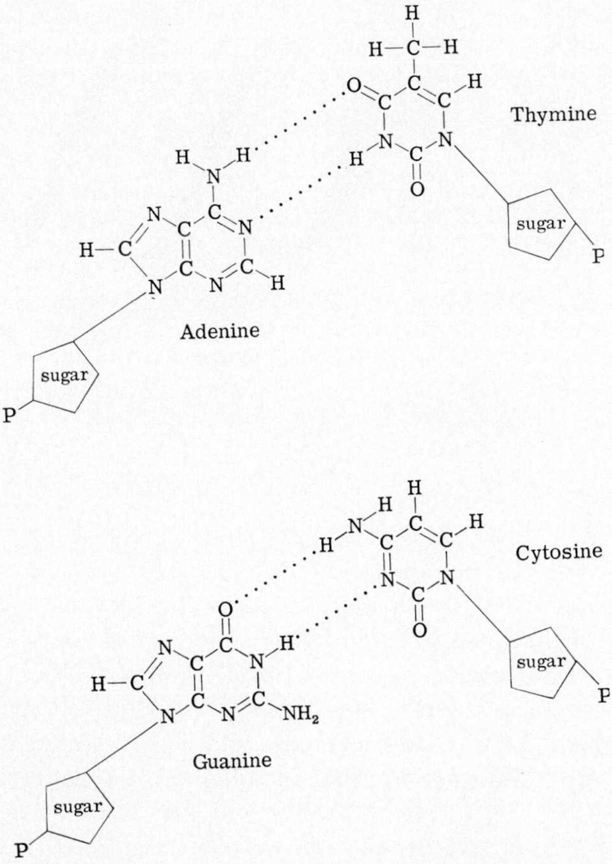

Fig. 11.4. Hydrogen bonding between pairs of nucleotides. The sizes of the purine and pyrimidine bases are such that, in order to be accommodated within the Watson-Crick double helix, the only pairings possible in DNA are those between adenine and thymine and between guanine and cytosine.

cause the dimensions of this structure prescribe that adenine be hydrogen-bonded to thymine and that guanine be similarly bonded to cytosine, the ratio of adenine to thymine, and of guanine to cytosine, must always equal one. The structure places no restriction on the sequence of bases in one strand. However, because of the requirement for base pairing (A with T and C with G), once the sequence in one strand is established, the sequence in the other is predetermined. This special feature of DNA is termed *complementarity.*

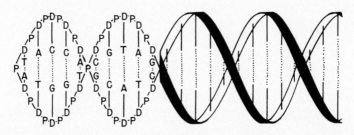

Fig. 11.5. The DNA double helix. This schematic representation indicates that the bases (A,T,C, and G) are located on the inside of the helix, whereas the phosphate groups (P) and deoxyribose sugar residues (D) are located on the outside. Hydrogen bonds between the bases of the two strands of DNA are indicated by dotted lines.

REPLICATION OF DNA

A fundamental problem of genetics concerns the molecular mechanisms involved in the replication of the genetic material during cell division. Since DNA is the chemical substance of genes, it must be replicated every time a cell divides. The element of complementarity in the structural model proposed by Watson and Crick served as the basis for an interesting hypothesis. If, during cell division, the two strands of DNA were to separate, and if each strand were to be replicated by the formation of its complement, the net result would be duplication. That is to say, each strand, after separation from the original double-stranded molecule, would serve as a template for the synthesis of a new strand. Let us suppose that the synthesis of the new strand starts at one end of the template and grows by the addition of one nucleotide at a time. Eventually, a double strand will be produced—one of the pair being the new strand, the other being the one that served as template. The rules of base pairing would dicate that the bases of the nucleotides used in building the new strand be able to form hydrogen bonds with those of the template to which they lie opposite. Thus, whenever there is a d-adenylic acid residue in the template, a thymidylic acid residue will be inserted opposite to it in the new strand; d-guanylic acid would require the insertion of d-cytidylic acid, and so on along the strand. As shown schematically in Figure 11.6, the net result is the

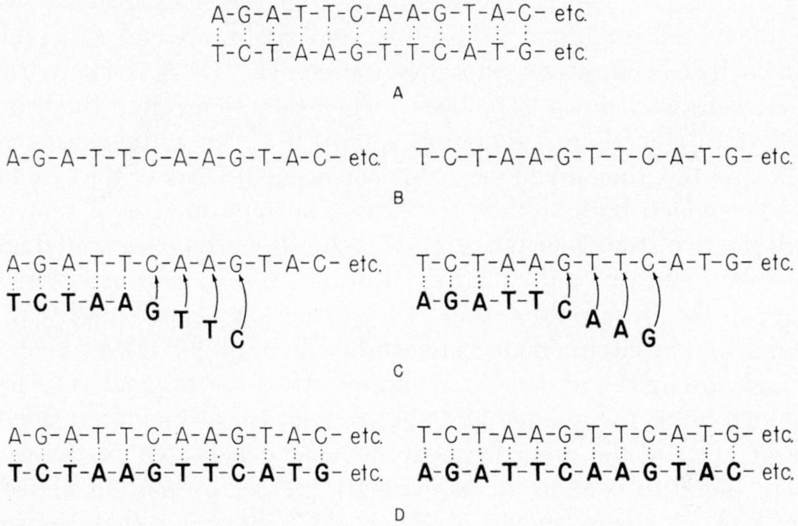

A-G-A-T-T-C-A-A-G-T-A-C- etc.
T-C-T-A-A-G-T-T-C-A-T-G- etc.

A

A-G-A-T-T-C-A-A-G-T-A-C- etc.   T-C-T-A-A-G-T-T-C-A-T-G- etc.

B

A-G-A-T-T-C-A-A-G-T-A-C- etc.   T-C-T-A-A-G-T-T-C-A-T-G- etc.
T-C-T-A-A G)))   A-G-A-T-T C)))
         G T T   C A A
            T C   G

C

A-G-A-T-T-C-A-A-G-T-A-C- etc.   T-C-T-A-A-G-T-T-C-A-T-G- etc.
T-C-T-A-A-G-T-T-C-A-T-G- etc.   A-G-A-T-T-C-A-A-G-T-A-C- etc.

D

Fig. 11.6. A model for the replication of DNA. A parent, double-stranded molecule (part A) first separates into two single strands (part B). Each of these strands then serves as a template for the synthesis of a new strand of DNA (part C). Because of the phenomenon of complementarity, the two daughter molecules (part D) are both identical to the parent. The dotted lines represent hydrogen bonds.

synthesis of a new, and completely complementary, strand of DNA from each of the original strands. At the start of the replicating cycle there is one double strand; at the end there are two. The two individual strands of the original DNA molecule are no longer paired with each other but are now paired with new partners. Since the new partners are still complementary in respect to base sequence (hence in respect to constituent nucleotides), the two new double-stranded molecules as a whole are both identical with the original.

This hypothesis for the mechanism of DNA replication was tested by Messelson and Stahl. In their experiments they took advantage of the fact that, when cells are grown in a medium in which the only source of nitrogen is a compound containing a heavy isotope (^{15}N), all the nitrogen-containing molecules synthesized by the cells are heavier than normal. For a macromolecule containing a great deal of nitrogen, such as DNA, the overall increase in weight is great enough to allow the separation of heavy molecules from light (normal) ones by the relatively simple technique of density-gradient centrifugation. Messelson and Stahl started with cells which had been grown on a ^{15}N source. The DNA isolated from these cells was shown to be heavy. Then they transferred the heavy cells into a medium containing a normal (^{14}N) nitrogen source. The question they asked was: Will the original DNA of the original cell, in which both strands are heavy, be replicated as a unit, or will the two strands of the original molecule become separated and each be replicated individually? After the original cells had divided once in the ^{14}N medium, they isolated the DNA and found that it had a weight intermediate between heavy and light DNA—that is, it had one light and one heavy strand. After the original cells had divided twice, the isolated DNA was of two types—one intermediate in weight and the other light. Subsequent generations of the cells were found to contain an increasingly greater proportion of light DNA. The scheme shown in Figure 11.7 illustrates these experimental findings, which prove that DNA is replicated in the manner predicted by the hypothesis described above.

Additional support for the hypothesis concerning the mechanism of DNA replication was obtained from studies with the enzyme *DNA polymerase*. The work of Arthur Kornberg and his associates established clearly that this enzyme, which they purified from cell extracts, catalyzes the synthesis of DNA when supplied with the four nucleotides and a DNA "primer." The unusual feature of this reaction is that the enzyme catalyzes the synthesis under orders of the primer. Thus, the primer acts as a template which directs the nucleotide sequence of the newly synthesized DNA. The fact that single-stranded DNA is a far more efficient primer for the DNA polymerase reaction than is double-stranded DNA suggests that single-stranded DNA is the natural template for DNA replication.

In investigating the problem as to whether both strands of the DNA molecule are essential to its function as a gene, Marmur and Doty used a technique they had developed for separating and re-combining the individual strands of DNA in a test tube. First, a double-stranded DNA molecule containing a specific gene was isolated and separated into two single strands. Each of the single strands was then combined with single-stranded DNA molecules that did not contain that gene. In this way, DNA molecules were produced in which only one of the two strands had come from a molecule containing the specific gene. This DNA was then tested in bacterial transformation experiments (see above), and was found

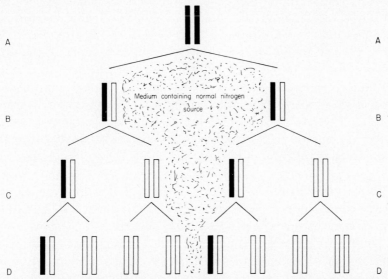

Fig. 11.7. Experimental proof for separation of strands during DNA replication. Messelson and Stahl started their experiment with cells grown on ¹⁵N, the DNA of which was heavy (row A). The cells were then transferred to a medium contain-ing ¹⁴N. In the next generation (row B) the cells were found to contain DNA of intermediate weight. In the third generation (row C) both intermediate and light DNA were found, and in succeeding generations (row D) the cells were found to contain progressively higher proportions of light DNA. Heavy strands of DNA are shown as solid lines; light strands, as open lines.

to confer upon the recipient bacteria the trait determined by the gene in question. Thus, only one of the strands of a DNA molecule need carry a particular gene for that gene to function.

Protein Synthesis

THE GENETIC CODE

We know that genes are made of DNA and are replicated prior to cell division in such a way that each daughter cell gets a complete copy of the original set of genes. What do genes do? It has now been convincingly shown that genes control the synthesis of proteins. In fact, it can be said that every protein of the cell is synthesized according to the specifications of a particular gene. This function of genes becomes obvious when one considers the problem of how DNA viruses are reproduced. When a virus of this type infects a bacterial cell, only its DNA may enter the cell; its coat of protein is discarded and left behind. Soon after being infected, the cell replicates the viral DNA, manufactures all the viral proteins, and assembles complete viruses. The cell may then burst open and release many new viral entities, each ready to infect a new cell with its own DNA. Since only the DNA of the virus enters the cell, all the specifications for synthesizing viral proteins must be carried by the viral DNA. Evidently, the metabolic apparatus of the infected cell is preempted by the viral DNA for building more viruses.

Certain genes also control the activities of the other genes and thereby affect the process of protein synthesis *indirectly*. The functions of these regulatory genes will be discussed in the next chapter. Here we are concerned only with the question as to how genes fulfill their primary function—the *direct* control of protein synthesis.

Proteins resemble nucleic acids in that they are macromolecules, made up of many monomeric units. Unlike nucleic acids, however, the monomeric units of proteins are amino acids. The specific sequence of amino acids in a given protein predetermines all of the characteristics that differentiate that protein from all others. Thus, the problem of how a gene controls the synthesis of a protein boils down to the problem of how the sequence of nucleotides in the DNA specifies the sequence of amino acids in the protein. It is often referred to as a coding problem, since information, stored in the "language" of DNA, must ultimately be translated into the "language" of protein in order to be meaningful in a functional sense— hence the term *genetic code.*

If proteins were made up of only four different amino acids, coding would be a straightforward matter. Each of the four nucleotides —A, T, G, and C—would then specify one of the amino acids, and so the sequence of nucleotides in the DNA could be used directly to fix the sequence of amino acids in the protein. However, proteins are composed of twenty different amino acids. How can only four different varieties of nucleotides be sufficient to specify twenty amino acids? Obviously, there must be some device such as that used in the Morse code (in which only two kinds of symbols are used to specify the twenty-six letters of the alphabet). Several solutions to the biological coding problem have been proposed, but we will restrict ourselves to the one that has withstood the tests of biochemical experimentation, the *nonoverlapping triplet code* proposed by Frances Crick. It was suggested by Crick that each amino acid is specified by a triplet of nucleotides (three nucleotides in a row). There are sixty-four different ways in which the four nucleotides can be arranged into triplets, which theoretically would allow the DNA molecule to specify sixty-four different amino acids.

In the linear DNA molecule, then, the sequence of nucleotides directs the sequence of amino acids in the linear polypeptide chain of a protein molecule, a characteristic arrangement of three nucleotides specifying each amino acid. A segment of DNA such as G-G-T-C-T-T-C-A-G- would specify the amino acid sequence proline-glutamic acid-valine-, if G-G-T specified proline, C-T-T, glutamic acid, and C-A-G, valine. A single molecule of DNA is long enough to encompass many genes, and can therefore direct the synthesis of many proteins.

TRANSCRIPTION

The major site of protein synthesis is not the nuclei of cells, where the chromosomal DNA is located, but the ribosomes, which are located in the cytoplasm of the cell. The mechanism for communicating the directions encoded in the chromosomal DNA from the nucleus to the cytoplasm of the cell involves RNA. This RNA is also required as an intermediary between DNA and the site of protein synthesis in bacteria (in which the chromosomes are not enclosed by a nuclear membrane). In the cells of higher organisms the ribosomes are part of a membrane system known as the endoplasmic reticulum. In bacterial cells no endoplasmic reticulum exists, but some other membrane system is thought to be involved, together with the ribosomes, in the process of protein biosynthesis.

As described in the preceding section, RNA is very similar to DNA in structure. The characteristic differences are that the sugar residue of the RNA nucleotides is ribose, rather than deoxyribose, and that one of the pyrimidine residues of RNA is uracil rather than thymine. Thus, whereas the four nucleotides of DNA are G, C, A, and T, those of RNA are G, C, A, and U (uridylic acid). An important feature of the chemistry of uridylic acid is that, like thymidylic acid, it can form hydrogen bonds with d-adenylic acid when it comes to lie opposite the latter nucleotide in a nucleic acid molecule. A strand of RNA can, therefore, be complementary to a strand of DNA, as shown in Figure 11.8, two such strands forming a "hybrid" nucleic acid molecule. This possibility for hybridization was utilized by Spiegelman and his colleagues to study

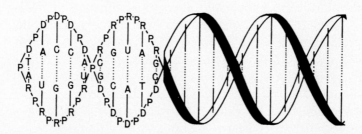

Fig. 11.8. Hybrid nucleic acid molecule. By virtue of the fact that the base moiety of the uridylic acid residues in RNA (like the base of the thymidylic acid residues in DNA) is of just the right size to form a hydrogen bond with the base of the adenylic acid residues in DNA, complementary single strands of the two kinds of nucleic acid may be accommodated in a double helical structure; thus, a hybrid molecule may be formed, as shown here.

the nature of the RNA involved in protein biosynthesis and to further define its role.

One of the first steps in the synthesis of a protein is the synthesis of a molecule of RNA complementary to the DNA of a gene. This process occurs in the nucleus of the cell, and is thought to proceed by a mechanism similar to the one utilized for the replication of DNA, except that it is catalyzed by a different enzyme. First, the double-stranded DNA probably separates into two strands; then, a segment of one strand is "copied" by the synthesis of a complementary new strand. In the present case, each time the growing chain comes to a d-adenylic acid residue in the DNA template, uridylic acid is inserted rather than thymidylic acid (and ribonucleotides are used rather than deoxyribonucleotides), since the product is to be RNA. Otherwise, the base pairing is the same as for DNA replication. Once the complementary strand of RNA has been synthesized, it bears the same coded information as does the segment of DNA copied.

After the RNA has been formed, it detaches from the genetic template, and the two separated strands of chromosomal DNA are thought to return to the double-stranded form. In the next phase of the process, the newly synthesized molecule of RNA becomes bound to ribosomes, the site of protein synthesis, as shown in Figure 11.9. It is possible that the binding to ribosomes begins even before the RNA has left the genetic template.

Because this RNA molecule carries the information concerning amino acid sequence from the gene to the ribosome it is called messenger-RNA (m-RNA). There are several species of RNA in the cell, such as ribosomal RNA and transfer-RNA (see below), and all species are apparently involved in the process of protein biosynthesis. Only m-RNA, however, actually functions as the bearer of genetic information concerning the amino acid sequences of proteins. The concept of m-RNA was first elucidated by Jacob and Monod of the Pasteur Institute. The process by which m-RNA is synthesized on the genetic template has often been referred to as a transcription, since the coded information of the genes is not "translated" directly into amino acid sequences; it is simply put into another form, or dialect, of the same language (the language of nucleic acids). It is the transcribed m-RNA which is actually used for making a translation into the language of proteins. Since only a portion of the chromosomal DNA is utilized as a template for the synthesis of each m-RNA molecule, the DNA must contain information which dictates where the transcription of each m-RNA is to begin and where it is to end.

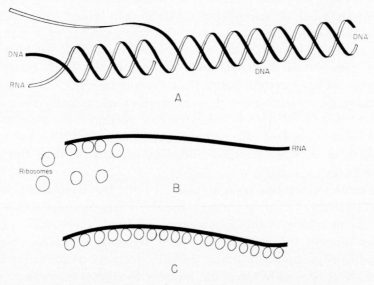

Fig. 11.9 Information encoded in the nucleotide sequence of DNA is transcribed into the nucleotide sequence of a complementary strand of RNA. After the RNA molecule has been synthesized (part A), it becomes detached from the genetic template and associates with ribosomes in the cytoplasm of the cell (parts B and C).

TRANSLATION

The next phase in the synthesis of protein is the lining up of amino acids along the m-RNA, the particular amino acid chosen at each position being determined by a triplet of nucleotides in the m-RNA. Actually, however, this phase involves a complex series of reactions. We will have to digress for a moment from the m-RNA to examine how the amino acids are prepared for their ultimate alignment and polymerization.

Before amino acids can be brought to their specified positions on the m-RNA, they must undergo two chemical reactions. First, they are converted to a highly reactive form by specific enzymes (synthetases), in reactions energized by ATP. Next, each activated amino acid becomes attached to its own specific transfer-RNA (t-RNA) molecule. The t-RNA's are so called because they transfer amino acids to their proper positions along the m-RNA molecule. The t-RNA must not be confused with m-RNA; it is a relatively small molecule, (composed of approximately eighty nucleotides) whereas m-RNA is relatively large (between three hundred and thirty thousand nucleotides). There are at least twenty different species of t-RNA molecules, one kind being specific for each amino acid.* Thus, there is a valine t-RNA, an alanine t-RNA, and so on, each one capable of reacting with, and becoming attached to, only one amino acid. In addition, the attachment of each species of amino acid to its specific t-RNA is catalyzed by a specific enzyme. There are thus at least twenty such enzymes. All of the t-RNA molecules are very similar chemically. They appear to be single chains of nucleotides folded in an orderly manner. Each species of t-RNA must have at least two unique sites—one for the attachment of its specific amino acid and one for its own attachment to m-RNA (see Figure 11.10).

Now we will return to the long strand of m-RNA which is in contact with ribosomes in the cytoplasm of the cell and which has a sequence of nucleotides complementary to that in the DNA of a particular gene. This sequence determines the sequence of amino acids in the protein to be synthesized in the following manner (cf. Figure 11.11). The triplets of nucleotides in the m-RNA do not specify amino acids directly, but rather the amino acid-specific t-RNA's. If alanine is the first amino acid to be brought into place, then the first three nucleotides of the m-RNA will specify the t-RNA for alanine. The t-RNA for alanine finds its way to this triplet, and attaches itself there, bearing an alanine residue. If the next triplet of nucleotides of the m-RNA specifies valine t-RNA, such a molecule, bearing a valine residue, will come to occupy this site. As the valine t-RNA comes into position on the m-RNA, it will sit

* Actually, there are several species of t-RNA for each amino acid, which brings the total number to well over twenty. The function of the "extra" t-RNA molecules is at present under investigation.

next to the alanine t-RNA, and the valine residue it carries will be adjacent to the alanine residue of the first t-RNA molecule. Thus, the two amino acids will have been brought together in the order specified by the m-RNA. An enzyme-catalyzed transfer now takes place, in which the first amino acid (alanine) is transferred to the amino group of the second amino acid (valine); this forms a di-peptidyl-t-RNA (alanylvalyl-t-RNA). The next triplet of nucleo-tides in the m-RNA specifies some other t-RNA, which attaches at that site and carries its amino acid into line with the other two. As before, the dipeptide is now catalytically transferred to the amino group of the third amino acid to form a tripeptidyl-t-RNA.

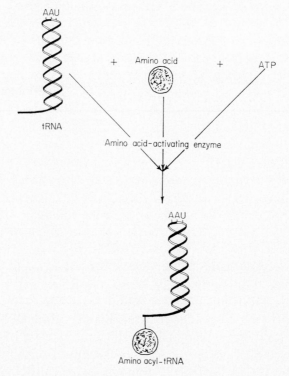

Fig. 11.10. Prior to the assembly of amino acids into proteins, the amino acids must be activated and enzymically attached to specific t-RNA molecules. In the drawing shown here, the process is represented as a single step. No attempt has been made to draw the various components to scale.

Then the fourth t-RNA is positioned on the m-RNA, and the tri-peptide already formed is transferred to the amino acid it carries, and so on. Thus, by the sequential attachment of t-RNA molecules along the m-RNA, amino acids are positioned together in the pre-

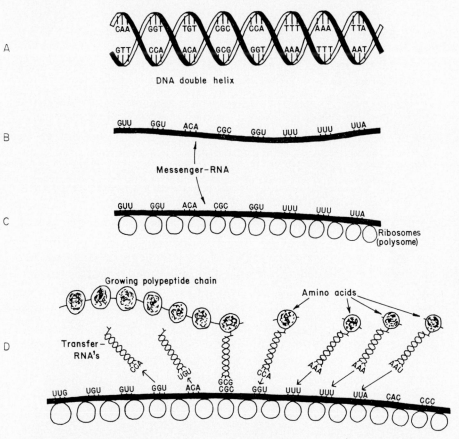

Fig. 11.11. The process by which a polypeptide chain is formed in accordance with the information encoded in DNA is summarized here. The code implicit in the nucleotide sequence of a portion of chromosomal DNA (part A) is transcribed into a molecule of m-RNA (part B). The m-RNA then associates with ribosomes (part C) and its nucleotide sequence is translated, by means of t-RNA, into the amino acid sequence of a polypeptide chain (part D). Gaps are shown between nucleotide triplets only for the sake of clarity; actually no gaps exist. No attempt has been made to draw the various components to scale. Redrawn from figure of M. W. Niren-berg, *Sci. Am.* **208**, 80 (1963).

determined sequence. The polymerization of amino acids occurs in a stepwise fashion, the growing polypeptide chain being added to the next amino acid-t-RNA as the latter molecule is brought into place by attachment to the m-RNA. It must be noted that, although amino acids never make contact with the gene, nor even with the m-RNA, it is the gene which ultimately determines how they are to be ordered. The various steps in this process are summarized in Figure 11.11.

During the translation process described above, the m-RNA must be in contact with ribosomes, which form an integral part of the translation apparatus. Although relatively little is known about the mechanism by which ribosomes act, it is evident that more than one ribosome may be engaged in the translation of any given m-RNA molecule. Electron micrographs have revealed that many ribosomes (known collectively as a *polysome*) may be associated with each m-RNA molecule, the number being proportional to the size of the m-RNA.

Soon after it became apparent that the amino acid sequences of proteins are encoded in the DNA of genes, biochemists tried to crack the code. If it takes a triplet of nucleotides in DNA to specify an amino acid, which triplet specifies which amino acid? The nature of this problem called for an experimental approach that would utilize a cell-free system. If all the ingredients necessary for protein synthesis were mixed together in a test tube, and a molecule of DNA were added, a polypeptide chain could be formed. If one knew the nucleotide composition of the DNA and could determine the amino acid composition of the polypeptide, then the details of the code could be inferred. The experiments by which the problem was actually studied utilized this idea, but with several important differences. By using preformed RNA as the coded message bearer, the whole process of m-RNA synthesis from DNA could be bypassed. The direct use of RNA had the additional advantage that synthetic RNA of known nucleotide composition could be used. It was M. Nirenberg and J. Matthaei who were first able to obtain a cell-free system capable of forming a polypeptide chain according to the directions encoded in a synthetic RNA. Their system included ribosomes from *Escherichia coli,* all the amino acids, activating enzymes, and t-RNA's, and ATP. When they added an RNA molecule, a polypeptide was formed. The first RNA molecule they used was composed entirely of uridylic acid residues. The polypeptide synthesized according to the information encoded in this molecule consisted entirely of residues of the amino acid phenylalanine. Thus, if it takes a triplet of nucleotides to specify a single amino acid, then U-U-U must be the "code word," or *codon*, for phenylalanine. Next, other synthetic RNA molecules were used, both by Nirenberg and his collaborators and by Ochoa and co-workers, to direct polypeptide synthesis in the cell-free system. However, since only the composition, and not the sequence, of these RNA molecules was known, codon assignments were made on the basis of statistical methods. Because there was an absolute requirement that all the synthetic RNA molecules contain uridylic acid, codons which do not contain U could not be assigned. Furthermore, experiments of this type can reveal only the nucleotide *composition* of the codons, and not the sequence. For instance, if we learn that G-U-U is a codon for valine, we do not know whether the actual codon for valine is G-U-U, U-G-U, or U-U-G. Recently, Nirenberg and his collaborators have devised a method for determining the nucleotide sequence in codons, utilizing synthetic trinucleotides of known sequence to direct the binding of specific amino acids to ribosomes in a cell-free system. The most elegant solution to the problem of codon assignments has been accomplished by Khorana and co-workers. They synthesized DNA molecules of known nucleotide sequence, used these molecules as templates for the synthesis of complementary RNA molecules, and then used the RNA (of known nucleotide sequence) to direct the incorporation of amino acids into polypeptides in a cell-free system. The different biochemical techniques applied to this problem by several groups of investigators have given results which agree excellently. Thus, the genetic code has been cracked successfully. The codon assignments for the various amino acids are shown in Table 11.1. The data in the table are taken from the independent work of Nirenberg, Ochoa, and Khorana and their collaborators; each group of biochemists utilized different experimental procedures.

The data in Table 11.1 demonstrate that the genetic code is *de-*

generate—that is, there are more than one triplet of nucleotides that constitute code words for any given amino acid. Thus, degeneracy helps to account for most of the sixty-four possible nucleotide triplets alluded to above. The value of degeneracy of the code in biological systems, however, remains a mystery, although some interesting guesses have been made. It is possible, for instance, that it serves as a means for regulating protein biosynthesis, or for minimizing the possibility that mutations may be lethal. Furthermore, it is obviously of protective value that single base

Table 11.1

ASSIGNMENT OF THE CODONS OF m-RNA TO SPECIFIC AMINO ACIDS

First[a]	Second				Third
	U	C	A	G	
U	Phe	Ser	Tyr	Cys	U
	Phe	Ser	Tyr	Cys	C
		Ser	Ochre		A
	Leu[b]	Ser	Amber	Try	G
C	Leu	Pro	His	Arg	U
	Leu	Pro	His	Arg	C
	Leu	Pro	Gln	Arg	A
	Leu	Pro	Gln	Arg	G
A	Ileu	Thr	Asn	Ser	U
	Ileu	Thr	Asn	Ser	C
	Ileu	Thr	Lys	Arg	A
	Met[b]	Thr	Lys	Arg	G
G	Val	Ala	Asp	Gly	U
	Val	Ala	Asp	Gly	C
	Val	Ala	Glu	Gly	A
	Val	Ala	Glu	Gly	G

[a] The first column represents the base at the 5′-hydroxyl terminus of the codon (usually written on the left), the four center columns represent the center nucleotide of the codon, and the last column represents the base at the 3′-hydroxyl terminus of the codon (usually written on the right). Thus, the codons A-A-A and A-A-G specify the amino acid lysine.

[b] The codons U-U-G and A-U-G, when present at the 5′-hydroxyl terminus of a polynucleotide, specify N-formylmethionine.

changes (such as occur in many types of mutation) often give rise to a new codon assignment involving a *chemically related* amino acid. Thus, the mutation is likely to cause the insertion of a related amino acid into the protein being synthesized, and the chance of a large change occurring in the overall chemical character of the protein is minimized. The codons U-A-G and U-A-A are designated in Table 11.1 as specifications for Amber and Ochre, respectively. These codons do not specify amino acids at all, but instead specify "end chain." Thus, during translation of a molecule of m-RNA, from one end toward the other, the growing polypeptide chain is terminated at any point where the translation apparatus reaches one of these codons. Since some m-RNA molecules are known to contain information for the synthesis of more than one protein, it is apparent that punctuation marks must occur in the nucleic acid language which serve to render a proper translation into the language of proteins. There must be some mechanism for recognizing where, along the m-RNA molecule, the specifications for each protein start and where they end. It appears that Amber and Ochre codons serve as signals for "end here," but the question as to whether either one serves this function naturally has not yet been settled, since neither has yet been identified in a natural m-RNA molecule. The codon for "start here" has not yet been identified with certainty, but very recent experiments indicate that U-U-G and A-U-G are likely possibilities.

By utilizing the cell-free system of Nirenberg it has also been possible to show that the genetic code is universal—that is, a given triplet of nucleotides codes for the same amino acid in all types of cells. Zinder and his collaborators at the Rockefeller University have shown, for instance, that when RNA from a certain virus was added to the cell-free system, a protein was synthesized which was shown to be identical with the coat protein of that virus. Thus, the code inherent in the viral RNA was recognized and translated correctly by a cell-free system derived either from *E. coli* or from *E. gracilis* (the latter organism not being a natural host for the virus). Several other experiments showing a similar cross-recognition between different species provide ample evidence that the genetic code is universal.

ASSUMPTION OF THREE-DIMENSIONAL CONFORMATION

The newly completed, linear polypeptide chain is still not a native protein. It has a relatively simple, two-dimensional structure, whereas a native protein has a highly complex structure, organized in three dimensions. Up to this point in our discussion of protein biosynthesis we have dealt with essentially linear macromolecules— the DNA of the gene, the m-RNA, and the polypeptide chain. Linear structures are ideally suited for the storage, transcription, and translation of linear information. By contrast, proteins function in an entirely different way, three-dimensional conformation being a most important structural feature (cf. Fig. 11.12). The next step in the process of protein biosynthesis must, therefore, involve

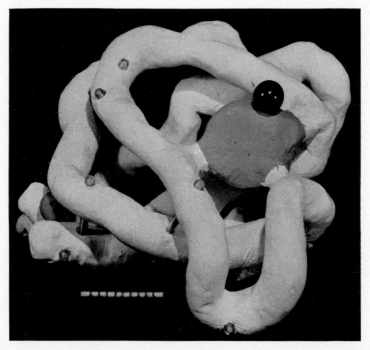

Fig. 11.12. A three-dimensional model of the myoglobin molecule, constructed from X-ray crystallographic data at 6Å resolution. The heme group is represented by the flat disc. Photograph supplied by Dr. J. C. Kendrew.

the folding of the polypeptide chain into the form characteristic of the completed protein molecule.

The three-dimensional protein molecule is held together not only by its covalent bonds (peptide bonds between adjacent amino acids and disulfide bonds between pairs of cysteine residues), but it is also stabilized by many other intramolecular and interatomic forces such as hydrophobic, electrostatic, and hydrogen bonds. Most of the nonpolar amino acid side chains project into the interior of the molecule, whereas most of the polar side chains project out-

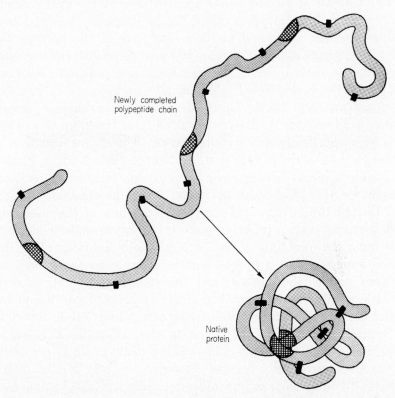

Newly completed
polypeptide chain

Native
protein

Fig. 11.13. A newly completed polypeptide chain must fold up in a specific way in order to bring certain amino acid residues together to form the active site of the native protein. In this drawing, the amino acid residues participating in the active site are indicated by the cross-hatched areas. The sulfhydryl groups of cysteine residues are depicted as solid squares. Disulfide bonds formed between pairs of such groups are depicted as solid rectangles.

ward into the aqueous medium. The native protein, in contrast to the simple polypeptide chain, has only a single unique conformation, which can be defined by various physiocochemical and crystallographic criteria. A three-dimensional model of the myoglobin molecule, the structure of which was worked out by John Kendrew and his colleagues from data obtained by X-ray crystallography, is shown as an example in Figure 11.12. The polypeptide chain of native myoglobin is never folded in any way under physiological conditions other than the one shown.

The active site of an enzyme may involve amino acid residues from several different segments of the polypeptide chain. If these residues, widely separated in the linear form of the polypeptide, are to participate *as a unit* in the active site, the native enzyme must be folded in such a way as to bring them into proximity with one another. This is illustrated schematically in Fig. 11.13 (p. 295). Bovine pancreatic ribonuclease, for example, an enzyme protein which catalyzes the hydrolysis of RNA, can function only when it is in a specific (*native*) conformation. The native structure of ribonuclease is stabilized, in part, by four disulfide bridges, formed by covalent bonds between pairs of cysteine residues. It is quite simple for the biochemist to break apart the disulfide bridges and disrupt the tertiary and secondary structure of this molecule, and, by using certain tricks, to make it fold again under conditions that favor the formation of the "wrong" disulfide bridges. The distorted molecule that is formed has the same amino acid sequence as does native ribonuclease, and the same *number* of disulfide bridges, yet its three-dimensional structure differs from that of the native enzyme. When tested for enzymic activity, it is found to be entirely inactive. As indicated in the schematic drawing of Figure 11.14 an incorrectly folded polypeptide chain is not likely to function enzymically because its active site may not be intact.

How, then, is the newly synthesized polypeptide chain, which cannot be properly folded during the period of its formation, finally converted into the highly specific conformation of the native protein it is destined to become? When biochemists first considered this question, two possibilities were entertained. The first was that, in addition to the m-RNA template on which the amino acids are assembled, another genetically determined template might be employed for the molding of the chain into the native conformation. This possibility seemed unlikely, because it would require some sort of supertemplate with three-dimensional characteristics not in keeping with our knowledge of the linear structure of the genetic material. The second possibility, termed the *thermodynamic hypothesis,* was that the native conformation is the form in which the chain is most stable under physiological conditions. If the three-dimensional structure of a native protein is determined solely by thermodynamic considerations—that is, if it is the most stable arrangement of the polypeptide chain—then under the appropriate

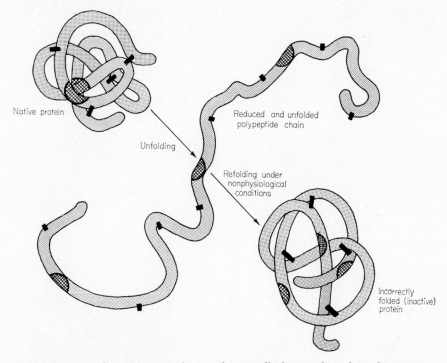

Fig. 11.14. In the experiment shown schematically here, a hypothetical protein is unfolded, and its disulfide bonds are cleaved *in vitro*. It is then allowed to refold and its disulfide bonds are allowed to reform under distinctly nonphysiological conditions designed to yield an incorrectly folded molecule. Due to the incorrect folding, the amino acid residues of the active site (cross-hatched areas) are not brought together; therefore, the molecule is functionally inactive.

conditions the transition from linear polypeptide to three-dimensional protein should be a spontaneous process, driven by the difference in free energy of conformation between the extended and the folded forms. According to this hypothesis, if a protein were artificially opened into an extended polypeptide chain, it should fold spontaneously into the native conformation. This point was put to the test by Christian B. Anfinsen and his colleagues, who used the enzyme bovine pancreatic ribonuclease as the model protein. They found that after the disulfide bridges of this molecule had been broken, and the tertiary structure had been disrupted, the opened polypeptide chain did, under appropriate conditions, return spontaneously to the native form of the enzyme. This phenomenon is illustrated schematically in Figure 11.15. The correct disulfide bridges were formed, and all other characteristics of the

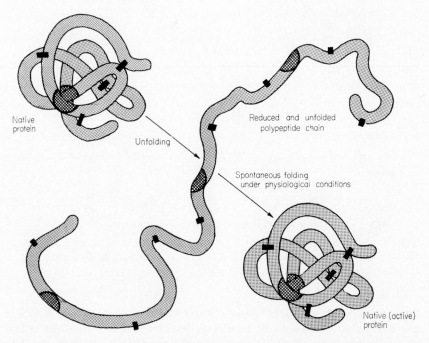

Fig. 11.15. The experiment of Anfinsen, represented here, shows that the native form of a protein is the one form spontaneously assumed by the extended polypeptide chain under physiological conditions.

native tertiary structure were again assumed by the molecule. The final product had the full enzymic activity enjoyed by the protein at the beginning of the experiment. A similar test of a number of other proteins has led to the same finding; the native conformations tended to reform spontaneously after the proteins had been opened into linear polypeptide chains. Thus, it appears that the thermodynamic hypothesis is correct. Genetic direction is required only for determining the sequence of amino acids in a polypeptide chain. Once the sequence is fixed, the chain automatically folds into its most stable arrangement, the arrangement that corresponds to the native conformation of the protein molecule.

Although the spontaneous folding of a polypeptide chain can easily be demonstrated by experiments such as the one described above with ribonuclease, the process *in vitro* is relatively slow. Investigations of the rate of protein synthesis *in vivo,* however, indicate that the folding process is a very fast one. It therefore seemed reasonable to expect that there is an enzyme whose function is to catalyze the process as it actually occurs in the cell. Such an enzyme was readily found; it has now been isolated from the endoplasmic reticulum of cells, and purified. In the presence of this enzyme, the open-chain form of ribonuclease, for example, is converted into the native form of the protein very quickly *in vitro*— at a rate consistent with the rate of protein synthesis *in vivo.* The enzyme does not contribute any information concerning three-dimensional conformation, a conclusion that is obvious from the finding that the same enzyme catalyzes the proper folding of the polypeptide chains of a large number of different proteins. It simply catalyzes disulfide interchange, and thereby allows the pairings of cysteine residues in the polypeptide chain quickly to reshuffle until the most stable pairings are attained. The folding reaction is driven by the energy made available when a polypeptide chain which has a relatively unstable conformation is converted into the native protein (which has the most stable conformation possible). The enzyme merely increases the speed of this reaction. It is interesting that this enzyme is located only in the endoplasmic reticulum— the membranous system that contains the machinery for the assembly of polypeptide chains. Thus, the protein-synthesizing system appears to be well organized for carrying out the entire process of converting amino acids into native proteins.

SYNTHESIS OF ORGANIZED PROTEIN SYSTEMS

By virtue of the extraordinary success of investigations on the mechanism of protein synthesis, a fairly good picture of this process has been developed in the last few years. Although many details are still lacking, the broad outlines of the picture are quite clear. The available information about the mechanism of protein synthesis is, however, limited to the synthesis of individual protein molecules. The problem of how organized protein structures are synthesized by cells is only now coming under investigation by biochemists. No solutions to this problem are yet in sight, but several relevant questions can be posed with some clarity. We shall briefly discuss these, and describe some of the possible ways that they may be approached experimentally. We shall use, as an example of an organized protein structure, an organelle—specifically, the mitochondrion—because it is the system for which most information at the molecular level is available. The problem, then, is how a mitochondrion is synthesized—how the synthesis of its many parts is carried out so that all the required components are present in a specific stoichiometry, aligned in their appropriate positions in the membranous structure of the finished product.

As described in Chapter 10, the mitochondrion is composed of protein and lipid, arranged in the form of two membranes—an inner and an outer membrane. The two membranes appear first to be assembled individually in a linear form and then to be fused together to form a single organelle with no open ends. The inner membrane contains more than twenty-five different species of protein in the electron-transfer chain alone, and probably an equal number is concerned with various aspects of the coupling process. At least twelve different oxidation-reduction groups are present in the electron-transfer chain, each attached to a particular protein in a distinctive, stoichiometric manner.

Associated with the protein molecules of the inner membrane is a special blend of lipids, with a specific set of phospholipids, each with a characteristic degree of unsaturation in its fatty acid residues. In addition to phospholipids, a group of neutral, small lipid molecules—including coenzyme Q, vitamin E, carotenoids, and cholesterol—are present in smaller amounts, but in constant proportions.

Thus, for the inner membrane alone, approximately fifty different species of protein have to be synthesized, linked to their appropriate functional groups, linked to various lipids, and assembled into a set of repeating units; these subunits must then be assembled into a membranous structure. There are four different kinds of repeating units—each apparently identical in size and shape, but different in composition and function. Each repeating unit contains the components of one of the four complexes of the electron-transfer chain, as well as the proteins concerned with the coupling process. The outer membrane of the mitochondrion is an equally complex structure (see Chapter 10 for a more detailed discussion of membrane systems).

Together with this picture of the complexity with which the parts of the mitochondrion are arranged, we must consider three other factors involved in mitochondrial synthesis. (1) Almost all of the mitochondrial proteins tend to polymerize when isolated in pure form. In the case of the structural protein this tendency is utilized by the cell, but in the case of such proteins as the electron carriers, polymerization is attended by loss of function, and must therefore be avoided *in vivo*. (2) Many of the protein components of the mitochondrion tend to combine with lipid. Such combination must not occur during mitochondrial synthesis if the hydrophobic binding sites of the proteins are to remain available for interaction at the specific sites at which they are destined to lie in the finished organelle. (3) Each prosthetic group must be attached to its proper protein so that it will be brought into proper alignment with all other functional groups when the parts of the mitochondrion are fitted together. While the three factors listed above are, to some degree, valid with respect to the synthesis of many individual proteins not associated with organized systems, they become far more troublesome when considered within the context of the logistic problems posed by the mitochondrion.

Because of the fantastic complexity of design and because of the

special problems ennumerated above, it seems reasonable to speculate that some degree of organization is built into the very mechanism by which mitochondrial synthesis is carried out. The ideas
that several hundred different building blocks—proteins, lipids, and
coenzymes—are all synthesized in a random fashion, and that all
these components must find each other by chance, are not in
keeping with the precision of mitochondrial synthesis or with the
stoichiometry found for the components of the mitochondrion. If
one is to discover a system for the synthesis of organized proteins,
designed to fabricate organized complexes, mitochondrial synthesis
surely presents a problem to be investigated.

Robert Lester and Anthony Linnane are two among a number of
biochemists who have, in recent years, turned their attention to
the problem of mitochondrial synthesis in yeast. When yeast cells
are grown anaerobically, no mitochondria are formed, but when
they are transferred into an aerobic medium containing the proper
substrates, mitochondrial synthesis begins immediately. Thus, when
yeast is transferred from one medium into the other, the synthesis
of mitochondria is initiated *de novo*, and the process may be studied
from the very beginning. The earliest anabolic activity appears to
be the synthesis of cardiolipin. Electron micrographs at this stage
reveal deposition of lipid micelles, or lipid-protein micelles, in con-
centric rings within the cytoplasm near the nucleus. It is only
after the burst of lipid biosynthesis that synthesis of cytochromes
is initiated. Then there ensues the appearance of structured elements, a process which continues until the adult mitochondrial
form is attained.

Isolation of the structured units in which mitochondrial assembly
is proceeding has disclosed the presence of DNA in relatively large
amounts, with a base composition distinctly different from that of
nuclear DNA. Active protein synthesis is demonstrable in these
premitochondrial particles, and when protein synthesis is arrested
by inhibitors, such as actinomycin D, the development of mitochondria comes to a halt at the stage that existed when the inhibitor
was added. This finding of active protein synthesis within the developing mitochondrion is very recent and requires verification.
Such an idea was considered in the past, partly because of the

demonstration that adult mitochondria contain a small amount of DNA. However, the amount of DNA in adult mitochondria is indeed miniscule, and the minimal protein synthesis reported to occur in mitochondrial preparations could be due to bacterial contamination. If, however, active protein synthesis does occur in mitochondria during their development, it is tempting to suggest that, in a sense, mitochondria synthesize themselves. That is to say, although all the information for the structure of every part of the mitochondrion must be encoded in the DNA of the nucleus of a yeast cell, it would be *extranuclear* DNA that actually directs the synthesis of those parts. According to this idea, the information encoded in the chromosomal DNA is not transcribed directly into m-RNA, but is first duplicated in another molecule of DNA. This copy of part of the chromosomal DNA would then leave the nucleus and direct the synthesis of mitochondrial structures, presumably via m-RNA. One of the advantages of such an arrangement could be in localizing the production of mitochondrial components and thereby increasing their effective concentrations. Furthermore, as suggested by the finding of cardiolipin synthesis as the first identifiable step in the synthesis of mitochondria, the synthesis of the various parts of the mitochondrion may be carried out in a temporal sequence that corresponds with the positional sequence of those parts in the finished organelle. Upon such an organized biosynthetic system numerous other degrees of organization could be imposed, but at the present time it is too early to speculate further. The foregoing discussion is not intended as a definitive statement on the synthesis of organized protein systems, but merely as a tentative probe of the kinds of phenomena that will have to be dealt with in considering this problem. There is no doubt that the highly ordered structure of an organelle, such as the mitochondrion, requires something more for its formation than does the system for the synthesis of individual proteins discussed previously in this chapter. It is not necessarily correct to invoke the mechanism by which one protein is synthesized in order to come up with an answer to the question of how a hundred proteins are synthesized. If the hundred proteins are part of a complex and specific structure, then one must strive to understand the forces involved in achieving that complexity and specificity. Biochemistry has now, for the first time, reached the stage at which it is feasible to investigate the question of organized protein synthesis. It is safe to predict that the answers to come will be among the most exciting developments of biochemistry in the next decade.

Suggested Reading

Books

Hartman, P. E., and Suskind, S. R., "Gene Action," Prentice-Hall, Englewood Cliffs, New Jersey, 1964.

Ingram, V. M., "The Biosynthesis of Macromolecules," W. A. Benjamin Inc., New York, 1965.

Jacob, F., and Wollman, E. L., "Sexuality and the Genetics of Bacteria," Academic Press, New York, 1961.

Levine, R. P., "Genetics." Modern Biology Series, Holt, Rinehart and Winston, New York, 1962.

"Papers on Bacterial Genetics," Adelberg, E. A., ed., Little, Brown, Boston, Massachusetts, 1960.

Perutz, M. F., "Proteins and Nucleic Acids: Structure and Function," Elsevier Publishing Co., Amsterdam, 1962.

Stahl, F. W., "The Mechanics of Inheritance," Prentice-Hall, Englewood Cliffs, New Jersey, 1964.

"Synthesis and Structure of Macromolecules," *Cold Spring Harbor Symp. Quant. Biol.* **28**, 1963.

Watson, J. D., "Molecular Biology of the Gene," W. A. Benjamin, Inc., New York, 1965.

Special Articles

Anfinsen, C. B., *Harvey Lectures Ser.* **61** (1965–1966). In press: on the conversion of polypeptide chains to native proteins.

Avery, O. T., MacLoed, C. M., and McCarty, M., *J. Exptl. Med.* **79**, 137 (1944): on the chemical nature of the substance inducing bacterial transformation.

Crick, F. H. C., *Sci. Am.* **207**, 66 (1962): on the genetic code.

Goldberger, R. F., and Epstein, C. J., *J. Biol. Chem.* **238**, 2988 (1963): on the identity of native and reoxidized proteins.

Goldberger, R. F., Epstein, C. J., and Anfinsen, C. B., *J. Biol. Chem.* **239**, 1406 (1964): on an enzyme which catalyzes the refolding of reduced proteins.

Jacob, F., and Monod, J., *J. Mol. Biol.* **3**, 318 (1961): on the role of messenger-RNA in protein biosynthesis.

Kornberg, A., *Science* **131**, 1503 (1960): on the enzymic synthesis of DNA.

Leder, P., and Nirenberg, M. W., *Proc. Natl. Acad. Sci. U.S.* **52**, 420 (1964): on the genetic code.

Linnane, A. W., *in* "Oxidases and Related Redox Systems" (T. E. King, H. S. Mason, and M. Morrison, eds.), Vol. 2, p. 1102, John Wiley and Sons, New York, 1965: on the biosynthesis of mitochondria by *S. cerevisiae*.

Luck, D. J. L., *in* "Organizational Biosynthesis" (H. J. Vogel, J. O. Lampen, and V. Bryson, eds.), Academic Press, New York, 1967, in press: on the formation of mitochondria in *Neurospora crassa*.

Mazia, D., *Sci. Am.* **205**, 101 (1961): on cell division.

Muller, H. J., *Proc. Roy. Soc.* **B134**, 1 (1947): on the gene.

Nirenberg, M. W., and Matthei, J. H., *Proc. Natl. Acad. Sci. U.S.* **47**, 1588 (1961): on protein synthesis induced by synthetic polynucleotides in a cell-free system.

Nirenberg, M. W., *Sci. Am.* **208**, 80 (1963): on cracking the genetic code.

Rich, A., *Sci. Am.* **209**, 44 (1963): on polysomes.

Singer, M. F., and Leder, P., *Ann. Rev. Biochem.* **35**, 987 (1966): on messenger-RNA.

Speyer, J. F., Lengyel, P., Basilio, C., Wahba, A. J., Gardner, R. S., and Ochoa, S., *Cold Spring Harbor Symp. Quant. Biol.* **28**, 559 (1963): on the genetic code.

Spiegelman, S. S., *Sci. Am.* **210**, 48 (1964): on hybrid nucleic acids.

Watson, J. D., and Crick, F. H. C., *Nature* **171**, 737 (1953): on the molecular structure of nucleic acids.

Watson, J. D., and Crick, F. H. C., *Nature* **171**, 964 (1953): on the genetic implications of the structure of DNA.

Yanofsky, C., *in* "The Bacteria" (I. C. Gunsalus and R. Y. Stanier, eds.), Vol. 5, p. 373, Academic Press, New York, 1964: on gene-enzyme relationships.

CHAPTER 12 ────────────────────

Control Mechanisms for Regulation of Living Systems

One of the striking characteristics of living systems is that they function in an orderly manner despite their high degree of complexity. In this chapter we shall discuss a number of the principles involved in the control and regulation of life processes in individual living organisms. Some regulatory mechanisms operate within the confines of a single cell, whereas others involve interactions between widely separated cells.

It is important to realize that organization and regulation were not superimposed upon living systems; they are inherent biochemical characteristics. Nature does not "use" regulatory mechanisms to impose order on biochemical processes. Orderly processes are simply more successful than disorderly ones, and therefore tend to be preserved through the evolutionary process by conferring advantages upon organisms. The tests of natural selection are not tests for clever or imaginative solutions, but tests for the ones that work, or work better than others, in solving the problems of survival.

Traffic Control

Within the cell hundreds of different chemical reactions go on simultaneously. Most are catalyzed by specific enzymes, each requiring a different substrate and producing a different product. Add to these cellular components the thousands of other molecules, such as inorganic salts, cofactors, enzyme activators, and enzyme inhibitors, and one has the makings of a colossal traffic jam. In fact, however, a traffic jam does not occur. The vast numbers of

306

cellular materials travel about and interact in a fairly orderly manner. It is not possible to describe in detail all the control systems that help to solve the problems of molecular traffic within the cell, but we shall discuss some of the more important ones, with special emphasis on principles of molecular interaction.

The high degree of selectivity of the *cell membrane* is one of the key determinants of orderly molecular traffic within the cell. In general, only those molecules and ions that participate in the normal metabolic reactions of the cell, can penetrate readily, whereas most other molecules either fail to penetrate or penetrate slowly.

Once inside the cell, the molecules move within the fluid of the cytoplasm by random motion. The cytoplasm is not a vast ocean in which the dissolved molecules are free to move endlessly in any direction. Inside cells of many types, an extensive system of membranes, such as the *endoplasmic reticulum,* divides the cytoplasm into channels. The flow of cytoplasm within each channel may be in one direction—toward the center of the cell in some channels and toward the periphery in others. The dissolved molecules are swept along in the flowing cytoplasm guided in these channels; entering metabolites may be carried toward the center of the cell, and waste products away toward the periphery. Thus, both random and directed movements of molecules are operative within the interior of the cell.

Within the cell are numerous *organelles,* such as the mitochondrion, the ribosome, and the nucleus, each of which carries out specialized activities. The organelles are enclosed by membranes which restrict the entry of solute molecules into their interiors. Compartmentalization of cells, through the device of organelles, imposes an additional degree of order upon the molecular population of the cell. It also provides discrete localized environments in which there exist very high concentrations of specialized macromolecules appropriate to the specialized functions of the organelles.

Another factor that helps to organize the huge number of molecules within the cell is the existence of *immiscible phases* at the molecular level. In the cell there are lipid areas, into which only nonpolar compounds can penetrate, and aqueous areas, from which nonpolar compounds are excluded. On the basis of the solubilities of the various molecules, the molecular traffic is thus directed along two separate lanes—one for the lipid-soluble molecules, the other for the water-soluble molecules.

Sets of functionally related protein molecules are sometimes joined together in what are known as *organized enzyme systems.* The components of an organized enzyme system are not merely confined within the same limited area; they are actually part of a single, physically and chemically integrated, unit which performs a single, although complex, function. The principles of molecular interaction with and within such a unit differ from those governing the interaction between individual molecules in solution. Since the discrete enzymes collectively forming a functional unit are physically attached to one another, they cannot move about independently. Therefore, collisions between these enzymes and their substrates cannot be entirely random. The advantages of such systems may be clarified by examining a hypothetical example—a metabolic pathway beginning with a metabolite (A) and proceeding through the mediation of various enzymes $(a, b, c,$ and $d)$ to a product (E).

$$A \xrightarrow{\text{enzyme } a} B \xrightarrow{\text{enzyme } b} C \xrightarrow{\text{enzyme } c} D \xrightarrow{\text{enzyme } d} E$$

If all of these enzymic components were separate, a molecule of substrate A would have to collide with a molecule of enzyme a in order to be transformed into B; B would have to collide with enzyme b in order to be transformed into C, and so on—four completely random collisions being required for the conversion of one molecule of A into one of E. If, on the other hand, enzymes $a, b, c,$ and d were all bound together in a single structural unit, only one collision would be necessary—that between substrate A and the enzyme unit. Naturally, the intermediates $B, C,$ and D would still have to be formed, and contact would have to be made between them and the appropriate enzymes, but the mechanism would be far less haphazard than that of chance collisions. Indeed, in some organized enzyme systems there seems to be a device for transferring intermediates from one enzyme to the next, like water in a bucket brigade, so that contact need be made only once—when the primary substrate and the integrated enzyme unit collide—and broken only once—when the final product is ejected from the unit.

Many enzymes are organized into multimolecular units; the number known continues to grow as biochemical research progresses. A few of them, such as the mitochondrial electron transfer system, have been studied in some detail (see Chapters 9 and 10).

Control of Reactions by Chemical Equilibria

The vast majority of biochemical reactions are reversible. They are written with double arrows to indicate their reversibility:

$$\text{Substrate (X)} \rightleftharpoons \text{Product (Y)}$$

The equilibrium of the reaction is defined by the ratio [Y] : [X],* which obtains at the point at which the reaction appears to come to a halt—that is, when the rates of the opposing reactions are equal. A reaction tends to proceed in the direction that will result in establishing the ratio, [Y] : [X], that is defined by the thermodynamic equilibrium for that reaction. When this ratio is attained, the reaction is said to have "reached equilibrium," and no further net change will occur spontaneously. The equilibrium point will determine whether there will be a net conversion of X to Y or of Y to X. The equilibrium point inexorably compels the direction of a reversible chemical process unless the equilibrium is displaced by other conditions or by an interposing system that can react with X or Y.

By and large, throughout the evolutionary process the pathways of metabolism which have persisted are those in which the equilibria are favorable to the reactions required by the organism; that is, most reactions in living organisms reach equilibrium only when a relatively large ratio, [product] : [substrate], has been attained. However, a number of cases of unfavorable equilibria have managed to persist. We shall examine one such case to illustrate how this type of reaction may serve the living system despite the thermodynamic difficulty. When the reaction shown in Eq. (1) is carried out *in vitro* with the appropriate enzyme,

$$\text{Malate} + \text{DPN}^+ \rightleftharpoons \text{oxaloacetate} + \text{DPNH} + \text{H}^+ \qquad (1)$$

* The brackets denote the molar concentrations of the reactants.

equilibrium is reached when the value of the following ratio is extremely small:

$$\frac{[\text{oxaloacetate}]\ [\text{DPNH}]\ [\text{H}^+]}{[\text{malate}]\ [\text{DPN}^+]}$$

Thus, malate will not be converted spontaneously into oxaloacetate unless there is an extremely large concentration of malate relative to that of oxaloacetate. How, then, can this reaction serve a living organism which depends upon the production of oxaloacetate from malate? The dilemma is solved by the fact that oxaloacetate enters into a subsequent reaction that is irreversible, as shown in Eq. (2).

$$\text{Oxaloacetate} + \text{acetyl-CoA} \rightarrow \text{citrate} + \text{CoA} \qquad (2)$$

The net effect of this irreversible removal of oxaloacetate by formation of citrate is to decrease the value of the [product] : [substrate] ratio, and thus to pull the reaction

$$\text{Malate} \rightleftharpoons \text{oxaloacetate}$$

to the right despite the unfavorable equilibrium.

Control by Reaction Rates

The equilibrium of a chemical reaction defines only the *direction* in which the reaction tends to go, and the relative *proportions* of substrate and product at equilibrium. It has no bearing on the *rate* or the *mechanism* of the reaction. There are, however, a number of ways by which the rate of a reaction provides control over a biochemical process. This is illustrated below in the discussion of rate-limiting steps in a reaction sequence, and of changes in steady state attending changes in substrate concentration.

RATE-LIMITING STEPS

Enzymic processes are usually rapid. The great speed of reactions catalyzed by enzymes is of obvious advantage to the living organism. To ensure the smooth operation of certain biochemical processes, however, some restraints on the rates of reactions are required. For example, if the degradation of glucose to carbon dioxide and water proceeded at the rate of the fastest step in the reaction series, the organism in which this might occur would use up all its glucose very rapidly and soon would die, unless it could obtain large quantities of glucose quickly from its environment. Insurance against such a situation is provided by a rate-limiting step in this metabolic pathway for glucose utilization. No matter how fast other steps in the pathway may be capable of proceeding, the whole integrated process cannot go faster than the slowest step. Rate-limiting reactions prevent the great swings of overproduction and underproduction that could occur if all reactions proceeded at maximal speeds.

THE STEADY STATE

In the reaction

$$\text{Substrate} \rightleftharpoons \text{product}$$

the steady state is defined as the condition in which the substrate is supplied to the reaction precisely as fast as it is used up in the reaction. If the rate of the reaction is influenced by the concentration of substrate present, then an increase in the substrate concentration will cause a rise in the rate of the reaction. The reaction will speed up in response to the increased concentration of substrate until a new steady state is reached in which the new (faster) rate of the reaction is in keeping with the new (higher) substrate concentration. Thus, the response to an increased concentration of substrate is an increase in the rate of substrate utilization, and therefore a diminution in the effect of substrate on the rate of the reaction. Finally, a balance is reached, and the new steady state represents a compromise. In living systems this relation between substrate concentration and reaction rate provides a mechanism for minimizing the effects of changes in the environment.

Autocatalysis

Autocatalysis is a process in which the product of a chemical reaction catalyzes the reaction—that is, catalyzes its own formation. When such a reaction begins, there is a great deal of substrate but little product present. Since the product molecule is required as a catalyst, the reaction begins slowly. As it progresses, however, more molecules of the product-catalyst are formed, and the reaction speeds up correspondingly. Thus, autocatalytic reactions tend to proceed at ever increasing rates, rather like the explosion of gunpowder triggered by the detonation of a charge. It is the depletion of substrate which finally slows down such reactions and brings them to a halt. The advantage of the acceleration in rate is that it provides a means for the rapid production of some essential material that is required by the organism *only occasionally*. The hallmark of autocatalytic reactions is that they function periodically. They are triggered by some momentary need of the organism, such as the need for activating proteolytic enzymes when food enters the digestive tract.

Trypsin is an enzyme which catalyzes the hydrolytic breakdown of proteins into peptides within the intestinal tract. It is secreted by the pancreas in an inactive form known as trypsinogen. Trypsinogen is converted into trypsin by the action of an enzyme which cleaves a hexapeptide fragment from trypsinogen. The enzyme that does this job is none other than trypsin itself. This, then, is an autocatalytic reaction; the product of the reaction catalyzes its own production.

$$\text{Trypsinogen} \xrightarrow{\text{trypsin}} \text{trypsin} + \text{hexapeptide}$$

The question that remains unanswered by the above scheme is: How are the first molecules of trypsin produced, if only trypsinogen is present to begin with? The answer is that the reaction is initiated by another enzyme, enterokinase, secreted by cells in the wall of the intestinal tract. This enzyme works rather slowly, but sufficiently well to spark the conversion of trypsinogen to trypsin. Once a few molecules of trypsin have been formed, the reaction speeds up at an ever increasing rate until all the trypsinogen has been converted into the active enzyme. The secretion of enterokinase is initiated by the entrance of food into the gastrointestinal tract. Thus, digestive enzymes are put to work when their function is required by the organism.

End Product Inhibition

A fairly large number of biosynthetic pathways are now known in which the enzyme catalyzing the first step of the pathway is inhibited by the final product of the pathway. This phenomenon, first elucidated by H. Umbarger, is often described as *negative feedback control.* We shall take, as an example, the pathway by which ATP and phosphoribosyl pyrophosphate (PRPP) are converted into the amino acid, histidine, in *Salmonella typhimurium.* This pathway consists of ten sequential chemical reactions, each of which is catalyzed by a specific enzyme. The enzyme catalyzing the first reaction (shown here):

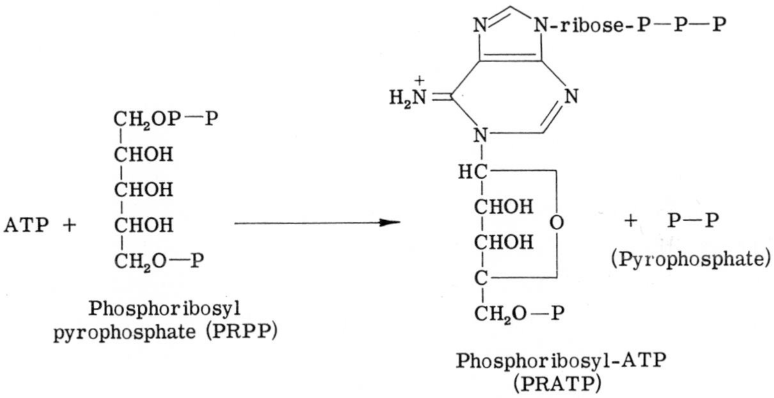

ATP + Phosphoribosyl pyrophosphate (PRPP) ⟶ Phosphoribosyl-ATP (PRATP) + P—P (Pyrophosphate)

is a protein molecule composed of subunits. It is specifically inhibited by histidine, which is the product of the tenth reaction of the pathway. This inhibition is not due to competition between histidine and PRPP for the same site on the enzyme, as one might surmise after examining the vastly different structures of the two small molecules shown here:

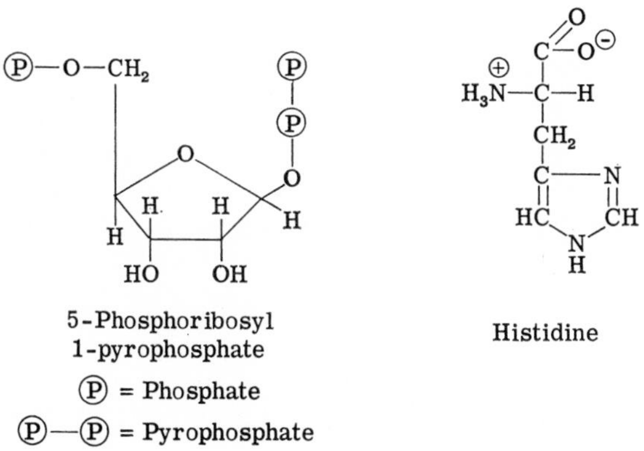

5-Phosphoribosyl 1-pyrophosphate

(P) = Phosphate

(P)—(P) = Pyrophosphate

Histidine

It has, in fact, been shown that there are at least two distinct and specific sites on the enzyme, one (the "active site") which binds PRPP, and another which binds histidine. When the enzyme is exposed to mercuric ions, its active site remains unchanged—that is, it still catalyzes the reaction between ATP and PRPP—but it now is insensitive to inhibition by histidine. When the mercuric ions are removed, sensitivity to histidine is restored. The general phenomenon of inhibition of an enzyme by combination with a small molecule at a site other than the "active site" has been explained in terms of a change in the tertiary or quaternary structure of the enzyme. Combination of histidine with the first enzyme of the pathway in question evidently causes a change in the three-dimensional structure of the enzyme which distorts the active site sufficiently to render it nonfunctional. This is an example of the more general phenomenon known as *allosteric transition*. An allosteric transition is a change in the structure of a functional protein, caused by the selective binding of a small molecule at a site other than the substrate site, which leads to an alteration in function. It appears that such transitions involve only proteins composed of subunits. It may be that the structural change is actually caused by a distortion in the association of the subunits in the protein. (cf. Figure 12.1)

In all cases that have been carefully studied so far, end product inhibition has been found to involve an allosteric interaction between the final product of a metabolic pathway and the first enzyme of that pathway. However, it is quite possible that there may be cases of end product inhibition that involve competitive inhibition (competition between substrate and final product for the *same* site on the enzyme). What of branching metabolic pathways that display end product inhibition? Which end product would be expected to inhibit? There are a few well-documented instances in which *all* the final products are required to act together to cause inhibition.

The value of end product inhibition as a control mechanism in cellular metabolism may be its economic nature. Let us say that a *Salmonella* cell is growing in a medium devoid of histidine. Starting with PRPP and ATP, the cell synthesizes histidine by a series of ten enzymic steps. It goes on producing histidine until the concentration of histidine in the cell is sufficient to inhibit the first enzyme of the pathway. Production of histidine will cease until enough of the cellular histidine is used up (in forming proteins) to allow the first enzyme to function again. In this way, the cell produces histidine only at such a rate as it is required; this avoids both the wastefulness of overproduction and the deprivation of underproduction. The extent to which end product inhibition plays

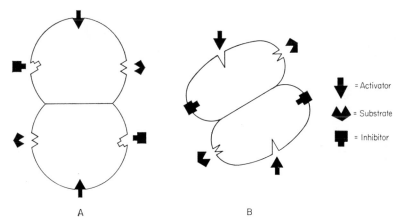

A   B

Fig. 12.1. Schematic representation of an allosteric protein. As shown at the left scheme (A), when the polymeric protein is combined with an activator its conformation is such that its substrate-binding site is capable of binding substrate. As shown at the right (scheme B), when it is combined with an inhibitor its conformation changes so that the substrate-binding site is sterically hindered.

a regulatory role in higher organisms has not been defined as yet, since microorganisms have been used for the vast majority of studies. However, in mammalian cells the phenomenon has been demonstrated, at least in a few pathways, and may well figure prominently in the overall biochemical regulation of such cells.

Control of Protein Biosynthesis

In Chapter 11 we discussed the mechanism of protein biosynthesis. Elegant though the mechanism may be, it is not sufficient for a cell to know *how* to make proteins; it must also know *how much* of each protein to make at any given time. Studies on microorganisms indicate that if the synthesis of any one protein were to proceed unchecked it would be produced at such a great rate that it could comprise more than 5% of the total cell protein. In other words, unrestrained synthesis of any twenty proteins might leave no room for the synthesis of the thousands of other proteins required in living organisms. It is clear, then, that without an extensive and versatile system for controlling protein biosynthesis, cellular chaos would be inevitable. Much of our current knowledge of control of protein biosynthesis comes from the work of Francois Jacob and Jacques Monod and their co-workers at the Pasteur Institute. Almost everything known has been derived from studies of bacteria, and it is not yet clear to what extent the control systems of microorganisms are operative in the cells of higher organisms.

REPRESSION AND INDUCTION

One of the mechanisms for the control of protein synthesis is *repression*. We shall return to our previous example of the pathway for histidine biosynthesis in S. *typhimurium*. We have already noted that histidine, the end product, inhibits the *activity* of the first enzyme of the pathway. We must now add that histidine also inhibits (represses) the *synthesis* of all the enzymes of the pathway. The case of histidine is by no means unique. A large number of metabolites are now known, each of which inhibits synthesis of the enzymes required for its own biosynthesis. It appears that the end product of a biosynthetic pathway does not itself act directly as the repressor. There is some evidence which suggests that the true repressor is the product formed by the attachment of the end product to another molecule, presumably a protein, formed under the direction of a *regulatory gene.**

In Chapter 11 we discussed the role of genes as controlling the

---

* The question as to the chemical composition of repressors is currently under intensive investigation, and even the best answer available at present will undoubtedly have to be modified in the future when more information becomes available. It appears, for example, that histidyl-t-RNA is involved in repression of the enzymes for histidine biosynthesis. However, since the basic principle appears to be quite sound, we shall continue, in the present discussion, with the idea as stated here.

synthesis of proteins by specifying, in coded form, amino acid sequences. We alluded to the fact that genes also have other important functions, and these functions, although related to protein synthesis, are regulatory in nature. There are thus two main types of genes—those which specify the amino acid sequences of cellular proteins (*structural genes*) and those which control the activity of structural genes (*regulator* and *operator genes*). It is quite likely that regulator genes do specify the amino acid sequences of specific proteins, but these proteins are specialized for regulating other genes.

To return to the repressor: this molecule, formed by combination of the protein product of a regulatory gene with a small molecule (such as the end product of a metabolic pathway), exerts its effect on the operator gene, presumably by combining with it. Operator genes are those genes which actually control the activity level of structural genes, and thus control the rate at which the structural genes are used for protein synthesis. When combined with an active repressor molecule, the operator gene is functionally inhibited, and as a result the structural genes it controls cannot be used for the synthesis of protein. Thus, the function of the operator gene is a negative one. When combined with a repressor molecule it inhibits transcription of the structural genes under its control; when not combined with a repressor molecule, or when absent altogether (as in the case of certain mutant organisms), the transcription of the structural genes is not inhibited. There may be an operator gene for each group of one or more structural genes controlling the synthesis of proteins with related functions. All the genes of one such group are known as an *operon*. In the case of the enzymes for histidine biosynthesis in *S. typhimurium,* the operon is unusually large; it contains nine structural genes (one for each of the enzymes). The structural genes of this operon are located one next to the other on the chromosome, and form one continuous segment with a length of approximately thirty thousand nucleotides.

The foregoing discussion is summarized in Figure 12.2. Here we have shown a hypothetical operon containing two structural genes which specify the amino acid sequences of two enzymes of a biosynthetic pathway. The end product of the pathway can combine with the protein produced by a regulatory gene and thus form an active repressor. The repressor interacts with the operator gene, located next to one of the structural genes, and thereby prevents the transcription of m-RNA from the operon. Thus, overproduction of the end product of the metabolic pathway results in activation of the repressor and consequently in a diminution in the synthesis of the enzymes of that pathway.

The advantages of repression of protein synthesis in cellular economy are clear. As mentioned above, this phenomenon serves to keep the functioning of structural genes at a level close to the requirements of the cell under a variety of conditions. For instance, the degree of repression of the histidine operon in *S. typhimurium* is

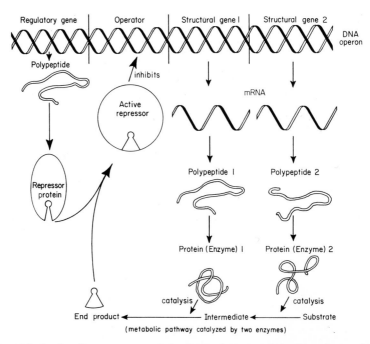

Fig. 12.2. In this drawing some of the basic elements of the hypothesis of Jacob and Monod are embodied. According to this hypothesis, one of the mechanisms for the regulation of protein synthesis involves the action of a repressor, which inhibits the transcription of DNA into m-RNA. As shown here, the repressor appears to be a complex molecule, composed of the product of a regulatory gene and a metabolite (in this case the metabolite is the end product of the metabolic pathway catalyzed by the enzymes made under the direction of the structural genes that are to be repressed).

determined by the needs of the organism, the rate of production of the enzymes for histidine biosynthesis being sufficient to ensure the manufacture of only the required amount of histidine. Much of our knowledge of control in the histidine system comes from the studies of Ames and Hartman and their associates; these studies have served as the basis for a number of important correlations between biochemistry and genetics. When histidine is available in the external medium, the operon is repressed, only small quantities of the enzymes are produced, and the organism uses the histidine from the medium preferentially. When little or no histidine is available in the external medium, the operon immediately becomes derepressed, the cell elaborates large quantities of the enzymes for histidine biosynthesis, and the production of histidine rises to a level sufficient to meet the needs of the organism. Even more dramatic derepression of the histidine operon is seen under certain conditions in which something has gone wrong with the metabolic pathway for histidine biosynthesis which prevents the manufacture of sufficient histidine. Under such conditions, the enzymes for histidine biosynthesis may be produced in sufficient quantity to comprise 10% of the protein of the cell.

Thus, because of repression, the cellular machinery for protein biosynthesis is ordinarily left free for the production of the thousands of proteins required by the cell. Only when an emergency arises, such as the histidine shortage mentioned above, is a larger part of that machinery preempted for the synthesis of one, or a few, specific proteins. In keeping with this economic principle, enzymes subject to repression are generally anabolic enzymes.

Another important phenomenon in the control of protein biosynthesis is *induction.* Just as the end product of a biosynthetic pathway may combine with a special protein molecule and act as a *repressor* (by "turning off" a structural gene), so also a substrate for a given enzyme may, under certain conditions, combine with another such protein molecule and act as an *inducer* (by "turning on" a structural gene). The gene "turned on" in the latter case would be the one controlling the synthesis of the enzyme for which the substrate is an integral part of the inducer.

By virtue of its inducible enzymes, a cell is able to adapt itself to a changing environment. For example, cells of *Escherichia coli,* growing in a medium rich in glucose, use glucose as their carbon source; however, when transferred to a medium rich in lactose, they use lactose as their carbon source as soon as they run out of glucose. This is possible because lactose, in combined form, acts as a specific inducer for β-galactosidase, an enzyme required for metabolizing lactose. In general, inducible enzymes are catabolic, ￼in keeping with the adaptive principle stated above.

CONTROL OF CONSTITUTIVE PROTEIN BIOSYNTHESIS

Although repression and induction operate in the control of the synthesis of many proteins, they do not appear to be universally operative. There are also many proteins which are synthesized at rates independent of the levels of end products or substrates. The synthesis of these proteins is not under the influence of repressors or inducers. The structural genes involved appear to operate at maximal (constitutive) rates all the time. How, then, can the levels of these proteins in the cell be controlled? Mechanisms other than repression and induction must be involved. One such mechanism could be variations in the stability of the m-RNA. If the m-RNA for a given protein were very stable, the same molecule could be used repeatedly to synthesize many molecules of that protein—that is, it could be translated many times—and therefore, the cellular level of the protein would be relatively high. If, on the other hand, the m-RNA were very unstable, it could serve for the synthesis of only a few protein molecules before it was degraded, and therefore, the cellular concentration of the protein would be relatively low. Another possible mechanism for controlling protein levels in the case of constitutive synthesis depends on the variable stabilities of proteins themselves. A protein which is degraded very rapidly would be present in low amount, even though it may be synthesized rapidly; a protein which is degraded very slowly would be present in high amount.

Other control mechanisms for protein biosynthesis can be imagined, but experimental verification is not yet complete. For instance, there may be differences in the rates at which different genes can be transcribed into m-RNA, even without the restraints of repression. Thus, constitutive synthesis of any two proteins may be unequal in rate. In addition, the rates at which various m-RNA molecules can be translated into protein may vary, so that some are able to give rise to many more protein molecules in a given time than are others.

DNA and RNA Synthesis

Regulation of the synthesis of RNA and DNA is a problem of great current interest, but little definitive evidence is available at present. In general, it appears that, as with protein biosynthesis, control of nucleic acid synthesis is economic in nature. For example, it has been shown that, when microorganisms are starved for an amino acid, net RNA synthesis ceases. The mechanism by which this inhibition is produced probably involves t-RNA; when the amount of uncharged t-RNA (t-RNA with no amino acid attached) reaches a critical level in the cell, it inhibits total RNA synthesis.

Studies with microorganisms indicate that replication of chromosomal DNA begins at a specific point on the circular chromosome, termed the *replicator,* and proceeds all the way around. The replication cycle is apparently started under the influence of a special molecule known as the *initiator.* The initiator is, in certain respects analogous to the repressor discussed above. Although their effects are different, the two regulator molecules both act on chromosomal DNA and serve as the determinants of whether or not it will be utilized as a template for nucleic acid (RNA or DNA) synthesis. Whereas the repressor *stops* the transcription of DNA ("turns off" genes for m-RNA synthesis), the initiator *starts* the replication of DNA ("turns on" genes for DNA synthesis). After one complete cycle the entire chromosome has been duplicated, but the two copies are held together at a site near the replicator. Before separation of the copies can occur and another replication cycle can be started, growth of the microorganism, leading to cell division, is probably required.

Control in Higher Organisms

As organisms evolved from the single cell into larger and more complex forms, a new sort of regulatory apparatus had to be added.

Control systems which operate on a local level cannot fulfill the need for control at a distance. When the concentration of oxygen in the brain is low, the heart must beat harder and faster to correct the deficiency; when the uterus expels a mature fetus, the mammary glands must secrete milk to nourish the newborn infant. These phenomena at the gross functional level must have their counterparts at the molecular level. Indeed, if one simply examines the quantity of DNA in a mammalian cell, one finds approximately a thousand times more than in a bacterial cell. It is probable that this difference in the amount of genetic material indicates a comparable difference in the number of different genes, and hence in the potential number of different proteins. It is clear that regulation and control become correspondingly more complex as one ascends from bacterial to mammalian cells.

To keep pace with the need for more complex regulation in the increasingly complex organism, three main systems evolved: a system of hormones, a system for differentiation (specialization of cells), and a nervous system. At the present time, little can be said about these systems except in phenomenologic terms. As a consequence of intense interest in the biochemistry of these systems, a number of important inroads have been made in the last several years, but the final story has not yet been told.

HORMONES

The hormones are a diverse group, ranging in structure from steroids to proteins. Each one is secreted by the specialized cells of a particular endocrine gland and, at least in higher organisms, is distributed throughout the body by the blood. Hormone secretion is characteristically controlled by mechanisms involving feedback inhibition. For example, when the concentration of water in the blood of a mammal is too low, the posterior pituitary gland is stimulated to secrete the hormone vasopressin, which, in turn, influences the kidney to excrete only minimal amounts of water in the urine. Conversely, when the concentration of water in the blood is raised to a sufficient level, the secretion of the hormone is inhibited, and the kidney excretes a more dilute urine.

Although we know that hormones exert their effects at the molecular level—that is, by influencing specific chemical reactions—there are very few instances in which we can define, in molecular terms, the precise mechanisms involved. We know that insulin, for example, causes a drop in blood sugar—we even know that it does this by facilitating the transport of glucose across cell membranes (cf. Figure 12.3)—but we do not know the exact nature of the chemical reaction which this hormone influences.

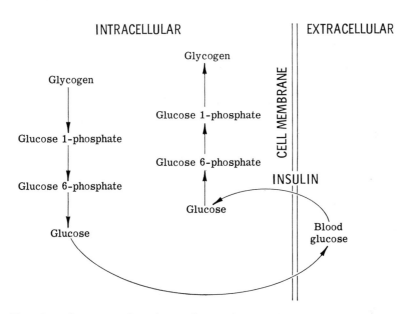

Fig. 12.3. The action of insulin in the regulation of blood sugar is shown here. Insulin facilitates the transport of glucose across the cell membrane, thereby allowing cells to build up a store of glycogen.

One of the most important inroads into the understanding of hormonal control mechanisms has been made through investigations on the insect hormone ecdysone. Ecdysone is a steroid elaborated by the prothoracic gland in the class of insects known as Diptera. The life cycle of these insects involves a number of stages, from egg to larva to pupa to adult—all transitions from one stage to the next being under the influence of a delicately balanced system of controls. Ecdysone is secreted in Diptera at certain periods during the larval and pupal stages, its function being to facilitate the molting of one form into the next (metamorphosis). Injection of the pure hormone into the larvae of Diptera causes rapid molting. It appears, however, that the hormone does not directly influence a chemical reaction involved in the molting process; instead, it acts on the chromosome and stimulates certain genes to activity in protein biosynthesis. It is evidently the protein thus synthesized that actually induces molting.

The identification of the chromosome as the site of action of ecdysone was first made possible by experiments with the "puffing phenomenon," a process (identifiable under the microscope) which gives rise to local swellings, or puffs, on the chromosome. It has been found that the puffs represent active genes—that is, genes that are in active use for the synthesis of specific m-RNA molecules (hence for subsequent synthesis of specific proteins). The correlation of the location of puffs with the function of particular genes became possible only after extensive mapping of the genes of the insect chromosomes. When ecdysone was injected into larvae, puffs were seen to appear within minutes on a particular chromosome. The larger the dose of hormone, the longer the puffs lasted; when ecdysone was depleted, the puffs regressed. It is notable that normal puffing at the same sites on the chromosomes occurs just prior to the normal molting process.

On the basis of these and other experimental findings, P. Karlson has proposed an extremely interesting hypothesis for the mode of action of ecdysone, which may apply to other hormones as well. According to this hypothesis, the hormone acts on protein biosynthesis at the stage at which the information encoded in the DNA of the gene is transcribed into m-RNA (as shown schematically in Figure 12.4). The specific gene thus activated by the hormone would be the structural gene for a specific protein. In the case of ecdysone, the active protein would probably be an enzyme required for the molting process. The hypothesis has been tested by investigating the effects of a number of chemicals that inhibit protein biosynthesis. If the hypothesis is correct, then substances (such as streptomycin and puromycin) that inhibit the translation of m-RNA into protein should inhibit the molting process by preventing the synthesis of the required protein, but should not inhibit the puffing phenomenon, elicited by injection of ecdysone. On the other hand, substances (such as actinomycin D) that act on genes themselves, and thereby inhibit the transcription of DNA into m-RNA, should inhibit both the molting process and the puffing phenomenon. Investigations into the effects of these inhibitors on insect larvae have shown that they act as predicted by the hypothesis.

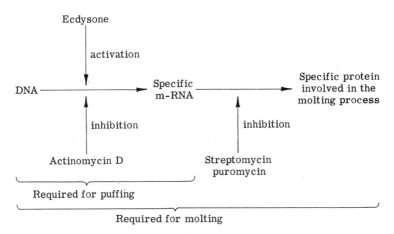

Fig. 12.4. Proposed site of action of ecdysone in the insect larva. Apparently, ecdysone affects a segment of the chromosome and activates the transcription of m-RNA from a specific gene. Experiments with various inhibitors pinpoint the processes required for the phenomena of puffing and of molting.

Additional evidence for the hypothesis comes from experiments which suggest that the specific protein synthesized when ecdysone exerts its effect on the insect chromosome is the enzyme dopa-decarboxylase. This enzyme is present in Diptera only at the time of molting, and appears to be involved in the formation of the proper outer skin for the molting process. Furthermore, it has been possible to demonstrate that ecdysone stimulates the synthesis of a specific m-RNA; when this m-RNA is introduced into a cell-free system for protein synthesis (obtained from rat liver), it is able to direct synthesis of the insect enzyme dopa-decarboxylase (see Chapter 11), as shown schematically in Figure 12.5.

As mentioned above, the mechanism of hormonal action deduced from studies with ecdysone may have rather wide applicability. This is not to say that all hormones act by a mechanism similar to that of ecdysone. Rather, the control of specific protein biosynthesis may be the principle underlying the mechanisms by which one group of hormones acts. For example, the recent studies of Garren suggest that the mechanism by which the hormone, adrenocortico-

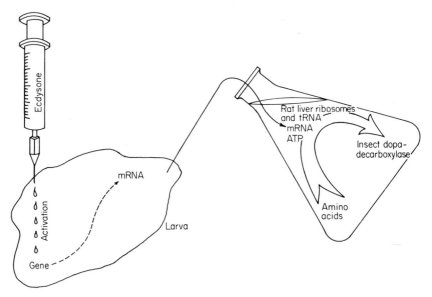

Fig. 12.5. As shown above schematically, the m-RNA formed from the specific gene activated by ecdysone can be transferred to a cell-free system for protein synthesis, and the protein whose synthesis it directs can be identified as dopa-decarboxylase.

tropin (ACTH) stimulates the production of corticosterone in the rat adrenal gland involves increasing the rate at which a specific m-RNA is translated into a specific unstable protein. In the absence of ACTH this m-RNA is translated slowly; because the protein produced is destroyed rapidly, only low levels of the protein can be maintained. In the presence of ACTH the m-RNA is translated rapidly; because the production of the protein now outstrips its destruction, the level of the protein rises. It appears to be the latter protein which, in turn, influences the rate of production of corticosterone. As in the case of ecdysone, continuing levels of the hormone are necessary to achieve a continuing effect.

By extension of Karlson's hypothesis, one might anticipate that the site of action of many hormones would be at any of the various stages in the process of protein biosynthesis: transcription of genes into m-RNA; translation of m-RNA into polypeptide chains; folding of polypeptide chains into proteins; or the association of protein subunits into proteins with complex quaternary structures. Indeed, there is evidence suggesting that certain steroid hormones affect the quaternary structure of the enzyme glutamic dehydrogenase, and thereby may produce changes in its specificity. The hypothesis could be extended even further to include hormones that might be involved in the processes of repression and induction, discussed in preceeding sections of this chapter.

If the lessons learned from studies with such hormones as ecdysone and ACTH are applicable to a larger group of hormones (as indeed seems to be the case) some generalizations may be made. As an agent for controlling the biosynthesis of a specific protein, a hormone of this group could do nothing to dictate *how* to make the protein, since that question is settled by the structure of the genetic material. It could, however, influence the expression of an existing gene, by acting at one of the stages in protein biosynthesis and dictating *how much* of the specific protein is to be made. It is known that hormone secretion itself is a finely regulated process; through a delicately balanced set of control mechanisms, the needs of the body are translated into the secretion of a hormone that can act to satisfy those needs. Thus, by feedback control, hormones of the type of the ecdysone group may be able to dictate not only *how much* of a specific protein is to be made, but also *when* it is to be made. In this way, specific requirements of the body may be met by the appropriate amount of synthesis of the appropriate protein at the appropriate time.

DIFFERENTIATION

One of the most interesting but poorly understood areas of biological control is the differentiation of cells during embryogenesis.

What causes the two daughter cells of a parent cell to be dissimilar? In what ways are they dissimilar? How is the dissimilarity maintained? These are among the many unanswered questions of the embryologist today. In the introduction to Chapter 11 we described the process of cell division and emphasized the exactness with which the parent cell is copied. However, during the development of higher organisms there are crucial stages at which the progeny must *not* be identical copies of a parent cell, since the complete organism is not a mass of identical cells.

Because the differences which arise among cells during embryogenesis are heritable—that is, when a differentiated liver cell divides it produces two liver cells, and not two of any other kind of cell— it is clear that differentiation involves genetic differences among cells. However, it is known that all the genes of the original parent cells are present in every cell of an organism (with the exception of the germ cells). The genetic differences among the differentiated cells of an organism therefore cannot be a result of the presence or absence of certain genes. An alternative hypothesis appears more likely: that the genetic differences among the various cell types of an organism are primarily expressions of the variable degrees to which particular genes are either functional or nonfunctional. In a mammalian muscle cell the structural genes for actin and myosin must be very active, whereas those for producing hemoglobin must be entirely inactive (the converse being true in the developing red blood cell). Thus, differentiation appears to be a problem of how certain genes are "turned on" or "turned off" in cells of the embryo destined for specialized function.

Although there are several coherent theories about the mechanism of differentiation, none has been substantiated by experimental evidence. It appears likely that the histones, positively charged proteins associated with chromosomal DNA in higher organisms, may be involved in the mechanism of how certain genes may be functional and other genes nonfunctional. For one thing, histones do not exist in the cells of undifferentiated organisms, such as bacteria. Furthermore, genes known to be dormant are found to be associated with histones. Thus, the histones presumably have an inhibitory effect and cause genes to be inactive. The idea that histones are involved, however likely it may be, does not really bring us any closer to the heart of the matter of differentiation. Assuming that histones are the molecular agents for inactivating certain genes during the differention of cells, by what mechanism are particular genes selected for inactivation? By what mechanism do the histones remain associated with the same genes in the progeny of differentiated cells? What controls the exact moment in embryogenesis when differentiation of certain cells should begin? Again we are left with these and many other unanswered questions. It has been apparent to embryologists for some time that such questions could not be answered before the proper experimental system had been devised for studying them. One such system consists of cultures of differentiated and undifferentiated cells outside organisms (tissue cultures of pure cell lines), which can survive and grow on defined media. This system was developed relatively recently, and there are still many technical problems to be contended with. But at least it is now available, and important inroads into the mechanism of differentiation may be expected in the near future.

CENTRAL NERVOUS SYSTEM

The most elegant control system in living organisms is the brain. All the control systems referred to thus far are important, to various degrees, for the development and survival of organisms in their environments; however, the brain, at least in the more complex species, surpasses them all by endowing organisms with the capacity to change the environment to fit their biological needs. The brain is far more complex than any of the other systems we have discussed, although the principles of molecular interaction which subserve its function are not likely to be different. Even if we consider only that system of the brain which constitutes the human "mind," the complexity is phenomenal. The psychological dynamics of behavior were extensively explored and systematized by Freud and his followers, who were able to synthesize their observations into an integrated theory of human behavior. Although this theory has withstood the tests of scientific observations on the phenomenologic level, it cannot at the present time be described in biochemical terms. We are still far from understanding the chemical mechanisms by which memories are recorded, stored, and recalled, by which affects are experienced, by which drives are discharged, and by which psychological defenses are brought into play. However, the belief that these phenomena of the mind are explicable in chemical terms is an important first step that has been taken. Until recently, the mind was considered to be outside the domain of biochemistry, just as all biological systems were so considered by medieval man. Although research in this area has only just begun, there is little doubt that it will some day constitute a fascinating chapter in the chemistry of biological control.

Suggested Reading

Books

Anfinsen, C. B., "The Molecular Basis of Evolution," John Wiley and Sons, New York, 1960.

Jacob, F., and Wollman, E. L., "Sexuality and the Genetics of Bacteria," Academic Press, New York, 1961.

Lascelles, J., "Tetrapyrrole Biosynthesis and Its Regulation," W. A. Benjamin Inc., New York, 1964.

Sherrington, C., "Man on His Nature," Cambridge University Press, London and New York, 1951.

Smith, H. W., "From Fish to Philosopher," Doubleday & Co., Inc., New York, 1953.

Watson, J. D., "Molecular Biology of the Gene," W. A. Benjamin Inc., New York, 1965.

Special Articles

Ames, B. N., and Hartman, P. E., *Cold Spring Harbor Symp. Quant. Biol.* **28**, 349 (1963): on the histidine operon.

Changeux, J.-P., *Sci. American* **212**, 36 (1965): on the control of biochemical reactions.

Garren, L. D., Ney, R. L., and Davis, W. W., *Proc. Natl. Acad. Sci. U.S.* **53**, 1443 (1965): on the mechanism of action of ACTH.

Gerhart, J. C., and Pardee, A. B., *Cold Spring Harbor Symp. Quant. Biol.* **28**, 491 (1963): on end product inhibition and allosteric interactions.

Goldberger, R. F., and Berberich, M. A., *in* "Organizational Biosynthesis" (H. J. Vogel, J. O. Lampen, and V. Bryson, eds.), Academic Press, New York, in press, 1967: on repression and derepression.

Jacob, F., and Monod, J., *J. Mol. Biol.* **3**, 318 (1961): on control of protein biosynthesis at the genetic level.

Jacob, F., and Monod, J., *Cold Spring Harbor Symp. Quant. Biol.* **26**, 193 (1961): on the regulation of the activity of genes.

Jacob, F., Brenner, S., and Cuzen, F., *Cold Spring Harbor Symp. Quant. Biol.* **28**, 329 (1963): on the mechanism by which DNA replication is regulated.

Karlson, P., *Perspectives Biol. Med.* **6**, 203 (1963): review of ecdysone.

Monod, J., and Jacob, F., *Cold Spring Harbor Symp. Quant. Biol.* **26**, 389 (1961): on regulation of protein biosynthesis and differentiation in higher organisms.

Monod, J., Changeux, J. P., and Jacob, F., *J. Mol. Biol.* **6**, 306 (1963): on allosteric proteins and cellular control.

Sekeris, C. E., and Lang, N., *Life Sci.* **3**, 625 (1964): on ecdysone.

Tomkins, G. M., Yielding, K. L., Talal, N., and Curran, J. F., *Cold Spring Harbor Symp. Quant. Biol.* **28**, 461 (1963): on the effect of hormones on protein structure.

Tomkins, G. M., Thompson, E. B., Hayashi, S., Gelehrter, T., Granner, D., and Peterkofsky, B., *Cold Spring Harbor Symp. Quant. Biol.* **31** (1966), in press: on the influence of hormones on enzyme induction.

Umbarger, H. E., *Cold Spring Harbor Symp. Quant. Biol.* **26**, 193 (1961): on end product inhibition.

Umbarger, H. E., *Science* **145**, 674 (1964): on intracellular regulatory mechanisms.

Vogel, H. J., *in* "The Chemical Basis of Heredity" (W. D. McElroy and B. Glass, eds.), Johns Hopkins Press, Baltimore, 1957, p. 276: on end product inhibition.

CHAPTER 13 _____

Biochemistry and Disease

In the sixteenth century the anatomy of the human body was extensively studied, but this knowledge had little influence on medical practices. Physicians continued to administer drugs and to apply procedures developed through superstitious beliefs or empirical findings. Some of the remedies were quite effective, but most had no specific pharmacological activity. Through the succeeding centuries, while the sciences of chemistry and physics flourished, problems of biological function were sparingly investigated in the scientific laboratory. It is true that from the time of Galen small inroads into functional biology had been made, but these were sporadic and few. It was not until the nineteenth century that the foundations were laid for the new science of physiology. Fathered in Germany by Müller, and in France by Magendie, Bernard, and Pasteur, this science quickly flourished and spread throughout Europe and the United States. Once the scientific method was applied to investigations of the function of living systems, instead of the intuitive "methods" that had been used for many centuries, it became apparent that an extremely fruitful approach had been found. Along with many new insights into the functioning of living systems in general came a greater understanding of the function, and dysfunction, of the human body. Thus, the roots of modern medicine are deeply implanted in the soil of physiological investigation.

More recently, the medical sciences have undergone another spurt in development, due to the flowering of a new science—biochemistry. The beginnings of this new science can be traced almost to the beginnings of physiology in the nineteenth century. In fact, it is only in recent years that biochemistry has developed suffi-

332

ciently to be considered a separate discipline. With the emergence of biochemistry, new concepts were brought to bear on age-old problems in medicine, and the results have been both interesting and useful. The purpose of this chapter is to examine some of the salient features of this comparatively recent development.

The biochemical concept of greatest importance to medical science is that all disease has a molecular basis. In a number of cases, the investigation of the molecular basis of a disease has led to the most precise definition of the cause of the disease, and to a detailed understanding of the mechanisms by which the disease progresses and by which symptoms are produced. Moreover, an understanding of the biochemical mechanisms of a disease provides a basis for the most rational attempt to devise a specific therapy. At the present time most of the new drugs are found by empirical methods. The potentialities, however, for designing drugs to fulfill specific chemical tasks by means of known biochemical mechanisms are tremendous. We have just begun to realize some of the potentialities of such an approach, and it is in this area of medicine that the future holds the greatest promise (see Chapter 14). Occasionally, the study of the molecular basis of disease leads to a greater understanding of normal human biochemistry. There have been several instances in which a normal metabolic pathway in the human was first elucidated through the biochemical study of patients suffering from a derangement of that pathway. Thus, the investigation of the molecular basis of disease may yield information of importance not only to the practicing physician, but also to the biochemist himself.

For the purpose of the present discussion only, we shall divide diseases into categories according to the degree to which their chemical nature is understood at the present time. The first category consists of "simple chemical diseases"—diseases in which the etiology and pathology have been clearly elucidated on a chemical basis. The second category consists of "complex chemical diseases"—diseases in which the abnormalities are clearly chemical in nature, but not all the symptoms are explicable in terms of these abnormalities. The third category consists of "seemingly nonchemical diseases"—diseases in which chemical abnormalities are not immediately apparent. Close examination reveals that even in the diseases of the last category the fundamental abnormalities do exist at the molecular level, although the mechanisms by which the molecular abnormalities produce the symptoms of these diseases may be obscure. The job of the biochemist is to elucidate the molecular mechanisms operating in all diseases, and thereby to place them all, eventually, into the first category.

Simple Chemical Diseases

Diseases Involving the Hemoglobin Molecule

The hemoglobin molecule is composed of a porphyrin derivative (heme) and a protein (globin). The protein moiety is made up of four polypeptide chains—two α- and two β-chains; these are folded and held together in a highly specific arrangement, the three-dimensional conformation achieved by the tetrameric molecule with its four heme groups attached, being a highly specific one. The primary function of hemoglobin is the transport of oxygen and carbon dioxide. Essentially all of the hemoglobin in the body is contained within the red cells of the blood. As these cells pass through the capillaries of the lung they are exposed to a relatively high partial pressure of oxygen. The particular chemical characteristic that qualifies hemoglobin to perform its specific functions is that, under these conditions, oxygen forms a complex with the heme group. As they pass on and travel throughout the body, the red blood cells, containing hemoglobin molecules which now carry oxygen, are exposed to lower oxygen tensions. Under these conditions the oxygen dissociates from the hemoglobin and is made available for use by the cells. Thus, with recycling of the blood, the hemoglobin molecules alternately pick up oxygen in the lungs and release it to the peripheral tissues. Also, they pick up carbon dioxide from the tissues and release it in the lungs.

A new phase of modern medicine began in 1949 when Linus Pauling and his colleagues first reported on the electrophoretic behavior of a variant form of human hemoglobin. This, and subsequent work, has now firmly established the fact that the red blood cells of the human adult may contain large amounts of various types of hemoglobin other than the normal adult hemoglobin (HbA). The other types of hemoglobin are found in individuals suffering from any one of a number of diseases, and differ from HbA in the structure of the protein moiety. Because of the altered structures of some of these hemoglobins, their electrical charge differs from that of HbA. It is this property which led to the detection of one of the abnormal hemoglobins by Pauling, through the use of the electrophoresis apparatus (which separates molecules having different charges). Before the difference in charge between HbA and the abnormal hemoglobin, HbS, had been explained, Pauling surmised that it was due to the substitution of one amino acid by another of different charge in the protein moiety of the molecule. Subsequent work has proved this hypothesis correct.

By subjecting hemoglobin to the digestive action of trypsin it is possible to split the molecule into a number of peptide fragments. Since trypsin catalyzes the hydrolytic cleaveage of arginyl* and lysyl* bonds, the number of peptides produced by tryptic digestion will equal one more than the total number of arginine plus lysine residues in the protein. The amino acid sequence in each of the peptides remains the same as it was in that segment of hemoglobin from which the peptide was derived, as shown in a simple schematic way in Figure 13.1. When the tryptic peptides from HbA were applied to a large sheet of filter paper and were then subjected to chromatography in one direction and to electrophoresis in the other, a "peptide map" of the molecule was obtained. Such a peptide map of HbA is shown in Figure 13.2A. Each spot in the map represents one peptide. The positions of the various spots are determined by the physical characteristics of the peptides they represent. In Figure 13.2B is shown an analogous peptide map prepared from a tryptic digest of the abnormal hemoglobin isolated from the red blood cells of a person suffering from a condition known as *sickle-cell disease*. The map of this hemoglobin (HbS) is identical with that of the normal HbA with one exception; a single spot is missing from the expected location, and a new spot appears in a different location. This spot corresponds to peptide No. 4 of the β-chain of

* Arginyl and lysyl bonds are the peptide bonds by which the carboxyl groups of arginine and lysine residues, respectively, are joined to other amino acids.

hemoglobin, a peptide containing eight amino acids. The peptide No. 4 in the map of HbA and the abnormal peptide in the map of HbS were cut out and eluted from the paper, and their amino acid sequences were determined and compared. The findings were as follows: for the normal peptide, Val—His—Leu—Thr—Pro—Glu—Glu—Lys; for the abnormal peptide, Val—His—Leu—Thr—Pro—Val—Glu—Lys. The only difference is the presence of

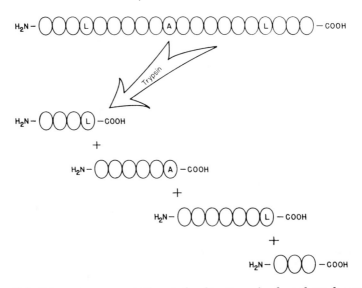

Fig. 13.1. Schematic representation of the digestion of a hypothetical protein by trypsin. The amino acid residues are represented by circles, the letters L and A being used to designate lysine and arginine, respectively. Trypsin catalyzes the hydrolytic cleaveage of lysyl and arginyl bonds uniquely, and the number of peptides produced equals one more than the sum of the numbers of lysine and arginine residues in the protein.

valine in HbS in a position in the peptide chain where glutamic acid is found in the normal molecule. Since the exposed side chain of valine is uncharged, and that of glutamic acid is negatively charged, the substitution brings about a difference in charge (hence, a difference in electrophoretic behavior) between the two analogous peptides, and also between the two types of hemoglobin from which these peptides were derived.

We shall briefly consider how a simple substitution of one amino acid for another may come about. It cannot be due to an accident during the synthesis of the protein, since the abnormality is a consistent one—that is, essentially all molecules of hemoglobin from an individual with sickle-cell disease are of the HbS type. The error must, therefore, be built into the protein-synthesizing system. The fault is unlikely to lie only in m-RNA, since this substance is

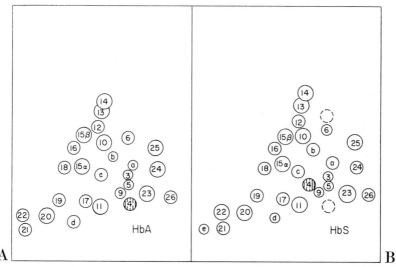

A   B

Fig. 13.2. Peptide maps of tryptic digests of HbA (left) and HbS (right). Peptide No. 4 of the β-chain of HbA is missing from the analogous position in the map of HbS, but appears in a different location (hatched lines). Redrawn from figure of C. Baglione, *in* "Molecular Genetics" (J. H. Taylor, ed.), Part I, Academic Press, New York, 1963.

simply a coded copy (transcription) of the DNA of the gene. (See Chapter 11). An abnormality of t-RNA is not likely to be responsible, since glutamic acid appears in its appropriate place in HbS in all but one position—therefore, the t-RNA for glutamic acid must be functioning properly. This leaves the DNA as the most likely source of error. As described in detail in Chapter 11, the amino acid sequence of a protein is encoded in the sequence of nucleotides in a particular stretch of chromosomal DNA, each amino acid being specified by a triplet of nucleotides. Thus, a mistake in the particular triplet that specifies the first of the two glutamic acid residues in peptide No. 4 of the hemoglobin molecule would lead to a consistent mistake in the amino acid appearing at that point in the protein. The error in the DNA might be one which gives a nucleotide sequence such as G-U-A instead of G-A-A (which are known codons for valine and glutamic acid, respectively). This hypothesis of a substitution of one nucleotide for another (A for U) is consistent with the fact that sickle-cell disease is genetically determined. The DNA of the individual with this disease is accurately copied in the offspring, so that the error in nucleotide sequence persists. Thus, HbS can always be found in the red blood cells not only of a person with sickle-cell disease, but also in those of the offspring as well.

Now we shall examine the ways in which the *function* of HbS differs from that of HbA, and the question of whether such differences can account for the symptoms of sickle-cell disease. When red blood cells from a patient with sickle-cell disease are examined under a microscope, they are found to appear normal until the hemoglobin within them becomes deoxygenated. When this occurs, many of the cells take on elongated and sickled shapes. The latter phenomenon is the basis for the name of the disease. Biochemical studies show that the deoxygenated form of HbS is far less soluble than the deoxygenated form of HbA, and tends to form a semisolid gel. Under the microscope this gel appears to be made up of small bodies shaped much like the typical sickle cells found in the blood of patients afflicted with the disease. Apparently, when a sufficient amount of HbS in the red blood cell becomes deoxygenated and remains so for a sufficient time, it precipitates from solution. Deformation of the cell into the characteristic sickle shape is a consequence of this precipitation. Any condition *in vivo* that strongly favors deoxygenation of the hemoglobin (such as flight at high altitudes in an unpressurized airplane) or a condition that prolongs the normal period for deoxygenation (that is, the time when the red blood cell is on the venous side of the circulation) would increase the tendency of cells containing HbS to assume an abnormal shape.

As long as the hemoglobin of the red blood cells remains in solution, the patient with sickle-cell disease has no symptoms. The red blood cells, shaped like smoothly contoured plates, glide through the capillaries with no difficulty. However, when sickling occurs the cells assume jagged shapes and therefore tend to get caught in small vessels. Some of the vessels become completely blocked. The areas of tissue ordinarily supplied by blood from these vessels are consequently cut off from oxygen and nutriment, with the result that cells in these areas may die. The pain caused by multiple small infarctions (death of groups of cells) characterizes the symptoms associated with the sickle-cell "crisis." Thus, the symptoms of the disease are due to acute stoppage of blood flow through small vessels clogged with sickled red blood cells; the sickling of the erythrocytes is due to precipitation of HbS under certain specific conditions with concomitant deformation of the red blood corpuscle; the insolubility of deoxygenated HbS is due to substitution of valine for glutamic acid at one position in the protein moiety of the molecule; and the amino acid substitution is due to a substitution of one nucleotide for another in that portion of the DNA (the gene) in which is encoded the primary structure of the β-chain of globin.

The abnormal gene which controls the synthesis of HbS must have arisen as a random mutation. The question as to why the carriers of the mutant gene flourished and caused the spread of the gene in certain populations has been answered quite satisfactorily.* It appears that red blood cells which contain HbS are not conducive to the survival of one of the parasites that cause malaria, and therefore individuals with the mutant gene are relatively immune to that disease. The mutant gene would be expected to confer a selective advantage upon carriers in a population for which the parasitic disease is a threat to life. Indeed, epidemiological evidence indicates that the mutant gene arose in just those areas in which the disease due to the malarial parasite in question was endemic. The mutant gene became frequent in these populations because it made death from malaria less likely; the disadvantages due to the presence of HbS itself were evidently not so great in comparison with the advantage gained by the diminished susceptibility to ma-

* For most genetic diseases this question remains unanswered.

laria. Thus, the force behind the spreading of the mutant gene was natural selection.

Since the discovery of the structural defect in the hemoglobin of people with sickle-cell disease, a large number of abnormal hemoglobins have been identified in the blood of individuals suffering from other blood diseases. In many of these variant hemoglobins the abnormality consists of a simple substitution of one amino acid for another, as is the case in HbS. It is very likely that a large number of other abnormal hemoglobins exist which are able to function properly, and therefore do not cause symptoms. Because the "diseases" due to the presence of such hemoglobins would not have any manifestations, "patients" would not be brought to the attention of doctors, and the abnormal hemoglobins would not ordinarily be identified. It should be noted that most of the known abnormal hemoglobins are able, at least partially, to carry on their major function, the transport of oxygen and carbon dioxide, while they usually cause symptoms for other reasons. Were it not for the insolubility of HbS, for instance, sickle-cell disease would probably be asymptomatic.

In at least a few diseases, however, the oxygen-carrying capacity of hemoglobin is impaired by an amino acid substitution—two or more of the group of diseases in which the abnormal hemoglobin is designated by the letter M. People whose red blood cells contain any of the M-hemoglobins have a disease known as congenital methemoglobinemia. Methemoglobin is hemoglobin with the iron of its heme group in the ferric $(3+)$ state; in normal hemoglobin the iron atom is in the ferrous $(2+)$ state. Ordinarily, when the iron of any hemoglobin becomes oxidized to the ferric state it is readily reduced again to the ferrous state. In hemoglobin-M, however, this reduction is inhibited, and therefore a large proportion of it remains as methemoglobin-M. The significance of this abnormality is the fact that hemoglobin is unable to function as a carrier of oxygen when the iron of its heme group is in the ferric state. The structural defect in one form of HbM is the replacement of one of the histidine residues in the α-chain (residue 58) by a tyrosine residue. On first inspection it is difficult to see how the substitution of a single amino acid in one of the two types of polypeptide chains of hemoglobin could so drastically affect the iron in the prosthetic group which constitutes such a small proportion of the mass of this molecule. The key to the explanation lies in the *three-dimensional* structure of the molecule. The polypeptide chains of hemoglobin are folded in such a way that the particular amino acid in question comes to lie immediately adjacent to the iron atom in the heme group of the molecule. Moreover, the amino acid that occupies this position in normal hemoglobin (histidine) would not be expected, on theoretical grounds, to affect the oxidative state of the iron, whereas the amino acid in this position in HbM (tyrosine) has a chemically reactive side chain which would be expected to stabilize the iron in the ferric state, as illustrated in Figure 13.3. Thus, the characteristic chemical reactivity of the heme group of the HbM under consideration is understandable on the basis of the known structural defect in the protein moiety of the molecule.

The symptoms of congenital methemoglobinemia are explicable on the basis of the tendency of the HbM to remain as methemo-

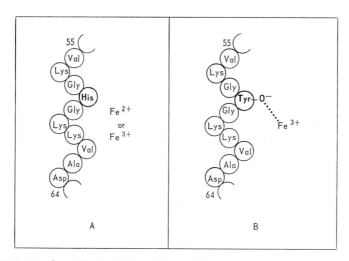

Fig. 13.3. Residues 55–64 of the α-chain of hemoglobin-A (part A) and of hemoglobin-M$_{Boston}$ (part B). Residue 58 of HbA (histidine) does not interact with the iron of the heme group, whereas the analogous residue in HbM (tyrosine) interacts strongly with the ferric form of the heme iron and stabilizes it in this form. Redrawn from figure of C. Baglioni in "Molecular Genetics" (J. H. Taylor, ed.), Part I, Academic Press, New York, 1963.

globin—that is, with the heme iron in the 3+ state: this interferes with its ability to form a dissociable complex with oxygen. Because much of the hemoglobin (20–50%) is in the form of methemoglobin, and because of the distinctive color of methemoglobin, afflicted persons tend to have a slate grey appearance. Also, because of the diminution in oxygen-carrying capacity, people with the disease tend to become short of breath on exertion, and to become fatigued easily—both symptoms of oxygen deficiency.

ALBINISM

Next, we shall discuss a disease in which the primary abnormality is the lack of an active enzyme. In most diseases of this type it is difficult to distinguish among three possible defects: synthesis of an abnormal variant of the enzyme (which is catalytically inactive); complete failure to synthesize the enzyme; and abnormally rapid destruction of the enzyme. In all three cases the apparent result is the same: the activity normally associated with the enzyme is deficient. A well studied disease caused by the lack of a specific enzymic activity is universal albinism. This is a heritable disease, characterized by deficiency of melanin. Melanin is a pigment normally produced within specialized cells, *melanocytes,* found in the skin, the hair bulb, and the retina. In one of the varieties of universal albinism the melanocytes of these regions fail to produce their normal pigment; the resulting clinical picture includes lack of pigmentation in the affected areas.

Careful biochemical studies have revealed the fact that the failure of the melanocyte to produce melanin in this type of albinism is due to blockage of the reaction sequence normally initiated by the enzyme tyrosinase. The role of tyrosinase in the normal metabolic pathway for the synthesis of melanin is shown in the following scheme (an asterisk indicates that intermediates have been left out of the formulation of the sequence). Because of the lack of tyrosinase activity the albino cannot convert tyrosine into dopa quinone; consequently, the metabolic pathway leading to the formation of melanin is blocked. The cause of the lack of tyrosinase activity in the melanocyte appears to be an abnormality in genetic information, transmitted from the parents of the albino, such that

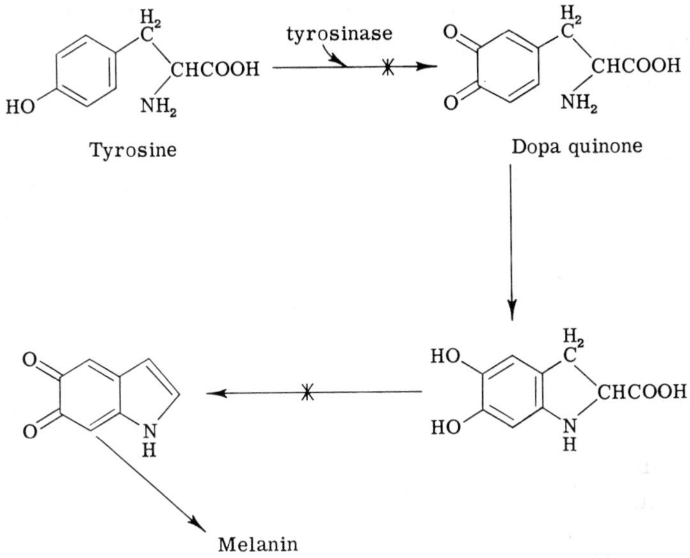

Tyrosine

Dopa quinone

Melanin

either a faulty tyrosinase molecule, or perhaps no tyrosinase at all, is produced. According to present concepts of protein synthesis, the portion of chromosomal DNA (gene) in the nucleus of the melanocyte that normally directs the synthesis of tyrosinase is defective; the precise chemical nature of the defect is not known.

Many of the clinical manifestations of universal albinism can be explained on the basis of the known block in the pathway of melanin synthesis: these are milk-white coloring of the skin; a tendency to develop carcinoma of the skin;* white or yellow hair; light blue iris; and depigmentation of the retina, leading to decreased visual acuity and increased sensitivity to light.

The two diseases discussed above, one involving abnormalities in an oxygen-carrying hemoprotein (hemoglobin) and the other involving abnormalities in (or absence of) an enzymic protein (tyrosinase), are among the simplest and most thoroughly studied of a larger group of diseases known collectively as *inborn errors of metabolism*. Although inborn errors of metabolism vary widely in their clinical manifestations, they are related by the fact that each of

---

* Melanin is thought to be a protective factor against the development of carcinoma of the skin since this lesion occurs more rarely in Negroes than in Caucasians.

them is caused by a hereditary defect in the synthesis of some protein molecule. Or, to go to the primary cause, each of them is due to a defect in that portion of the DNA molecule that contains coded information for the structure of the particular protein involved. The defect may result in the synthesis of an abnormal protein, which may or may not function properly, or in total lack of synthesis of the protein. Many "diseases" characterized by structurally abnormal, but functionally competent, proteins probably go undetected because these "diseases" cause no symptoms. Symptoms are produced only when a structural abnormality in a protein impairs the function of that protein, as in HbM, or is in some other way dangerous, as in HbS.

Most often, diseases caused by abnormalities in specific proteins are manifested by derangements of those processes in which the proteins participate. Thus, if there is an abnormality in the hemoglobin molecule, the manifestation involves the function of the red blood cell; if there is an abnormality in an enzymic protein, the manifestation involves the metabolic pathway in which that enzyme normally functions; if there is an abnormality in a protein necessary for cell differentiation in the early development of the embryo (an organizer substance), the manifestation involves a congenital defect of one or more organ systems of the body; if there is an abnormality in a protein that has a structural function, the manifestation involves a structural defect, such as occurs in some forms of muscular dystrophy. A number of inborn errors of metabolism are listed in Table 13.1, together with the specific protein that is abnormal in each case and the tissue or metabolic system affected by the abnormality.

Vitamin Deficiency

Vitamins are small organic molecules which are required for the normal metabolic activities of a given organism, but cannot be synthesized by that organism. In the event that they are inadequately supplied from an external source, disease will result. The disease state associated with each vitamin deficiency usually has characteristic symptoms. Often, especially if the disease is discovered early in its course, a cure can be effected by the administration of the appropriate vitamin. Basic research on the structure and function of the vitamins has contributed greatly to our understanding of the biochemical basis of the vitamin deficiency diseases. Many of the

Table 13.1
DISEASES INVOLVING INBORN ERRORS OF HEREDITY

Disease	Abnormal or deficient protein	Tissue or metabolic system involved
Acatalasia	Catalase	Susceptibility to oral infections
Phenylketonuria	Phenylalanine hydroxylase	Conversion of phenylalanine to tyrosine
Alcaptonuira	Homogentisic acid oxidase	Metabolism of phenylalanine and tyrosine
Albinism	Tyrosinase	Melanin synthesis
Galactosemia	Galactose 1-phosphate uridyl transferase	Conversion of galactose to glucose
Maple syrup urine disease	Branched-chain keto acid decarboxylase	Catabolism of valine, leucine, and isoleucine
Favism and primaquine sensitivity	Glucose 6-phosphate dehydrogenase	Red blood cell metabolism
Hemolytic anemia	Pyruvate kinase	Red blood cell metabolism (glycolysis)
Sensitivity to suxamethonium	Pseudocholinesterase	Hydrolysis of choline esters
Sickle cell disease	Hemoglobin (β-chain)	Red blood cell function
Afibrinogenemia	Fibrinogen	Blood coagulation
Hemophilia	Antihemophilic globulin	Blood coagulation
Wilson's disease	Unknown	Copper metabolism
Gout	Unknown	Purine metabolism
Primary familial lipoidoses (several varieties)	Unknown	Lipid metabolism
Cystinuria	Unknown	Renal tubular and intestinal epithelial amino acid transport

vitamins have been found to function as coenzymes, or as prosthetic groups, or to be essential to the synthesis of such groups *in vivo*. These groups are parts of enzymes involved in important metabolic activities (see Chapter 5). A list of a few of the vitamins, together with their biological functions, is shown in Table 13.2. It should be understood that the function of most vitamins pertains to all cells and is not limited to the cells or organ in which symptoms are first manifest.

Vitamins must be defined in terms of single species. Those listed in Table 13.2 are vitamins for man; they are not necessarily vitamins for other organisms. For instance, the rat possesses an enzyme system that implements the synthesis of ascorbic acid (vitamin C);

Table 13.2

VITAMINS AND THEIR FUNCTION

Vitamin	Area of function	Disease or symptom caused by deficiency
A	Vision (prosthetic group of rhodopsin) and somatic role (ill-defined)	Night blindness and skin changes
D	Bone development (regulation of concentration of inorganic phosphate)	Rickets
K	Blood clotting (may be prosthetic group of enzyme(s) required for the synthesis of several clotting factors)	Bleeding diathesis
Thiamine	Energy metabolism (coenzyme for decarboxylation of α-keto acids)	Beriberi
Riboflavin	Intermediary metabolism (coenzyme of flavoproteins)	Glossitis, cheilosis, etc.
Niacin	Electron transport (the functional group of DPN and TPN)	Pellagra

therefore, ascorbic acid is not a vitamin for this animal. It is a vitamin for man because human tissues lack an enzyme system essential for its synthesis. Each compound which functions as a vitamin for one organism must be synthesized by some other organism, plant, or animal; otherwise, there would be no natural external source of that compound, and the organism for which it is a vitamin could not survive.

As an illustration of the molecular basis of vitamin deficiency states, we shall briefly discuss vitamin A. This molecule is a large organic alcohol, the structure of which is shown below:

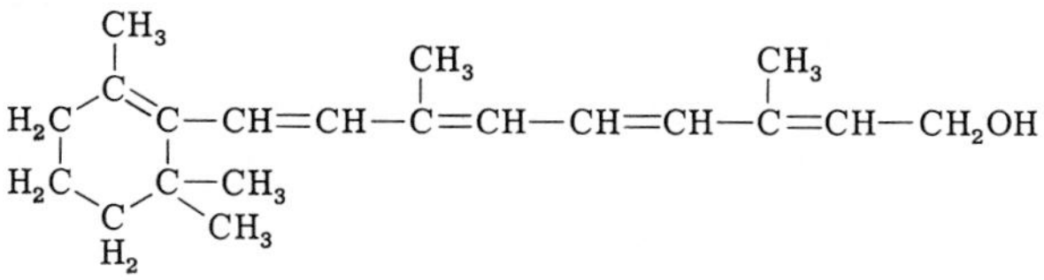

Vitamin A
(coenzyme for rhodopsin)

Vitamin A functions as the prosthetic group for rhodopsin, one of the pigment proteins of the retina. When exposed to light the retinal pigments undergo chemical changes. The chemical change in the pigment molecule brought about by exposure to light serves to activate a nerve filament at the surface of the retina. An impulse is then carried through the optic nerve to the brain, where it is perceived as light. Summation of thousands of such events—the chemical change in the pigment molecule, the nerve impulse, and the reception of the impulse by the brain—constitutes visual perception. It is clear, then, that any chemical abnormality in a pigment of the retina that would interfere with its light sensitivity would necessarily interfere with the entire process of vision. The retinal protein for which vitamin A normally acts as the prosthetic group is totally inactive—that is, totally insensitive to light—in the absence of vitamin A. It is no wonder, then, that one of the most striking features of the disease state associated with vitamin A deficiency is a visual disturbance. Other symptoms of vitamin A deficiency still await further biochemical studies for explanation at the molecular level.

Complex Chemical Diseases

PRIMARY GOUT

Gout is a disease involving purine metabolism. The cardinal manifestations are an elevated level of uric acid in the blood and abnormalities of the joints. The latter are of two types. One is characterized by repeated attacks of acute arthritis (inflammation in the joints), often involving the great toes, but often involving many other joints as well. The other type of joint pathology is characterized by the deposition of large quantities of urates in and about the joints. These deposits, called *tophi,* are associated with a chronically progressive destruction of the joints. Typically, the disease progresses through three stages, the first stage being asymptomatic and characterized by increased production of uric acid which results in an elevation of the concentration of uric acid in the blood (hyperuricemia). In the second stage, in addition to the hyperuricemia, recurrent attacks of acute arthritis occur. The third stage is known as chronic tophaceous gout because it is characterized by the progressive deposition of urates in and about the joints, with consequent joint destruction. Although the manifestations of gout tend to progress in this order, the symptoms vary markedly from one individual to the next. For instance, there is no clear relationship between the occurrence of acute arthritis and either the degree of elevation of blood uric acid or the size and location of tophi. In the late stages of gout, kidney damage often occurs. Renal involvement is especially pernicious in this disease because it may cause a decreased ability to excrete urates and thereby may accelerate the accumulation of urates in the body.

Uric acid is one of the normal end products of the metabolism of purines in humans. The purines are a group of bases that serve as building blocks for certain nucleotides, which in turn are building blocks for the nucleic acids (see Chapter 3). They also form an integral part of certain coenzymes (see Chapter 5). Uric acid is produced by deamination and oxidation of the purine bases while still in combined form in the normal course of the turnover of the nucleic acids, as shown schematically in Figure 13.4. The purines may also be formed *de novo* by synthesis. The origins of the various atoms of the synthesized purine ring are indicated in Figure 13.5.

Uric acid, which is not used or metabolized further by the human body, is carried by the blood to the kidneys and is excreted in the urine. Under normal conditions the rates of uric acid production and excretion are in balance; therefore, the serum level and the total amount of uric acid in the body are maintained within relatively narrow limits. In patients with gout, this balance is no longer maintained. As a result, both the serum level of uric acid and, more significantly, the total quantity of uric acid increases. Obviously, the cause of such an imbalance could be either an increase in the production (or intake of precursors) of uric acid or a decrease in the excretion of uric acid by the kidney. Probably

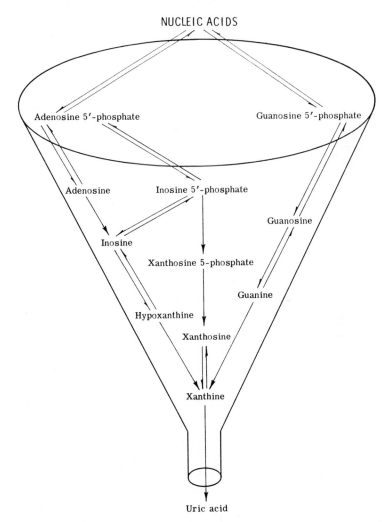

Fig. 13.4. Metabolic pathways for the degradation of purines arising from the breakdown of nucleic acids. The final product is uric acid.

in all cases of primary gout there is an overproduction of uric acid, and in some cases there is also an abnormally low excretion. So far, no single metabolic defect has been found to explain gout as uniquely as the single deficiency of tyrosinase explains albinism. However, gout is known to be a heritable disease, and experience has taught us to suspect that somewhere behind such a disorder lies a faulty gene which is responsible for the synthesis of a faulty protein (or for the inability to synthesize the protein altogether). The biochemical findings in gout indicate that the protein in question is an enzyme involved in purine metabolism.

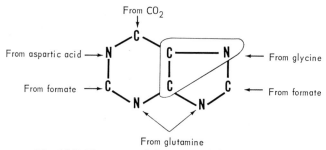

Fig. 13.5. The origin of the atoms of the purine ring.

Two drugs that have been of the greatest therapeutic value in the treatment of gout—probenecid and colchicine—have also been useful in studying this disease. Probenecid induces increased excretion of uric acid by the kidney. By the use of this drug it is possible not only to restore the normal production-excretion balance, but even to raise the rate of excretion over that of production and thereby to deplete the excess stores of urate in the body. This drug is obviously most effective in the treatment of the chronic, tophaceous stages of gout; it has no effect on acute, gouty arthritis. For the latter purpose the drug of choice is colchicine. Until recently, little has been known about the mechanism of action of colchicine in alleviating the acute arthritis of gout. Recent work appears to be leading to some understanding of this mechanism.

Examination of samples of fluid removed from the joints of patients with acute gouty arthritis reveals the presence of urate crystals inside phagocytes, cells responsible for ingesting foreign materials in the body. The phagocytes in the joint fluid of asymptomatic patients with gout do not contain urate crystals, even though the fluid itself may contain a large amount of urate. On the basis of these observations it appeared that the ingestion of urate crystals by phagocytes in the joint fluid was in some way involved in the production of the acute arthritis. To test this possibility, the effects of injecting crystalline vs. amorphous urates into the joints of normal individuals were compared. No symptoms developed in those individuals whose joints had been injected with the amorphous urates. However, in the individuals whose joints had been injected with crystals, typical symptoms of acute gouty arthritis developed, and phagocytosis of the crystals was demonstrated in fluid later removed from these joints. Studies carried out *in vitro* gave similar results: when normal joint fluid was incubated with amorphous urates, no phagocytosis of urate was noted, whereas crystalline urates were rapidly ingested by the phagocytes of joint fluid. Addition of colchicine to the incubation mixture in the latter case prevented the phagocytosis of the crystals. Administration of colchicine to patients suffering an acute attack of gouty arthritis reverses the clinical symptoms and prevents phagocytosis of urate crystals, as judged by examination of joint fluid. It is possible that the phagocytosis of urate crystals in the joint is related to the occurrence of attacks of acute gouty arthritis, yet the exact nature of this relationship remains unknown. An attractive hypothesis is that the arthritic pain results from production of large amounts of lactic acid. It has been known for some time that phagocytosis is associated with the production of lactic acid. According to this hypothesis, the effect of colchicine is exerted by preventing phagocytosis of urate crystals in the joint fluid, thereby preventing the production of lactic acid and the consequent painful symptoms of acute arthritis.

Seemingly Nonchemical Diseases

Myocardial Infarction

Myocardial infarction is currently among the leading causes of death in the United States. As mentioned above, the word *infarction* means death of a group of cells due to lack of oxygen. In myocardial infarction it is a group of heart cells that dies, and the anoxia is due to partial or complete occlusion of the artery supplying the area of the heart in which these cells are located. As a result of the infarction, which varies in size and position, depending upon the particular vessel occluded, the function of the heart as a whole may be impaired. If the impairment is severe, death of the individual may result. In cases in which death does not occur, the dead cells of the infarcted area of myocardium are gradually removed and are replaced with fibrous (scar) tissue. The scar tissue strengthens the injured wall of the heart but cannot replace the contractile function of the dead myocardial cells. Thus, a heart that contains one or more of these scars may function less well than a normal heart.

Since infarction results from the obstruction of blood flow through a vessel, the problem is essentially one of faulty plumbing, and no molecular mechanism is immediately apparent to explain the mechanical failure. However, through extensive investigation of myocardial infarction by the pathologist, the clinician, and the biochemist, some clues to the molecular basis of this disease are now emerging.

Occlusion of a coronary artery almost always occurs by one of three mechanisms: by gradual narrowing of the lumen due to thickening of the vessel wall; by the formation of a blood clot (thrombus) within the vessel; or by obstruction of the vessel by some foreign matter (embolus) carried there through the blood stream. Although the first two of these mechanisms are interrelated, it will be instructive to discuss them separately. The third mechanism is by far the least common.

Narrowing of a coronary vessel is most often the result of a rather complex series of pathological changes that are known collectively as *atherosclerosis*. Although there is still some question about detail, it is generally agreed that atherosclerosis begins with the deposition of lipids within the inner layer (*intima*) of the vessel wall. Concomitant with the deposition of lipids, both proliferation and necrosis (death) of intimal cells occur; this leads gradually to thickening of the inner lining of the vessel. In addition, a mass of platelets (small cellular elements normally present in the blood stream) and fibrin are deposited in layers on the inner surface of the vessel. As a result of this combination of intimal thickening and layering of platelets and fibrin, the lumen becomes narrowed. Another factor which may aggravate the condition is the accumulation of calcium salts within the necrotic areas of the intima.

The various factors influencing the rate and extent of lipid deposition in blood vessel walls are extremely complex. It appears that the process "normally" goes on throughout life. Whether or not clinical manifestations of atherosclerosis appear at or beyond middle age depends, in part, upon whether a person dies of some other cause before the process produces symptoms. The process appears to be influenced by diet. People who have a very high intake of lipids tend to develop atherosclerosis more commonly, and at earlier ages, than do people on diets that are very low in lipids. Another factor is sex; estrogen retards the development of atherosclerosis, and may be partly responsible for the fact that myocardial infarction occurs less frequently, and at a later age, in women than in men. Several diseases in which the concentration of lipids in the blood is elevated cause a predisposition to the development of atherosclerosis. Among them are diabetes and certain genetic disorders of lipid metabolism, such as familial hypercholesterolemia. Despite the rapid growth of our knowledge about the factors influencing the deposition of lipid in blood vessel walls, we are still quite far from being able to answer questions about the molecular mechanisms involved. Intensive research in this area of medical biochemistry holds promise of providing some of the answers in the next decade.

The formation of a thrombus within the lumen of a coronary vessel involves the complex mechanism of blood clotting. A thrombus consists of a tangled mass of fibrin in which red blood cells are caught. Although thrombi can form free in the blood stream, they most often begin on the inner surface of a vessel. They usually originate at a point where either the vessel surface, or the blood flow just above the surface, is abnormal. Thus, thrombi tend to occur either in conjunction with sites of lipid deposition (atherosclerotic plaques), over which there is a disturbance in the integrity of the vessel lining, or just beyond a branch point of the vessel, where the blood flow may be turbulent. In either case, once a thrombus has begun to form, it tends to grow in size until it has obstructed the vessel.

An embolus is usually a small piece of a thrombus that has broken loose from a large clot, or a fragment of an atherosclerotic plaque which has broken down. It arises either in the heart itself or in a large vessel, and is swept along, in the blood stream, into a coronary artery until it becomes caught in one of the smaller divisions of the vessel. At this point it may serve as the basis for the formation of an even more extensive thrombus and may obstruct the flow of blood.

The molecular mechanisms involved in blood coagulation are far too numerous to be detailed in this chapter. The schematic representation shown in Figure 13.6 gives a picture of the complexity of the coagulation system. We shall focus on just a few points in this system to illustrate the molecular nature of the process.

As shown in Figure 13.6, the system consists of a long series of chemical reactions, the product of each one catalyzing the next. The series may be summed up by the statement that, in response to some stimulus which activates the process, fibrinogen is converted into fibrin. Fibrinogen is a soluble protein, normally present in the blood at all times, ready to be converted into fibrin whenever the coagulation system is activated. It is a large protein (molecular weight 330,000), made up of six polypeptide chains held together by disulfide bonds. The six chains are comprised of three pairs of different chains. Fibrin is formed from fibrinogen by the action of the proteolytic enzyme thrombin. Unlike most proteolytic enzymes, thrombin has an exceedingly high degree of specificity. The only protein it attacks is fibrinogen, and its attack on this molecule occurs at only two specific peptide bonds. In Figure 13.7 a rough "structure" of fibrinogen is shown, each pair of identical polypeptide chains being represented by one chain. The two bonds cleaved by the catalytic action of thrombin are indicated in the figure. They are the peptide bonds between specific arginine and glycine residues in two of the three different polypeptide chains. Since the fibrinogen molecule actually contains two of each type of chain, thrombin catalyzes the cleavage of a total of four peptide bonds in each molecule. The products of this cleavage are one fibrin molecule and two molecules each of two different peptides, peptide A (containing nineteen amino acids) and peptide B (containing twenty-one amino acids).

How does the conversion of fibrinogen to fibrin result in the

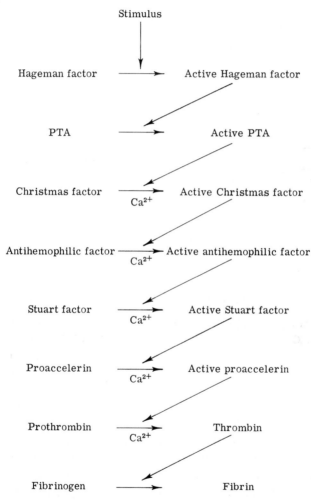

Fig. 13.6. A tentative scheme for the mechanism of blood coagulation modified from E. W. Davies and O. D. Ratnoff (see references). In response to an appropriate stimulus, the long series of reactions is started, the product of each reaction catalyzing the next in the series. The final effect is the conversion of fibrinogen to fibrin, which serves as the basis for the blood clot.

formation of a blood clot? The answer lies in the tendency of fibrin molecules to aggregate to such a high degree as to precipitate from solution, forming an insoluble coagulum. As this coagulum forms in whole blood, the cellular elements of the blood become trapped within it. The modification in the structure of fibrinogen brought about by the catalytic action of thrombin (which converts it into fibrin) serves to expose a number of chemically reactive sites through which fibrin molecules react with one another to form a

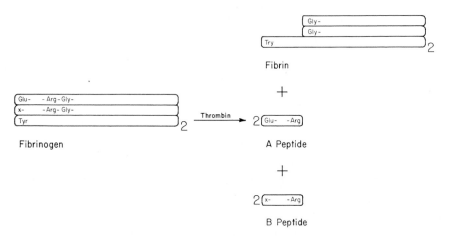

Fig. 13.7. A schematic structural representation of the conversion of fibrinogen to fibrin. The reaction, catalyzed by thrombin, yields from each molecule of fibrinogen one molecule of fibrin plus four peptides (two molecules of peptide A and two of peptide B). Only three of the six polypeptide chains of the proteins are shown, since the other three are identical.

multimolecular aggregation. Because these binding sites remain protected (unexposed) in the fibrinogen molecule, fibrinogen cannot aggregate and therefore remains soluble.

One of the peptides formed by the cleaveage of fibrinogen (the B peptide) displays a very interesting action *in vitro;* it potentiates the effect of the hormone bradykinin in causing contraction of smooth muscle. If this action operates *in vivo,* then the conversion of fibrinogen into fibrin may serve a twofold purpose in the stoppage of bleeding from a superficial wound: first, it causes the formation of a blood clot, which tends to seal the open ends of bleeding blood vessels; second, it releases a substance (B peptide) which may facilitate the contraction of smooth muscle in the wall of the vessel and thereby help to restrict the flow of blood.

It is easy to see why an efficient mechanism for blood clotting is important to life when one considers the importance of the clotting process in the body's defense against the dangers of a superficial wound. No doubt the mechanism was developed and preserved throughout evolution because of its beneficial nature. However, in the case of a coronary occlusion, it is essentially the same mechanism that leads to the stoppage of blood flow to part of a vital organ. In this condition the coagulation process is started by a stimulus such as a roughened area on the blood vessel surface, rather than by a laceration of superficial tissue. Thus, the very process that may be lifesaving in one situation can lead to death in another. The coagulation process, at least in its final effect, is simply not capable of discriminating between the different stimuli in the two cases. This paradoxical phenomenon is by no means unique to the process of blood coagulation. There are a number of physiological mechanisms which are ordinarily beneficial but may at times cause great harm. Prime examples may be found among the immune responses, certain types of which may be either life-saving or lethal, depending upon the circumstances.

Our discussion of the molecular basis of coronary occlusion has led us far afield—into a discussion of lipid metabolism and blood coagulation. Even so, we have not touched upon some of the other, perhaps even more complex, mechanisms which come into play during and after the occurrence of a coronary occlusion and which have profound effects on the course of the disease. The reason why our discussion has led to such digression is that coronary occlusion is only the end result of a large number of molecular events. It is this multiplicity of molecular factors which makes diseases such as myocardial infarction seem, at first sight, not to have molecular bases at all. When one probes the mechanisms involved in each of the events associated with these complex diseases, however, one finds that they are ultimately capable of precise definition at the molecular level.

Myocardial infarction is used here merely as an example; other seemingly "nonchemical" diseases can also be investigated by this approach. Infectious diseases, for instance, have been fruitfully studied from the standpoint of the molecular events involved. It is no longer sufficient for the physician to say merely that a person has certain symptoms because there are microorganisms growing in his throat. He now asks about the molecular mechanisms involved in bacterial toxins, in allergic reactions, and in tissue damage. Once the answers to such questions are found, the groundwork will have been laid for the most rational development of means to prevent, or to alter, pathological conditions. Cancer and schizophrenia are among the many disorders in which the medical world is beginning to probe for molecular mechanisms. The probing in these areas has only just begun, but, if judged from the fruitfulness of biochemical investigations in other areas of medicine, a successful conclusion cannot be far away.

Suggested Reading

Books

Dubos, R. J., "Biochemical Determinants of Microbial Disease," Harvard University Monographs in Medicine and Public Health, Harvard University Press, Cambridge, Massachusetts, 1954.

"Garrod's Inborn Errors of Metabolism," reprinted with a supplement by H. Harris, Oxford University Press, London, 1963.

Thompson, R. H. S., and King, E. J., "Biochemical Disorders in Human Disease," 2nd ed., Academic Press, New York, 1964.

Wagner, R. P., and Mitchell, H. K., "Genetics and Metabolism," John Wiley and Sons, New York, 1964.

Wagner, W. F., and Folkers, K., "Vitamins and Coenzymes," Methuen Co., London, 1964.

Special Articles

Baglioni, C., *in* "Molecular Genetics" (J. H. Taylor, ed.), Part I, Academic Press, New York, 1963: on genetics and chemistry of human hemoglobins.

Boyd, G. S., *in* "Biochemical Disorders in Human Disease" (R. H. S. Thompson and E. J. King, eds.), Academic Press, New York, 1964: on atherosclerosis.

Davie, E. W., and Ratnoff, O. D., *in* "The Proteins" (H. Neurath, ed.), Vol. III, pp. 359–443, Academic Press, New York, 1965: on proteins of blood coagulation.

Epstein, F. H., Block, W. B., Hand, E. A., and Francis, T., *Am. J. Med.* **26**, 39(1959): on familial hypercholesterolemia, xanthomatosis, and coronary heart disease.

Fitzpatrick, T., *in* "The Metabolic Basis of Inherited Disease" (J. C. Stanbury, J. B. Wyngaarden, and D. S. Fredrickson, eds.), pp 228–428, McGraw-Hill, New York, 1960: on albinism.

Gerald, P. S., *in* "The Metabolic Basis of Inherited Disease" (J. C. Stanbury, J. B. Wyngaarden, and D. S. Fredrickson, eds.), pp. 1068–1085. McGraw-Hill, Inc., New York, 1960: on hereditary methemoglobinemias.

Gutman, A. B., *Am. J. Med.* **29,** 545 (1960): on gout as an inborn error of metabolism.

Gutman, A. B., *Am. J. Med.,* **35,** 820 (1963): on the role of glutamine metabolism in gout.

Pauling, L., Itano, H. A., Singer, S. J., and Wells, I. C., *Science* **110,** 543 (1949): on sickle cell anemia, a molecular disease.

Symposium on "Inborn Errors of Metabolism," *Am. J. Med.* **22,** No. 5 (1957).

CHAPTER 14

Drugs and Poisons

Drugs and poisons may be classified in many ways, but simplification in this endeavor leads to inaccuracies. The field of pharmacology and toxicology are as diverse as is the field of biochemistry itself. Therefore, we shall not attempt to discuss all drugs and poisons or even to illustrate all the principles of pharmacology and toxicology. Our discussion of a few selected examples is intended to illustrate the premise that pharmacological and toxicological actions are the effects of specific molecules on specific biochemical systems. Most of the examples we have chosen illustrate mechanisms underlying the actions of both poisons and drugs. The very fact that the same compounds may exert both beneficial and harmful effects serves to underscore the idea that at the molecular level many of the basic principles apply equally to drugs and poisons.

The Concept of Poison and Drug

The concept of a poison is not absolute but relative: any substance, whether normal or foreign to a cell, may be poisonous when present above a critical concentration. It is sometimes difficult to distinguish between a poisonous concentration of a given substance and a poisonous substance *per se*. For instance, sodium chloride, at a concentration of about 0.1 M or less, is harmless to mammlian cells, but at a concentration of 1.0 M, sodium chloride—or any other salt—is highly toxic. There are cells of other types, however, such as those of marine microorganisms, that thrive in a solution which is 1.0 M with respect to sodium chloride. These cells, in turn, will die if the salt concentration is increased still farther. This differential sensitivity of cells of different types has been used to advantage in the field of antimicrobial chemotherapy. A substance may be poisonous to bacterial cells invading human tissues at a concentration which is harmless to mammalian cells—the opposite of the example of sodium chloride. Thus, a "poison" may be used as a "drug" when the metabolic machinery of the host is sufficiently different from that of the pathogen.

Drugs and poisons can never impose new characteristics on living cells. They can only suppress, stimulate, or modify biochemical processes which are inherent in normal cellular metabolism. Digitalis, for example, is an extremely useful drug in the treatment of congestive heart failure. The muscle cells of the failing myocardium contract with insufficient force; digitalis tends to correct this malfunction. Digitalis cannot, however, make the muscle cells contract more forcefully than they are potentially capable of doing. Once the myocardium has lost a great deal of its potential for forceful contraction, digitalis cannot be expected to have much beneficial effect.

Wide Spectrum Poisons vs. Single Target Poisons

There are some compounds that are poisonous at extremely low concentrations. These are the substances that are commonly called poisons. In general, poisons act by damaging the membrane systems, by inhibiting the enzymes, or by interfering with the control mechanisms of the cell. Some poisons, such as the heavy metal ions, are capable of reacting with a wide variety of cellular components. In a molecular sense, these are like bulls in a china shop. Although it is true that some sites within the cell may be more sensitive than others, these poisons act in a rather indiscriminate manner. A relatively large number of molecules of the poison are "wasted" in reacting with noncritical components of the cell before enough molecules have reacted with sufficient criticial components to cause toxic effects. This probably accounts for the relatively high concentrations at which these poisons cause symptoms. Other poisons, such as cyanide, do not squander their substance in "unimportant" areas, but react exclusively with one critical component of the cell. These are the single-target poisons. Any reagent which interferes with a biochemical mechanism of the cell at a very low concentration is likely to be a single-target poison. Moreover, it appears that at the molecular level all such poisons exert their effects by interacting, either directly or indirectly, with macromolecules. For this reason, highly selective poisons are of considerable interest to biochemists as reagents for probing chemically the structures and functions of macromolecular systems. The biochemical problems in which specific inhibitors have been of greatest importance are those involving multistep processes. Mitochondrial energy transduction is a prime example; the solution of this problem is being facilitated by the use of poisons that inhibit the process selectively at various specific points. Protein biosynthesis is another excellent example.

Penetration of Poisons

Unless a potential poison can reach the vulnerable site in a cell, no toxic consequences can develop. There are a number of biological barriers which can hinder the movement of a potential poison toward the susceptible site. In the case of snake venoms, most of these hindrances are bypassed, since the venom usually is injected directly into the soft tissues beneath the skin by the fangs of the snake and is widely distributed via the lymphatic system to other parts of the body. In the case of bacterial invasion through the skin, however, the barriers are numerous. The intact human skin is rather resistant to invasion by the many bacteria that normally live on its surface. However, certain bacteria are specialized for the production of substances that aid them to spread rapidly once they have gained entrance. One of the important barriers to bacterial invasion is the connective tissue network in the dermal layer of the skin. Hyaluronidase is an enzyme elaborated by some bacteria into their growth media, and by certain snakes and spiders into their venoms. This enzyme catalyzes the depolymerization of mucopolysaccharides, which are essential components of the connective tissue network. Once this network is damaged, the possibility is opened for the rapid spread of toxins or of bacteria into the dermal layer. Thus, hyaluronidase can facilitate the more extensive invasion of microorganisms, as well as a wider distribution of poisons.

Drug Dosage

Implicit in the term *drug* are the same provisions with respect to concentration that were discussed in relation to poisons. For each drug there is a minimal concentration below which it has no demonstrable effect. As the dosage is increased, the effect becomes more and more pronounced until a plateau may be reached, after which further increases in dosage are no longer attended by increases in the characteristic pharmacologic effect. Aspirin, for instance, is a highly effective antipyretic agent, but 10 gm of aspirin will not lower the temperature of a febrile patient more quickly, or to a greater extent, than will 5 gm, or 1 gm, because even 1 gm produces a level which exceeds that at which the plateau is reached. For many drugs, however, no dosage plateau exists. For instance, central nervous system depressants, such as the barbiturates, cause mental relaxation at low dosages, sleep at higher dosages, and progressively deeper anesthesia, leading finally to death, at progressively higher dosages. Thus, there may be a continuum in which greater concentrations of a drug are attended by more pronounced effects. It may be said of all drugs, however, that, beyond a certain maximal concentration, toxic manifestations will be elicited. One characteristic of a drug that is extremely important to the physician is the *therapeutic index*—that is, the ratio of the dosage at which a drug exerts its toxic action to the dosage at which it exerts its pharmacologic action.

$$\text{Therapeutic index} = \frac{\text{toxic dosage}}{\text{pharmacological dosage}}$$

If the value of the ratio is large, the drug is relatively safe to use. If it is small (close to unity), then the dosage must be controlled with utmost precaution. If the ratio is one or less, then the compound cannot properly be called a drug at all, except in certain special instances (see below under antitumor drugs), because it acts as a poison at concentrations lower than those at which it acts as a drug.

As with poisons, one must distinguish between the primary and secondary targets of drugs. Many drugs, at concentrations useful medically, act on more than one metabolic process or chemical reaction. Other drugs may act very selectively, but still affect a specific biochemical reaction in a number of different tissues; such a drug may appear to be affecting several different reactions because it may produce several different effects. In any case, the "side effects" must be taken into account by the medical practitioner when he uses drugs. Certain drugs appear to exert different effects at different dosages. Aspirin, for instance, acts as an antipyretic at relatively low concentrations, whereas it decreases the inflammation of joints in patients with certain types of arthritis only at much higher concentrations. It is likely that in instances of this type the drug acts in two fundamentally different ways in the two situations.

Selected Examples of Drugs and Poisons

DICUMAROL

The discovery of the first anticoagulant available for the treatment of human diseases, Dicumarol, has an interesting history. In the 1920's a new disease was noted in cattle by veterinarians. After surgical procedures, the cattle afflicted with this disease continued to bleed, and often died of hemorrhage. Soon the cause of this condition, known as *sweet clover disease,* was traced to a poisonous substance in plants growing in the meadows on which the afflicted cattle had been grazing. Intensive investigation of this substance by many workers, most notably by K. P. Link and H. A. Campbell and their colleagues at the University of Wisconsin, led eventually to the isolation and structural identification of the poison as 3,3'-methylenebis(4-hydroxycoumarin), otherwise known as Dicumarol. Biochemical studies on Dicumarol disclosed that its anticoagulant effect was due to the fact that it causes a deficiency of prothrombin.

A simplified scheme of the normal blood clotting mechanism is shown here, to point out this site of action.

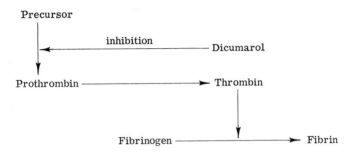

Prothrombin is a protein which is synthesized by the cells of the liver and is normally present in the circulating blood. When certain kinds of trauma occur, such as a surgical incision, a series of complex events leads to the catalytic conversion of prothrombin to thrombin; this, in turn, leads to the formation of a clot which helps to stop the bleeding. Thrombin is a proteolytic enzyme which rather selectively catalyzes the conversion of fibrinogen (normally present in the circulating blood) into fibrin, an insoluble protein that serves as the structural network of the blood clot. On the basis of these facts, the hemorrhagic symptoms of sweet clover disease may easily be explained as poisoning by Dicumarol. By preventing the formation of prothrombin, Dicumarol inhibits the clotting process. Although the mechanism by which Dicumarol poisoning causes a deficiency of prothrombin remains an unsettled question, we can make some guesses. Before doing so, however, we must digress to discuss another compound that may, in a certain sense, be considered a drug: vitamin K.

Deficiency of vitamin K produces hemorrhagic symptoms. Investigation of the cause of these symptoms has revealed that a deficiency of prothrombin is involved. Evidently, when insufficient quantities of dietary vitamin K are absorbed, the rate of prothrombin synthesis by the liver is markedly diminished, and the circulating level of prothrombin in the blood falls. Vitamin K deficiency thus mimics the toxic effect of Dicumarol. The remarkably similar chemical structures of vitamin K and Dicumarol are shown here:

Vitamin K   Dicumarol

Because of the structural similarities between these two compounds, and because they exert opposite effects on the synthesis of prothrombin, several hypotheses for the mechanism of their action can be proposed. Perhaps the most straightforward possibility is that vitamin K is the normal prosthetic group for an enzyme required for the synthesis (or release) of prothrombin by the liver. By analogy with the function of many other vitamins as prosthetic groups of enzymes, this assumption is not unlikely (see Chapter 13). Dicumarol, like vitamin K, may be able to bind to the same enzyme, but may be unable to provide the appropriate function. Thus, the enzyme bound to vitamin K would be functional, whereas the enzyme bound to Dicumarol would be nonfunctional. According to this hypothesis, Dicumarol acts by causing a vitamin K "deficiency"—that is, by displacing vitamin K from an enzyme which is required for prothrombin synthesis. It should be noted that a rapid and highly effective treatment for Dicumarol poisoning (or overdosage) is the administration of vitamin K. To continue with the same hypothesis: these facts could be explained by a competition between Dicumarol and vitamin K for the same site on an enzyme required for the synthesis of prothrombin. If the concentration of vitamin K were increased, the Dicumarol bound to the enzyme would be displaced by the normal prosthetic group, and the function of the enzyme could thus be restored.

Anticoagulants are now an important and well established part of medical treatment in a large number of conditions, such as thrombophlebitis and coronary occlusion, and also during vascular surgery. Over the past few years chemists have attempted to synthesize new anticoagulants, using the structures of Dicumarol and vitamin K as their guides. These attempts have proved extremely successful, and have yielded new drugs with far greater potency than Dicumarol.

DIISOPROPYLFLUOROPHOSPHATE

The most intensive early investigations on diisopropylfluorophosphate (DFP) were concerned with its potent toxic effects, and only later was this compound used as a drug. During World War II, DFP was studied as a possible agent for chemical warfare. It is one of the class of compounds known as nerve gases, which cause death by paralysis. The therapeutic usefulness of DFP has been in the symptomatic treatment of myasthenia gravis, a condition characterized by weakness and rapid fatiguability of muscles. Since the discovery of the beneficial effects of DFP in cases of myasthenia gravis, a number of more effective agents have been found. However, since the mechanism of action of most of these newer drugs is basically similar to that of DFP, we shall use DFP as the prototype. Before discussing DFP as a drug, we shall digress to consider first the mechanism by which motor nerve impulses stimulate muscles to contract, thence to the mechanism by which DFP exerts its toxic effect. We shall then return to the question of how DFP may alleviate some of the symptoms of myasthenia gravis, and consider drugs and diseases that illustrate similar mechanisms.

Studies on the transmission of nerve impulses have, since the elegant studies of Otto Loewi in the 1920's, brought to light the important role of specific chemical substances known as neurohumors. One of the most important of the neurohumors is acetylcholine, which functions in many parts of the nervous system. For the present discussion we are concerned only with the effect of this compound at the neuromuscular junction, the site at which a somatic motor nerve ending is applied to a skeletal muscle fiber. The process by which the nerve causes a contraction of the muscle involves the release of acetylcholine from the nerve ending. This neurohumor serves to transmit the nerve impulse across the neuromuscular junction. The mechanism by which acetylcholine causes the muscle to contract is complex, and still not entirely understood. For the present discussion it is sufficient to say that it changes a site on the surface of the muscle fiber from state A to state B, and that this change in state initiates the contraction. When the supply of acetylcholine is exhausted at the neuromuscular junction, the sensitive site on the muscle fiber quickly returns to state A, and is ready to be stimulated again. Were the acetylcholine to remain in the junction, the surface of the fiber would remain in state B, incapable of further stimulation. During normal muscular contraction, nerve impulses must be conducted through a given neuromuscular junction with very great frequency; it is therefore essential, especially for sustained or repetitive contraction, that the acetylcholine secreted with each nerve impulse be removed very rapidly. The device by which this rapid removal is accomplished involves the enzyme cholinesterase, which catalyzes the hydrolytic degradation of acetylcholine to choline and acetate, as shown in the formulation:

$$(CH_3)_3\overset{+}{N}-CH_2-CH_2-O-\overset{\overset{\displaystyle O}{\|}}{C}-CH_3 + H_2O \xrightarrow{\text{cholinesterase}} \begin{array}{c} (CH_3)_3\overset{+}{N}-CH_2-CH_2-OH \\ \text{Choline} \\ + \\ CH_3-\overset{\overset{\displaystyle O}{\|}}{C}-OH \\ \text{Acetic acid} \end{array}$$

Acetylcholine

Once the acetylcholine in the neuromuscular junction has been hydrolyzed, the surface of the muscle fiber returns to state A, and is ready to be stimulated again. The role of cholinesterase in scavenging residual acetylcholine has been thoroughly established by the extensive studies of David Nachmansohn.

DFP inhibits the enzymic activity of cholinesterase and thereby prevents the catalytic hydrolysis of acetylcholine. In the presence of DFP, acetylcholine secreted into a neuromuscular junction by a nerve ending, remains at the junction and maintains the surface of the muscle fiber in state B, incapable of further stimulation. Repeated nerve impulses impinging upon a neuromuscular junction which is inhibited by DFP serve only to raise the concentration of acetylcholine still farther, but cannot cause the muscle cell to contract. Failure to transmit the impulses to the muscle appears, symptomatically, as paralysis. Death due to DFP poisoning results from paralysis of the muscles of respiration.

An extremely effective antidote for DFP poisoning was synthesized by Wilson and Ginsberg in the laboratory of David Nachmansohn. They reasoned that, since DFP inhibits the activity of cholinesterase, it must be bound to the enzyme; however, if another molecule could bind DFP even more avidly than does the enzyme, such a molecule might be able to displace the poison from the cholinesterase. On the basis of the chemical properties of acetylcholine (the natural substrate for the enzyme) and DFP (the enzyme inhibitor), they designed the molecule known as pyridine-2-aldoxime (2-PAM); the structure of 2-PAM, and its reaction with DFP are shown here:

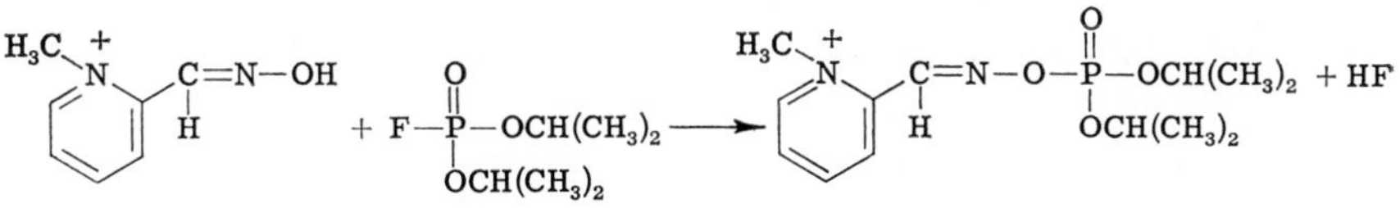

2-PAM   DFP   DFP-2-PAM complex

In studies of its potency in animals, 2-PAM was found to prevent death of mice which had received ten to twenty times the usual lethal dose of DFP. In addition, 2-PAM is a useful drug in humans, since it counteracts the effects of a number of drugs with actions similar to that of DFP. Overdosage with drugs of this type is not an uncommon happening because their therapeutic indices are close to unity. Therefore, 2-PAM has proved lifesaving in a number of instances.

In myasthenia gravis, a disease of unknown etiology, there appear to be both decreased synthesis (or release) of acetylcholine and also decreased sensitivity of muscle fibers to acetylcholine. At neuromuscular junctions the overall effect is that some nerve impulses do not suffice to initiate a contraction. Theoretically, the situation would be benefited by any substance which could increase the amount, or effectiveness, of the acetylcholine secreted at the neuromuscular junction with each nerve impulse. Compounds that inhibit cholinesterase do just this. By decreasing the catalytic hydrolysis, they allow what little acetylcholine may be available to persist for a longer time, so that, with succeeding nerve impulses, the concentration of the neurohumor is finally sufficient to initiate a contraction. There are several drugs, such as neostigmine, that are even more effective than DFP in achieving this effect; they are the drugs which are used today in the medical management of myasthenia gravis.

Myotonia congenita is a disease the pathology of which may, in a sense, be considered the reverse of that of myasthenia gravis. In this condition muscular weakness is also a prominent symptom, but the cause of the weakness lies in an *increased* sensitivity to acetylcholine at the neuromuscular function. The amount of the neurohumor normally secreted when a nerve impulse reaches the neuromuscular junction is so effective in a patient with myotonia congenita that, although one contraction can occur, the surface of the muscle fiber is unable to return from state B to state A (see above), and therefore remains refractory to additional nerve impulses. In this case the drug of choice would be one that would *decrease* the sensitivity of the muscle site to acetylcholine. Curare is a drug of this type, and has proved beneficial in the symptomatic treatment of myotonia congenita. Curare, like DFP, was first known for its toxic effects. For centuries it was used as an arrow poison by the Indians of South America as a means for paralyzing the victim. Curare and similar drugs are currently used to induce muscular relaxation. As an aid to anesthesia, for instance, these drugs are beneficial in certain surgical procedures.

Mechanistically, the pathologies involved in myotonia congenita and myesthenia gravis stand in an opposite sense to one another, although the symptoms are in certain respects similar. In the one disease, muscle weakness results from an exaggerated effect of acetylcholine, whereas in the other the weakness results from a diminished effect. As might be expected, drugs which are beneficial in one disorder aggravate the symptoms of the other. The toxic effects of both classes of drugs produce the same final symptom—paralysis of skeletal muscles—but the mechanisms are opposed.

VENOMS

The venomous reptiles, spiders, wasps, and coelenterates are among the many living organisms which produce highly potent toxins. Toxins are beneficial to these organisms for immobilizing prey and for repelling attackers. One of the active toxins in certain snake venoms is phospholipase A, an enzyme that catalyzes the hydrolysis of the phospholipids belonging to the class known as lecithins.

$$\begin{array}{c}
\overline{R}COOCH_2 \\
| \\
RCOOCH \quad\quad O \\
| \quad\quad\quad\quad \| \\
CH_2O{-}P{-}OCH_2CH_2\overset{+}{N}(CH_3)_3 \\
| \\
OH
\end{array}
\quad
\xrightarrow[\text{+ }H_2O]{\text{phospholipase A}}
\quad
\begin{array}{c}
\overline{R}COOCH_2 \\
| \\
HOCH \quad\quad O \\
| \quad\quad\quad\quad \| \\
CH_2O{-}P{-}OCH_2CH_2\overset{+}{N}(CH_3)_3 \\
| \\
OH
\end{array}$$

Lecithin   Lysolecithin + RCOOH (Fatty acid)

The fangs of poisonous snakes serve to inject the venom into the body of the victim, and the venom is then distributed widely via the lympatic system. A tissue most vulnerable to phospholipase A is the blood. The product of the reaction catalyzed by this enzyme, lysolecithin, has the properties of a detergent; it acts as a powerful hemolytic agent, causing rapid lysis of the red blood cell membrane. The massive hemolysis that occurs after bites by certain snakes is often due to phospholipase A and may cause the death of the victim.

Snake venoms have been important to the biochemist for a number of reasons. For example, they are an important source of phospholipase A. This enzyme is valuable in the biochemical laboratory in probing the chemical structures of phospholipids and in separating out those components of the cell which are membrane-bound.

Other poisonous substances found in the venoms of certain snakes include proteolytic enzymes, amino acid oxidases, and inhibitors of cholinesterase. It is the last of these substances that is responsible for the paralysis of the victim bitten by certain snakes. Cobra venom, for instance, contains a very potent inhibitor of cholinesterase which rapidly causes death due to paralysis of the muscles of respiration.

BACTERIAL EXOTOXINS

Many bacteria excrete into the growth medium substances which are toxic to man. Some of these bacterial exotoxins have been identified as enzymes. For instance, the α-toxin of *Clostridium perfringens* is a species of lecithinase, highly effective in causing hemolysis. Another enzyme elaborated by the same organism has collagenase activity; it catalyzes degradation of collagen, the most important structural element of connective tissue. Its effect is, therefore, a softening and, finally, disintegration of this tissue. Such a toxin allows the organism which produces it to invade more widely into the living tissues of the host.

Clostridium botulinum produces an exotoxin that is the most potent poison known. As little as 1 mg is enough to kill twenty million mice. Only rarely can a human be saved after oral intake of this toxin, death being due to damage of the central nervous system. Streptolysin S, one of the hemolytic toxins elaborated by certain streptococci, can induce the release of degradative enzymes from cellular organelles in which these enzymes are normally caged. The release of these degradative enzymes can then lead to a whole series of pathological changes. The toxin of murine *Pasteurella pestis* inhibits mitochondrial processes such as ion translocation and electron transfer at extremely low concentrations. It has, for this reason, become an important tool for the biochemical study of mitochondrial function.

ANTIMICROBIAL DRUGS

The first very effective chemotherapeutic agents used for the treatment of systemic infectious diseases in humans were the sulfonamides. We shall use sulfanilamide as the prototype of the several sulfonamide drugs. The mechanism of its bacteriostatic activity involves blockage of the pathway for folic acid synthesis. Folic acid, one of the essential coenzymes (see Chapter 5), must be synthesized by many types of bacteria. One of the essential building blocks in this synthesis is *p*-aminobenzoic acid (PABA). The enzyme that catalyzes the introduction of PABA into the folic acid molecule is the target of sulfanilamide. The formulae of PABA and sulfanilamide are shown here:

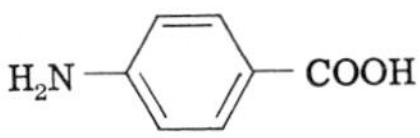

H_2N —⟨benzene⟩— COOH

PABA

H_2N —⟨benzene⟩— SO_2NH_2

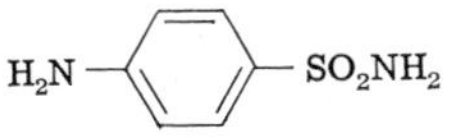

Sulfanilamide

Because of the structural similarity between these two molecules, sulfanilamide is able to displace PABA (the normal substrate) in the coupling system, and thereby to block the pathway of folic acid biosynthesis. When thus deprived of folic acid, bacteria are unable to grow; this is the mechanism by which sulfanilamide acts. Only those bacteria that synthesize folic acid by way of PABA are affected by sulfanilamide or its variants. Man is not bothered by drugs of this type because preformed folic acid is necessarily provided in his diet. An interesting corollary of the folic acid-sulfanilamide antagonism is the fact that folic acid in the host cell is not available to the pathogen. Otherwise, the pathogen would be able to grow in the tissues of the host even in the presence of sulfanilamide.

One of the most decisive events in the history of chemotherapy was the discovery of the bacteriocidal action of penicillin. This antibiotic is synthesized by molds of the genus *Penicillium*. There are actually several varieties of penicillin; the formula of one of them, benzylpenicillin (penicillin G), is shown below, with a dashed line surrounding the part common to all varieties:

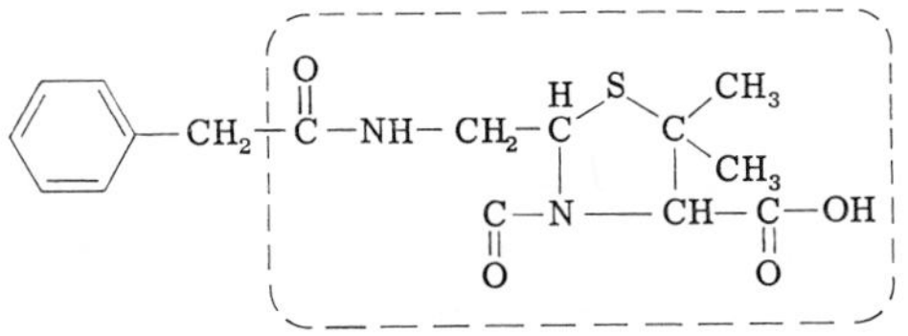

Benzylpenicillin

Penicillin interferes at some point in the sequence of reactions by which the cell wall of susceptible bacteria is synthesized. When the synthesis of the cell wall is inhibited, cell division leads to the death of the bacteria. For this reason, the bacteriocidal effects of penicillin are far more pronounced in a rapidly growing cell population than in a slowly growing one. Penicillin has no adverse effect on man because there is no comparable synthetic process in the cells of man.

As might have been anticipated, some pathogenic bacteria developed a resistance to penicillin. The particular form of resistance found in certain staphylococci was traced to the fact that these bacteria elaborated an enzyme, penicillinase, which catalyzed the degradation of penicillin to inactive products. This was a problem, not of resistance to penicillin as such, but of the disappearance of penicillin before it could be effective. By the chemical synthesis of variant forms of penicillin, this problem has been partly solved. In one of the variants recently synthesized, a β-ethoxynaphthyl group (shown below) replaces the normally occurring benzyl group:

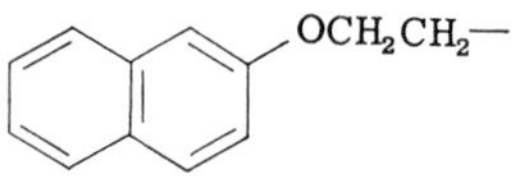

β-Ethoxynaphthyl group

Strains of staphylococci which are resistant to benzylpenicillin are vulnerable to the β-ethoxynaphthyl form of the drug because the penicillinase they produce is unable to catalyze the degradation of the latter form.

HEAVY METALS

Metals generally, and heavy metals in particular, are highly toxic to cells. Lead (Pb), mercury (Hg) and arsenic (As) are among the earliest known heavy metal poisons. They are all capable of reacting with proteins and with some coenzymes. The metalloprotein derivatives which are formed by the interaction of the ions of these heavy metals with cellular proteins may not retain the biological activities of the unmodified proteins. Lead, mercury, and arsenic all share the property of reacting readily with the sulfhydryl groups of proteins, although the modes of interaction differ. Compounds of trivalent arsenic (R-As$<$) can interact with neighboring pairs of sulfhydryl groups in proteins.

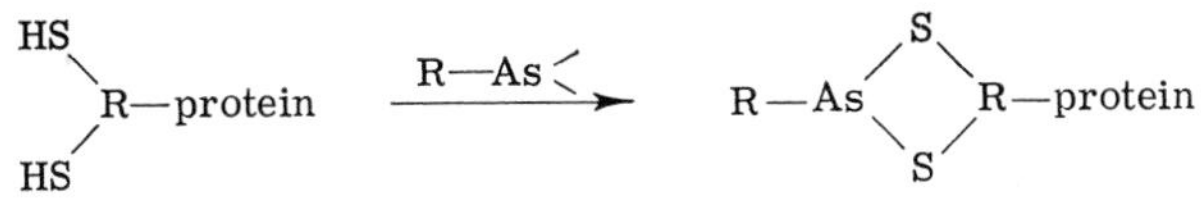

$$\begin{array}{c} \text{HS} \\ \diagdown \\ \text{R—protein} \\ \diagup \\ \text{HS} \end{array} \quad \xrightarrow{\text{R—As}<} \quad \begin{array}{c} \text{S} \\ \diagup\ \diagdown \\ \text{R—As}\text{R—protein} \\ \diagdown\ \diagup \\ \text{S} \end{array}$$

The pyruvic and α-ketoglutaric dehydrogenase complexes of the mitochondrion are particularly sensitive to the action of As_2O_3. This sensitivity can be referred to the presence in these complexes of bound lipoic acid

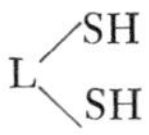

$$\text{L}\begin{array}{c} \diagup \text{SH} \\ \diagdown \text{SH} \end{array}$$

which carries two -SH groups in close proximity. Once the lipoic acid has reacted with the arsenical, it can no longer undergo oxidation and reduction (see Chapter 5) and is thus inactivated.

An organism poisoned with a heavy metal can be saved by the administration of reagents that displace the heavy metal from combination with the cellular proteins. The heavy metal ion can thus be solubilized by formation of a nontoxic complex with the drug; the complex can then be eliminated from the body of way of the kidneys. During World War II the British developed an antidote against arsenical war gases (such as lewisite) which was called BAL (British antilewisite). It has the following structure:

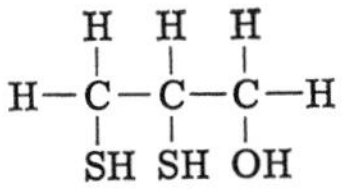

$$\begin{array}{ccc} \text{H} & \text{H} & \text{H} \\ | & | & | \\ \text{H—C—C—C—H} \\ | & | & | \\ \text{SH} & \text{SH} & \text{OH} \end{array}$$

This compound was designed for its job on the basis of the known mechanism of arsenical toxicity. Because BAL reacts with arsenicals much more avidly than do proteins, it can effectively displace the arsenicals from combination with proteins.

In addition, BAL also reacts with other heavy metals, such as cadmium, mercury and copper, and forms stable compounds with them. It has therefore been an effective agent for the treatment of heavy metal poisoning in general. The success of the search for an antidote for arsenic poisoning in the 1940's provides an excellent example of how the understanding of chemical mechanism can be a powerful tool for research in pharmacology.

More recently, ethylenediaminetetraacetate (abbreviated EDTA) has been found to be superior to BAL for the treatment of heavy metal poisoning. This compound forms stable complexes with the heavy metals by forming a ring structure known as a chelate:

Lead chelate of EDTA

The lead-EDTA complex, for example, is harmless and is readily excreted by the kidney.

CYANIDE

Cyanide combines avidly with the ferric iron of cytochrome oxidase in the electron-transfer chain, less avidly with the ferric iron of methemoglobin, and not at all with the ferrous iron of hemoglobin or that of oxyhemoglobin. Thus, its primary site of action is the mitochondrial electron-transfer chain. When cytochrome oxidase combines with cyanide, it loses the capacity to transfer electrons from reduced cytochrome c to molecular oxygen. With suppression of the electron-transfer process, synthesis of ATP is concomitantly reduced, and rapid death of the organism is inevitable if large amounts of the poison have been absorbed. Treatment of cyanide poisoning involves the clever application of well-known chemical principles. Methemoglobin can compete (with limited success) with cytochrome oxidase for cyanide. This competition is admittedly weak, but since there is 100–1000 times as much hemoglobin in the body as cytochrome oxidase, this competition would be effective, providing sufficient hemoglobin were transformed into methemoglobin. Administration of sodium nitrite accomplishes this transformation. Once a substantial amount of cyanomethemoglobin (the cyanide complex of methemoglobin) has been formed by displacement of cyanide from cytochrome oxidase, thiosulfate is administered intravenously. Thiosulfate avidly complexes with cyanide and thus dissociates cyanide from the methemoglobin-cyanide complex. The compound formed in the bloodstream by interaction of cyanide with thiosulfate (thiocyanate) is relatively harmless and is rapidly excreted by the kidney. The critical part of this treatment lies in the conversion of the desired amount of hemoglobin to methemoglobin by nitrite. A sufficient amount of hemoglobin must be left unaltered to carry out its vital function. In this particular method for treatment of cyanide poisoning, we have an elegant illustration of the use of drugs as devices for displacing a poison from combination with the susceptible site and for transferring it, through a series of reactions, to a compound with which it forms a harmless soluble complex.

ANTITUMOR DRUGS

A vast and continuing program aimed at finding reagents that can selectively suppress the growth of malignant cells has been under way for almost two decades. The yield thus far has been rather sparse; no drug has been found which is capable of curing any malignant disease. Some agents have been discovered, however, that are useful in obtaining remissions of the malignant process. Most notable among these is the group of drugs known as cytotoxic agents. The drawback to the use of cytotoxic agents is that they are toxic to all mammalian cells. Their somewhat greater lethal effect on malignant cells is due either to the fact that the malignant cells grow more rapidly than do normal cells, or to the fact that the malignant cell mass may selectively accumulate large amounts of the cytotoxin.

Of the cytotoxic agents, the folic acid antagonists are among the most interesting. The mechanism of action of these compounds involves their structural similarity to folic acid. The structure of methotrexate, one of the folic acid antagonists, is shown here, together with the structure of folic acid:

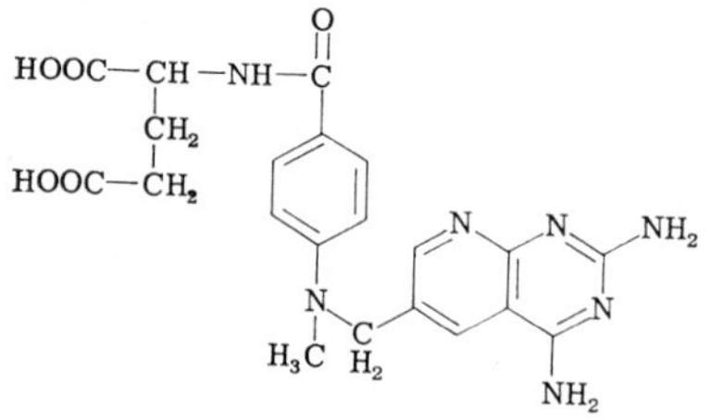

Methotrexate

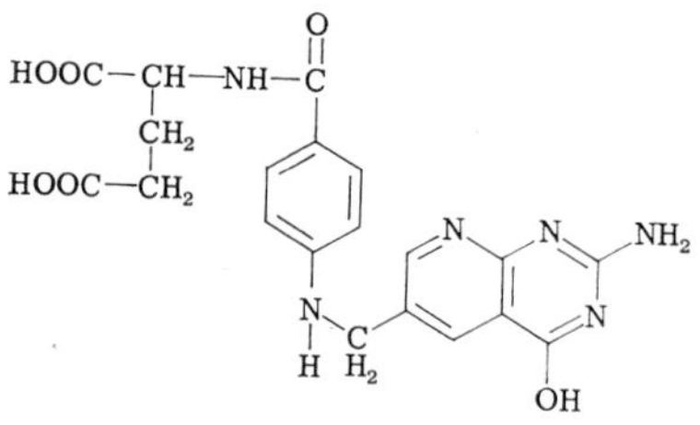

Folic acid

Methotrexate, by virtue of its resemblance to folic acid, can enter
into some of the same reactions as the vitamin, but cannot subserve
the same function. Methotrexate affects nucleic acid metabolism
primarily; the interference ultimately shows up as a defect in cell
division (in the presence of methotrexate, cell division is arrested
in metaphase). Because methotrexate exerts its toxic effects on all
dividing cells that require folic acid, it is entirely nonselective.
The principle involved here is simply that rapidly dividing cells
(malignant ones) must be more vulnerable to a poison that arrests
cell division than are slowly dividing cells (normal ones). The fact
remains, however, that the vulnerability of normal cell is considerable; high dosages, or prolonged use, of a drug such as methotrexate does produce the symptoms of folic acid deficiency.

    In a few special situations, the radioactive isotopes of certain
elements may be used with some degree of selectivity in the treatment of malignant diseases. The precise mechanism by which
exposure of cells to the ionizing radiation of radioactive isotopes
causes the death of the cells is still not established. It is known that

the ionizations lead to the production of free radicals which are of extremely high chemical reactivity. For instance, if a gamma ray strikes a molecule of water, the water molecule will eject an electron and form an unstable positive ion. The free electron may strike another water molecule and form an unstable negative ion. Both of the unstable ions will decompose immediately to form stable (hydrogen and hydroxyl) ions and highly reactive free radicals (OH· and H·).

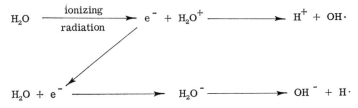

The reactions in which such free radicals participate appear to underlie the lethal effect of radiation. Because free radicals can persist for only one millionth of a second before entering into a chemical reaction, and therefore cannot travel far from the site in the cell at which they are produced, the cellular damage must be highly localized. In addition to producing free radicals, ionizing radiation may simply raise a molecule of the cell to an excited state in which it is highly reactive chemically. This could happen if the energy of the radiation was absorbed by a molecule but was insufficient to cause the ejection of an electron.

One important fact which makes ionizing radiation an effective treatment for malignant diseases is that rapidly dividing cells are more sensitive to the lethal effects of radiation than are slowly dividing ones. Another possibility for obtaining selective toxicity in malignant, as opposed to normal, cells of the body is by selective uptake. The ideal situation would be the localization of the radioactive isotope inside malignant cells exclusively. Although this situation has never been achieved, partially, selective uptake is possible in a few types of malignant diseases. For example, in certain malignant tumors of the thyroid, radioactive iodine may be used to kill the malignant cells. Iodine is taken up and concentrated in functioning thyroid tissue with great efficiency. If the tumor is functional glandular tissue,* it will take up an injected dose of radioactive iodine; thus, the source of ionizing radiation is placed within the malignant cells selectively. Even functioning metastatic lesions (groups of malignant thyroid cells in distant parts of the body) may take up the isotope. In this instance the function of the thyroid will usually be entirely abolished, and the patient will have to be maintained on doses of thyroid hormone sufficient for normal metabolic needs.

One may wonder why so little progress has been made in the chemotherapy of malignant diseases. The dilemma becomes even more puzzling when one considers the amount of money spent and the number of people involved in this endeavor. One possible explanation is that by far the greatest effort has gone into the rather heavy-handed approach of screening thousands of chemical compounds to determine whether they are curative. Such an approach must not be discredited because of its failure with respect to malignant diseases. It has proved extremely fruitful in other areas of pharmacology, such as the quest for new antibiotics. However, the problem of malignant diseases may require a more basic approach. It appears likely that only biochemical studies designed to characterize malignant cells at the molecular level will set the stage for a more rational search for chemotherapeutic agents. The problem boils down to one of establishing the biochemical differences between malignant and normal cells, and of gaining insight into the molecular bases of these differences. In the case of diseases caused by bacterial infections, for example, the problem is not nearly so difficult; bacterial cells have many characteristics that differ from those of mammalian cells. These differences provide the springboard for designing or discovering selective bacteriocidal agents. However, malignant cells *are* mammalian cells, and are even the cells of the same individual with the malignant disease. Differences here are rather few. Those that have been identified have so far been of little help in devising effective drugs. The most striking property of malignant cells is their rate of growth. Since growth is a property of normal cells also, there seems little hope of finding

---

* Many tumors of the thyroid are not composed of functional glandular tissue.

cures until the *biochemical basis* for the increased growth rate of malignant cells has been established.

Some Concluding Remarks

The field of pharmacology is a vast and growing one. Since it has been recognized that drugs act on specific chemical reactions, special attention has been paid to the structure-function relationships of pharmacologically active substances. In a number of instances, the synthetic chemist has been successful in so designing, or so modifying, a drug that it will fulfill a particular biochemical role. The synthesis of the newer anticoagulants illustrates this point, as does the synthesis of 2-PAM. The possibility of designing chemical compounds purposefully to display specific therapeutic effects holds the greatest promise for the field of pharmacology. Advances in this area are predicated upon prior knowledge of the precise structural elements involved in those normal biochemical processes that have been altered by the disease. Understanding of biochemical mechanisms will, therefore, provide the basis for the synthesis of new drugs. As illustrated above, studies in pharmocology can, in turn, serve to advance our knowledge of biochemical mechanism. Thus, the progress of biochemistry both feeds and is fed by advances in pharmacology.

Suggested Reading

Books

    Binns, T. B. (ed.), "Absorption and Distribution of Drugs," Williams & Wilkins Co., Baltimore, Maryland, 1964.

    Goodman, L. S., and Gilman, A. (eds.), "The Pharmacological Basis of Therapeutics," Macmillan Co., New York, 1965.

    Nachmansohn, D., "Chemical and Molecular Basis of Nerve Activity," Academic Press, New York, 1959.

    Schueler, F. W., "Chemobiodynamics and Drug Design," McGraw-Hill, New York, 1960.

Special Articles

    Bloom, B. M., and Laubach, G. D., *Ann. Rev. Pharmacol.* **2**, 67 (1962): on relationship of chemical structures and pharmacological activities of drugs.

Brodie, B. B., and Hogben, C. A. M., *J. Pharm. Pharmacol.* **9**, 345 (1957): physicochemical factors in drug action.

Burger, A., *New Engl. J. Med.* **270**, 1098 (1964): on the discovery of drugs.

Fastier, F. N., *Ann. Rev. Pharmacol.* **4**, 51 (1964): on structure-activity relationships of drugs.

Williams, R. T., *Clin. Pharmacol. Therapy* **4**, 234 (1964): on detoxication mechanisms.

Wilson, J. B., *Federation Proc.* **18**, 752 (1959): on molecular complementarity and an antidote for poisoning by fluorophosphate.

Biochemical Universals

In almost every chapter of this book there has been some mention of the concept of biochemical universals—of properties, systems, and principles that are applicable to all forms of life. This concept is worthy of systematic development inasmuch as the universals provide the framework for a logical and predictive science of life. The very fact that universals exist means that there has been no essential change in respect to certain basic properties and systems during at least the last two billion years of life on earth. These invariant features of living systems will be the subject matter of the present chapter.

Universal Systems

We must not overlook the fundamental fact that all living systems are based upon the principle of the cell. Circumscribed by one membrane system (the plasma membrane) is the complete apparatus for all the processes that characterize life. This is not the only conceivable way that a living system could be arranged. One could imagine, for instance, that the nucleus might constitute, or be located in, one module and the mitochondrion in another, and so on. However, the invariant feature of all living forms, and thus the most fundamental of all universals, is that the module of life is the cell.

Atoms and Molecules

The key structural atoms of all cells are the sextet C,H,O,N,S, and P, and the key ancillary atoms are the septet Na,K,Mg,Ca,Fe,Co, and Mn. There is no known case in which any of these atoms is replaced by an atom which is not part of the list. There may be additions to this basic list, but never subtractions. Thus, we can generalize that the particular atoms selected by Nature are invariant for all forms of life.

Among the myriad organic molecules that are possible there is a limited number of molecules that are found in living systems. We are concerned here with the particular set of molecules that have universal distribution. This set includes hexose sugars, such as glucose and fructose; trioses, such as glyceraldehyde; fatty acids, such as palmitic and stearic acids; purines, such as adenine and guanine; pyrimidines, such as thymine, uracil, and cytosine; steroids, such as cholesterol; and hydrocarbons, such as squalene. The invariance also extends to the optical or geometric isomers—for example, D- vs. L-glucose, fumaric vs. maleic acids, one isomer of squalene out of several dozens of possible isomers. The same set of twenty amino acids is also the common heritage of all cells. Amino acids additional to this basic list may also be found in specialized cells, but these never replace the staples. Many variations of any of the basic molecules are found in Nature, but these are supplements to, and not replacements for, the originals.

COFACTORS AND PROSTHETIC GROUPS

A limited number of cofactors and prosthetic groups represents the full repertoire of Nature's inventions in the way of catalytic, nonprotein, organic molecules; the same list turns up with monotonous regularity in cells of every type: DPN, TPN, CoA, lipoic acid, biotin, riboflavin, heme, thiamine, pyridoxine, coenzyme Q, vitamin K, folic acid, vitamin B_{12}, ATP—these are the molecules that implement all of the enzymic processes of living cells that are known to be dependent upon cofactors. No substitutions have been found for any of these catalytic species, but some variation in detail is occasionally noted. The isoprenoid side chain of coenzyme Q, for example, may be longer or shorter in different species, but the benzoquinone ring structure is essentially invariant; ATP may be replaced by CTP or some other nucleotide triphosphate in selected reactions, but, as we have already discussed in Chapter 2, this is not a significant variation since the triphosphate form of other nucleotides may be synthesized from the diphosphate by enzymic transfer of a phosphoryl group from ATP.

MACROMOLECULES

We cannot speak of specific macromolecules which are universal; rather, we recognize certain *types* of macromolecules. Thus, DNA and RNA as the respective determinants and instruments of heredity, are doubtless different in each type of cell, but the molecular architecture and the structural principles of these molecules are invariant, whatever differences there may be in detail. Thus, we find in nature only polynucleotides of a particular type as the instruments for the storage and transcription of genetic information. No other macromolecule is found in any known living cell to fulfill these functions. In the same way, proteins serve as the instruments of enzymic activity. No macromolecule of any type other than protein has been found to be capable of catalyzing chemical reactions *in vivo*. An invariant feature of biological membranes is micellar lipid which is, in a sense, a macromolecule. These micelles have a hydrophobic interior, attributable to the fatty acid residues, and a polar exterior, attributable to the polar groups in the molecule (phosphate, sulfate, choline, or some sugar). Whereas, in general, fatty acid residues make up the hydrophobic sector of phospholipid molecules, there are instances, such as in the membranes of halotolerant bacteria, of phospholipids with carotenoid fatty residues. In the membranes of the animal kingdom phospholipids are the predominant bimodal molecules, whereas in the membranes of plant cells glycolipids and sulfolipids are also found.

THE CELLULAR SYSTEMS FOR GENERATION AND UTILIZATION OF ATP

The general strategy for energizing cellular processes involves invariant modalities. The molecule which links the energy-transforming systems with the energy-requiring systems is ATP; this is universal, as is the particular P-O-P bond involved in the transaction. There are basically only three systems that couple oxidation to the synthesis of ATP; these systems have no substitutes in any known form of life. Moreover, the kinase principle for driving synthetic reactions with ATP has universal applicability. The particular form of the kinase is subject to species variation, but the principle appears to be inviolate.

Not all cells have all three primary systems for generation of ATP. Plant cells may have all three; animal and bacterial cells lack the chloroplast. Some anaerobic cells rely entirely on the glycolytic system. The mitochondrion and the chloroplast are analogous, closely related devices for the coupled synthesis of ATP, and these may be looked upon as alternative expressions of the same basic coupling mechanism. The difference lies essentially in the mode of generation of the electrons which traverse the electron-transfer chain.

METABOLIC SYSTEMS

The basic principles underlying the pathways and the enzymic catalysts of all the major metabolic processes of cells have proved to be extremely resistant to evolutionary change. Fatty acid oxidation, glycolysis, the citric cycle, fatty acid synthesis and elongation, synthesis of phospholipid, RNA, DNA, and protein are all achieved essentially by the same catalytic devices and sequential steps in all forms of life.

MEMBRANES

All cells contain membranous structures with invariant attributes. All membranes are vesicular or tubular lipoprotein systems with a structured periphery and a fluid interior. The structured sector is a composite of fused repeating units. All the energy-transforming systems are, without exception, membrane-associated, as are most integrated metabolic processes. The architectural features of membrane systems also have universal application. For example, phospholipids, or, more accurately, bimodal molecules are intrinsic to all membrane systems.

The mode of packing of lipid and protein, which imparts the special qualities characteristic of membranes, is another structural principle which has completely resisted change during the evolutionary process. There appears to be some variability in cells with respect to which membrane will fulfill a given function. In bacteria, the plasma membrane may carry out functions such as protein synthesis, or coupled phosphorylation, whereas special organelles, or internal membrane networks, are charged with these assignments in the cells of the animal kingdom.

Although it is not possible to specify in detail the mechanisms by which membranes are synthesized, the very fact of the universality of the architectural pattern of membrane structures indicates that these mechanisms are universal.

PROTEIN SYNTHESIS AND CELL DIVISION

The chain of command from DNA to RNA to protein, and all the principles which govern this command, apply with equal force to all cells. The DNA is always the final repository of information; m-RNA is the instrument for transmitting this information to the sites of protein synthesis; t-RNA and the ribosomes are the instruments for translating this information into protein structure. Moreover, the genetic code in which the information is stored is basically the same in all cells.

The processes by which DNA is replicated in cells and by which cells divide into two daughter cells are invariant. The unpairing of chromosomes, the replication of chromosomes, and the segregation of complete sets of chromosomes all appear to occur by the same mechanisms in all cells. We still do not know fully the list of events which enter into the act of cell division and the nature of all the supporting systems. However, at least at the cytological level, the essential events in all types of cells are basically the same.

CONTROL MECHANISMS

The molecular tactics by which biochemical control is exercised in cells have many features with universal applicability. The principles of end product inhibition, repression, and induction, so well studied in bacterial systems, appear to be equally valid in mammalian cells. Although a number of the control mechanisms that have evolved in higher organisms are missing in less complex forms of life, such as the hormonal system, the operational principles involved are not unique. The elaboration of trigger substances for the control of processes capable of being triggered, is applicable to all forms of life; hormones are simply one of the variations on this universal theme.

CATALYTIC PROTEINS AND THE MECHANISM OF CATALYSIS

It is a reasonable possibility that each of the catalytic macromolecules that have universal applicability embodies features of construction that are invariant. In the case of oxidation-reduction enzymes this possibility has been amply demonstrated. Cytochrome *c* invariably has the same prosthetic heme group and the same amino acid sequence near that group. The triosephosphoric dehydrogenase invariably reacts with a pyridine nucleotide and contains a functional sulfhydryl group. However, in addition to universal features of this type, there appears to be another parameter of enzymic structure and function with universal applicability. This parameter involves the nature of the active site, the nature of the functional groups which implement the catalysis, and the sequence of catalytic events. At that level, and in those terms, we may find underneath the bewildering array of different types of enzymes only a few strategic principles, equally valid for all forms of life.

Comparative Biochemistry and Biochemical Universals

As the name implies, comparative biochemistry deals with the biochemical systems, materials, and mechanisms found in different forms of life. Traditionally, the emphasis in this field has been placed on variation. Our concern in comparative biochemistry will be with variation in the context of biochemical universals. We shall consider a few examples of the types of permissible variations encountered in systems of universal applicability.

All green plants contain chlorophyll in their chloroplasts, but chlorophyll does not occur in all cells of the plant. That is not to say that the chloroplast has an alternative form.* The principles

---

* There are morphological differences between chloroplasts and other photosynthetic units in bacterial systems. At the functional level, however, the identity of the operational principles appears to hold.

underlying the *modus operandi* of the chloroplast are constant, and are generally applicable to all cells having photosynthetic equipment; however, some plant cells lack photosynthetic equipment. In the same way, all aerobic cells have the enzymes that implement the citric acid cycle, but anaerobic cells may lack them. Yeast cells, for example, can be grown either anaerobically or aerobically. When grown anaerobically, the cells contain no mitochondria; when induced to grow aerobically, the cells synthesize mitochondria (see the discussion of the origin of mitochondria in Chapter 11). Wherever we find contractile systems in nature, the contractile element is a species of actomyosin, and the mechanistic basis of contraction appears to be invariant. Although the available data are insufficient to describe and evaluate the mechanism used by all systems that respond to light, it would hardly seem rash to assume that the photosensitive systems in all animal tissues involve molecular species similar in chemistry to rhodopsin, and mechanistic principles similar to those used by the retinal systems of the eye. The mechanism by which a nerve impulse is generated is identical in the nerve cells of all animal organisms. Thus, we have a group of phenomena that is universal in respect to the basic mechanisms, but not universal in distribution.

There are processes in multicellular organisms that differ in detail from one organism to another but still involve basically the same molecular mechanisms. The embryological process varies widely from organism to organism at the gross morphological level, but the molecular features, insofar as these have been recognized, appear to be remarkably constant. The structured elements of animals and plants that subserve energy-transducing functions are all cellular universals. These elements differ greatly in gross form and in functional details, but the architectural principles upon which they are built and the molecular strategy of their operation are invariant. Thus, energy-transducing systems can all be identified as variations of a single system.

THE MITOCHONDRIAL SYSTEMS

The mitochondrion may be regarded as a prototype of membranes generally. The variations among mitochondria from different sources may well serve as an indication of the kind and extent of variation to be anticipated when other membranes are studied in comparable depth. The mitochondrion of the animal cell (as well as the chloroplast of plant cells) is made up of a system of interconnecting membranes—the outer membranes, with a full complement of enzymes that fulfill ancillary functions (such as the citric acid cycle, β-oxidation of fatty acids, fatty acid synthesis, and the oxidation of β-hydroxybutyrate), and the inner membrane, composed of cristae, which contains the repeating elementary particle. The elementary particle is concerned with the main function of the mitochondrion—that is, the coupling of electron flow to the synthesis of ATP and to the translocation of ions. The nature of the ancillary functions varies from one type of mitochondrion to another, but all mitochondria carry out the coupled synthesis of ATP and the translocation of ions. Mitochondria from some cells can oxidize β-hydroxybutyrate, whereas mitochondria from other cells cannot; one species of mitochondria can form hippuric acid by condensation of benzoate with glycine, another cannot; one species of mitochondria oxidizes fatty acids very rapidly, another slowly. Thus, there may be considerable variation in respect to the nature (and the amounts) of particular enzymes in the outer mitochondrial membrane. Cells of each type have their own characteristic spectrum of ancillary mitochondrial enzymes and their characteristic ratios among the enzymes associated with the outer membrane.

The relative amounts of inner and outer membranes are variable from one mitochondrial species to another. In some cells, the mitochondria are relatively large; in others, considerably smaller. Similar variation occurs in respect to shape. The cristae may extend from one side of the mitochondrion to the other, as in heart muscle mitochondria, or may take the form of tubular loops that extend only part way into the interior, as in liver mitochondria. The cristae may fill the interior of the mitochondria, as in heart muscle and kidney, or they may constitute a small percentage of the total internal volume, as in liver.

In bacteria, the relation of the outer mitochondrial membrane to the inner membrane is reported to be atypical, or at least undefined. As improved electron-microscopic techniques are applied more systematically to bacterial cells, the apparent differences between structures seen in bacterial membranes and those seen in true mitochondria are diminishing. For example, recent electron micrographs disclose the fact that tripartite elementary particles exist in membranes of the microorganism, *Micrococcus lysodeikticus*. The probability is high that bacteria contain the same types of repeating units as are found in mitochondria.

The inner mitochondrial membrane is built up of repeating particles which contain a segment of the electron-transfer chain plus ancillary proteins involved in the coupling process. In mitochondria of heart muscle, there are four different repeating units of this sort; three of which correspond to the three phosphorylating sites of the electron-transfer chain. Some mitochondria (those of *Ascaris lumbricoides*, for instance) with an abbreviated electron-transfer chain, may contain only one or two sites of phosphorylation and a correspondingly smaller number of species of elementary particles. The mitochondrion of *A. lumbricoides** appears to lack the terminal complex of the chain (the reaction with oxygen has the character of an autoxidation). Nitrate-reducing bacteria have a terminal complex that reacts specifically with nitrate, rather than with oxygen, and this specialized complex contains cytochromes a and a_3, but not copper. Similar variation has been noted at the point at which electrons enter the electron-transfer chain. In the mitochondria of locust flight muscle, for instance, α-glycerophosphate is the main donor of electrons to the chain. This capability can be explained in terms of an additional repeating unit being present in the inner membrane of the mitochondrion. Bacterial systems of the mitochondrial type have evolved the capacity to utilize a variety of substances which can donate electrons to the chain, including inorganic iron, molecular hydrogen, and formate. These capacities would require new or modified repeating units in the membranes containing the electron-transfer chain.

The nature of the lipids in mitochondria from various sources is

---

* *Ascaris lumbricoides* is a parasitic nematode worm found in the intestinal tract of the infected host. There would be a transition from an aerobic phase to a predominantly anaerobic phase in the adult stage of its life cycle.

highly variable. In the mitochondria of animal and plant cells, the fatty acid residues of the lipids are highly unsaturated, whereas these residues in the corresponding bacterial structures are generally monounsaturated. In the mitochondria of heart muscle, fatty aldehyde residues are present in the phospholipids (as vinyl ethers), whereas liver mitochondria contain no fatty aldehyde residues at all. However, the overriding consideration is that lipids of whatever structure are fundamental parts of all mitochondria.

The variations in mitochondrial structure and function cited above constitute only a representative selection. None of them modifies the basic operational principles of the mitochondrion. As mentioned before, the mitochondrion is, in essence, a device for coupling electron flow to the synthesis of ATP and to the translocation of ions. It does not matter to the device whether electrons originate from substrates of the citric acid cycle, from α-glycerophosphate, or from β-hydroxybutyrate. The fact that the phospholipids in mitochondria of one type contain fatty acids, and those in mitochondria of another type contain fatty aldehydes, does not modify the principle that lipids are an essential feature of mitochondria. It is not vital to the coupling process that certain oxidizing and synthesizing enzymes be present in the outer membrane. These are the optional features that are not relevant to first principles such as the nature of the coupling mechanism, the nature of the catalysts in the electron-transfer chain, and the arrangement of parts in the elementary particle.

Nucleic Acids and the Replicating System

The mitotic apparatus common to higher organisms is represented only partially in lower organisms. No asters or centrioles are seen during the division of plant cells. In protozoa the nucleus does not break down; the spindle forms within the nucleus. In certain cells, the nucleus divides and then the cell wall is laid down around the preformed nuclei. Muscle cells contain many nuclei per cell. In some cells, such as the gut cells of the mosquito and certain plant cells, there is no cell division at all and no separation of daughter nuclei; the chromosomes simply divide and remain together within the same nucleus. In some cellular forms division leads to unequal partition into one larger and one smaller daughter cell. In all of these examples the basic principles of cell division, nucleic acid replication, and protein synthesis, proceed as described in Chapter 11; the variations are due to differences in the details of what is fundamentally one basic plan.

In multicellular organisms, each cell has a number of DNA molecules distributed in a discrete number of chromosomes within the cell nucleus. In such a cell the separate DNA molecules—that is, the chromosomes—carry different genetic information. The total "blueprint" for the many activities of the cell is spread over a set of separate DNA molecules. In bacteria, the DNA is in the form of a single long molecule—a continuous thread which is not localized within a defined organelle. In higher organisms DNA is linked to basic proteins (histones) whereas the DNA of lower organisms is generally uncombined with protein. The cell nucleus of each species has its own characteristic number of chromosomes, and each of the different chromosomes has a distinct appearance. No matter how the DNA is packaged, however, no matter how many DNA molecules there are per cell, and no matter whether the DNA is combined with histones or is free, it is essentially a linear polymer of nucleotides, it is organized into a double helix, and it functions in the control of protein biosynthesis.

Undoubtedly, information directing amino acid sequences is encoded in all DNA molecules in the form of specific nucleotide sequences, and is thus given in linear form. It appears that m-RNA is always the agency by which the genetic information is made available to the protein-synthesizing system and that the latter system always involves ribosomes, t-RNA, amino acids, and activating enzymes, as described in Chapter 11.

The viruses are a notable exception to the rule of "DNA-to-RNA-to-protein." However, if the virus is considered in the context of the cell which it must enter before it can reproduce, the rule is followed exactly. The virus contains only its own structural proteins and its own genetic material. To reproduce, it must parasitize a cell and use the cell's apparatus for replicating its DNA, for synthesizing its proteins, and for assembling new virus particles. It is clear that the genetic code of the virus must be precisely the same as that of its host, since the host cell reproduces perfect whole viruses according to the directions encoded in the viral DNA. It is easy to imagine how such a system might have evolved: a given virus could have been selected because its DNA could be correctly "read" by a given host cell. However, in all likelihood no such evolutionary selection was necessary, since the genetic code itself appears to be universal.

Another variation of the hereditary mechanism is seen in the RNA viruses. These viruses contain, within their coat of protein, not DNA but RNA. Nonetheless, when they infect a cell they are able to take over the metabolic machinery of the cell and to direct the production of new virus particles. However, they take over the host cell's protein-synthesizing apparatus in a manner and at a step which differ from those of the DNA viruses. Their RNA evidently acts directly as m-RNA, and serves as a template for the synthesis of viral protein. Norbert Zinder and his colleagues have isolated the RNA from an RNA virus and have used it, instead of a synthetic polynucleotide, in the cell-free system developed by Nirenberg (see Chapter 11). They found that in the presence of this RNA the cell-free system incorporated amino acids into protein. When they examined the newly synthesized protein, they found it to be identical with the coat protein of their virus. Although this was an important achievement in the verification of the biological meaning of cell-free systems for protein synthesis, the result was not surprising. The cell-free system that was employed had been derived from *Escherichia coli,* the natural host of the virus from which the RNA had been obtained. *Escherichia coli* would be expected to be able to "read" the directions for making the proteins of a virus for which it is a natural host. A far more interesting result was obtained when the same workers tested the effect of the viral RNA in a cell-free system derived from *Euglena gracilis,* an organism which does not serve as host for the virus. They found, once again, that a protein identical with the viral coat protein was synthesized. This finding supports the thesis that the genetic code is universal.

It is now recognized that in some nucleic acids there are nucleotides other than those containing the well-known purine and pyrimidine bases. There are instances in which the pyrimidine base of viral DNA is slightly different from the corresponding base in the DNA of the host bacterial cell. Thus, the DNA of some viruses contains hydroxymethyl cytosine, whereas the DNA of the host cells contains cytosine. However, the virus must provide the host bacterial cell with instructions for the production of enzymes necessary for the synthesis of hydroxymethyl cytosine. Here again the virus and the host cell are perfectly geared to one another—they must share a common set of mechanistic principles. This interdependence of virus and host reminds us that the virus is not an independent form of life but rather a part of a living system which requires other parts for fulfillment.

Cytochrome *c*—Variables and Constants

Cytochrome *c* is one of the invariant components of the mitochondrial electron-transfer chain and of its bacterial counterpart. We shall consider only one class of cytochrome *c*, represented at all levels of living organisms; the cytochromes of this class have a molecular weight of around 13,000. Margoliash and Smith have determined the amino acid sequences in a set of cytochrome *c* specimens of this class—specimens isolated from a variety of organisms widely spaced on the evolutionary tree. Apparently, there have been changes and modifications in sixty of the one hundred and four amino acid residues in cytochrome *c*. Nonetheless, the molecular size, the nature of the heme group, the mode of attachment of the heme group to the protein, the capacity to form complexes with phospholipid (an expression of its positive charge)—in fact, all the properties essential to its catalytic role—have remained unchanged. It is significant that there are only limited sequences of amino acids which have entirely resisted evolutionary change; one such sequence includes the two cysteine residues through which the heme group is attached to the protein; another such sequence (amino acid residues 70–80) clearly fulfills some essential function in the protein, but this function cannot yet be specified. One of the conclusions to be drawn from this comparative survey is that there are regions in the protein molecule essential to catalytic activity that cannot be changed without incurring some functional damage to the molecule as a whole. Outside this privileged domain, variations may occur. Of course, even the variations in segments of the molecule outside the critical one mentioned above must obey certain rules. For instance, no amino acid substitutions may be made which would greatly interfere with the proper folding of the polypeptide chain during the formation of the native form of the protein, because an altered three-dimensional conformation might interfere with the catalytic activity of the molecule. The role of cytochrome *c* is to fulfill a unique function in the electron-transfer process. This role dictates a particular size, geometry, and chemistry of the enzyme. Providing these requirements are met, any change in the sequence of amino acids in the molecule would be permissible.

METABOLISM AND MEMBRANES

The association of integrated metabolic processes with membranes has important implications with respect to permissible variations in these processes. Each enzyme in a membrane-bound metabolic process serves in two capacities: (1) as one of a group of catalysts in a sequential process and (2) as an integral part of a membrane system. Any change in the sequence of catalytic proteins, for instance, would require many other synchronized changes if both the original metabolic function and the structural integrity of the membrane were to be maintained. Undoubtedly, this requirement of multiple simultaneous changes to achieve even the smallest modification in a sequence has been a formidable barrier to evolutionary change in membrane-bound metabolic processes. The enzymes of the glycolytic complex (associated with the plasma membrane) and the enzymes of the citric acid cycle (associated with the mitochondrial outer membrane) show remarkable constancy in sequence, and in mechanism of catalysis throughout the phylogenetic scale. The systems for the oxidation of fatty acids and for the elongation of fatty acids, both of which are associated with the outer membrane of the mitochondrion, also show no significant variation in mechanism from one species to another.

COFACTORS IN METABOLIC PROCESSES

In Chapter 5, the universality of coenzymes, and of the bound prosthetic groups of enzymes, was pointed out. It is perhaps appropriate, in the context of the present chapter, to seek out the basis for this universality. Flavin, thiamine, lipoic acid, biotin, nicotinamide, pyridoxal, thioethanolamine, hemin, and coenzyme Q are some of the cofactors concerned with membrane-associated metabolic processes. This association, as we have indicated above, makes it likely that evolutionary variation in chemistry will be blocked. Any change in the chemistry of a functional group would have to be compatible with a large number of interlocking requirements. First, the new functional group would have to be fitted to the apoprotein. Then, the altered protein would have to be fitted into the other proteins of the membrane. The more we know about the structure of membrane systems, the clearer it becomes that there are fine tolerances in the fitting of parts, and this automatically limits the permissible variation in the structure of any coenzyme. Some of the variations which do occur have yet to be understood. For instance, in certain bacteria coenzyme Q is replaced by vitamin K. Both these molecules are substituted quinones—one a benzoquinone, the other a naphthoquinone. The meaning of this change in coenzyme, found only in a few instances, is not known.

THE EVOLUTIONARY PROCESS IN RELATION TO THE UNIVERSALS

It would appear from available information, that the problems of replication and energy transduction were among the first to be solved in the evolutionary process. Once solved, the essential principles have never been varied, or, at least, there is no evidence that any currently* viable form has found an alternative solution. It might be reasonable to conclude that any change in the form of a solution would require such an enormous number of synchronized modifications as to be essentially impossible. We may take this type of immunity to evolutionary change as the springboard for predicting the general form and character of energy-transducing, and

---

* It is estimated that some 95% of all species which once inhabited the earth are now extinct.

replicating, systems in all forms of life. The same arguments may be applied to universals in general, although in some instances the generality is not so sweeping. This is not to say that evolutionary changes in the domain of the universals have been completely interdicted. On the contrary, there is evidence of wholesale variation, but always at the level of detail, never of principle.

A Concluding Thought

It is only in recent years that sufficient critical information has been accumulated to establish beyond any reasonable doubt the concept of biochemical universals. This concept had eventually to be verified at the molecular level. At the morphological or physiological level of experimentation, only inferences may be drawn about universals. The final proof had to be found in the molecular details—in the molecular properties of both the hereditary apparatus and the membrane systems. Now that the concept of biochemical universals rests on a solid body of experimental evidence, a reappraisal of the teaching of biochemistry is in order. A preoccupation with the variables in living systems can only lead to a meager appreciation of biochemical fundamentals.

Like the basic laws of the physical sciences, the universals of living systems provide a solid base for prediction and simplification. The full extent of the area encompassed by universals has yet to be determined; there is undoubtedly a vast territory yet to be explored. As we learn more about the molecular architecture of membranes, proteins, DNA, and RNA, additional principles of a universal nature are sure to be found.

Suggested Reading

Books

Baldwin, E., "An Introduction to Comparative Biochemistry," Cambridge University Press, London and New York, 1949.

Ebert, J. D., "Interacting Systems in Development," Modern Biology Series, Holt, Rinehart and Winston, New York, 1965.

Sistrom, W. R., "Microbial Life," Modern Biology Series, Holt, Rinehart and Winston, New York, 1962.

Stent, G. S., "Molecular Biology of Bacterial Viruses," W. H. Freeman and Co., San Francisco, 1963.

Special Articles

Bueding, E., and Farber, E., *in* "Comparative Biochemistry" (M. Florkin and H. S. Mason, eds.), Vol. I, Chapter 9, Academic Press, New York, 1960: on comparative biochemistry of glycolysis.

Conn, E. E., *in* "Comparative Biochemistry" (M. Florkin and H. S. Mason, eds.), Vol. I, Chapter 10, Academic Press, New York, 1960: on comparative biochemistry of electron transfer.

Florkin, M., and Mason, H. S., *in* "Comparative Biochemistry" (M. Florkin and H. S. Mason, eds.), Vol. I, Chapter 1, Academic Press, New York, 1960: an introduction to comparative biochemistry.

Hill, R. L., and Buettner-Janusch, J., *Federation Proc.* **23**, 1236 (1964): on the evolution of hemoglobin.

Kluyver, A. J., and Donker, H. J. L., *Chemie Zelle Gewebe* **13**, 134 (1926): on unity in biochemistry.

Margoliash, E., *Proc. Natl. Acad. Sci. U.S.* **50**, 672 (1963): on the primary structure and evolution of cytochrome *c*.

Margoliash, E., and Smith, E. L., *in* "Evolving Genes and Proteins" (V. Bryson and H. J. Vogel, eds.), p. 221, Academic Press, New York, 1965: on structural and functional aspects of cytochrome *c* in relation to evolution.

Mazia, D., *in* "The Cell," (J. Brachet and A. E. Mirsky, eds.), Vol. III, p. 77, Academic Press, New York, 1961: on mitosis and the physiology of cell division.

Nathans, D., Notani, G., Schwartz, J. H., and Zinder, N. D., *Proc. Natl. Acad. Sci. U.S.* **48**, 1424 (1962): on *in vitro* synthesis of *f*2 coat protein by extracts of *E. coli*.

Schwartz, J. H., Eisenstadt, J. M., Brawerman, G., and Zinder, N. D., *Proc. Natl. Acad. Sci. U.S.* **53**, 195 (1965): on *in vitro* synthesis of *f*2 coat protein by extracts of *E. gracilis*.

Smith, E. L., and Margoliash, E., *Federation Proc.* **23**, 1243 (1964): on the evolution of cytochrome *c*.

Wald, G., *in* "Comparative Biochemistry" (M. Florkin and H. S. Mason, eds.), Vol. I, Chapter 7, Academic Press, New York, 1960: on the distribution and evolution of visual systems.

Biochemical Universals
in Relation to Evolution

The notion that there are universal attributes of cells has had an honored place in biological thought for some decades. However, it was difficult to evaluate with precision how far this notion could be extended. Intensive exploration of the biochemical apparatus of a wide selection of cells not only has made exceptions unlikely, but, equally important, has also extended the range of phenomena, structures, and molecules that fall within the scope of the universals of cells. Only recently have sufficient data been accumulated to allow one to talk with confidence of the reality and importance of biochemical universals. Certainly, in respect to the picture of evolution some conclusions can now be drawn.

Concrete evidence for the evolutionary process actually concerns only the rather recent period for which there is a fossil record. Fossils can be dated with precision, and the organisms which produced them can thereby be assigned specific points in time. Because the organisms which predated these times have left no discernible record, we can only make guesses about them and the time periods in which they existed. Such guesses are actually based on rather sound evidence. For instance, one can extrapolate back from the evolutionary evidence derived from the examination of fossils. Alternatively, one can examine the whole spectrum of organisms living today, and from it construct a hierarchy based upon relative complexity. It is usual to assign the least complex organisms to the bottom of the phylogenetic scale and the most complex to the top. Indeed, the various inferential methods of arriving at an evolutionary scheme are in fairly good agreement, at least as far back in time when cells existed which resembled microorganisms. As for what preceded such cells, we have nothing but intuition to go on.

The very fact that there are biochemical universals indicates that the earliest form of life as we know it, from which all the species of the animal, plant, and microbial kingdoms evolved, contained most of the systems encompassed by the term "universals." Since the evolutionary tree is a luxuriantly branching one, it is safe to say that identities of biochemical systems at the tips of the branches must have their source at the very base of the trunk.* If we accept the premise about the early cells, which follows from the universality of a large number of systems, then a more restricted interpretation of the evolutionary process has to be imposed.

Now let us approach the question of the nature of the early cell from the genetic standpoint. The two most fundamental phenomena on which so-called Darwinian evolution operates are mutation and natural selection. It is important to realize that mutation comes first, and in a random manner not related to environmental conditions. In any population of cells, mutations occur with a definable (but low) frequency. Whether or not a mutant gene will be propagated, and thus persist, in a population of organisms depends upon whether or not it confers an advantageous attribute. If it does, it will tend to persist; if it does not, it will tend not to. That is where the environment comes into the picture. A mutation can confer an advantageous attribute upon an organism only within the context of the environment. Change the environment, and the attribute may change from advantageous to disadvantageous.

The peppered moth in the area of Birmingham in the industrial Midlands of England provides an excellent, if somewhat extreme, example of how these principles operate. The peppered moth has recently undergone a fabulous and extremely rapid change right before the eyes of contemporary scientists. This creature has always been white, as far back as anyone knows. It is almost invisible when it rests on the trunks of trees native to its environment, which have a light color referable to the lichen which covers the bark.

* The only way to arrive at identical ends from *different* sources would be through convergent evolution, a concept which the weight of evidence argues strongly against.

In this way it manages to escape detection by the local birds. When Birmingham became industrialized, and this happened very rapidly, the soot from the enormous number of smokestacks soon turned the local trees uniformly black. The white peppered moths now stood out clearly, and were summarily consumed by their predators (see Figure 16.1). However, mutations take place among the peppered moths just as in any other population of organisms. One such mutation of the moths is in a gene which determines coloration—the normal gene conferring whiteness, and the mutant gene conferring blackness. Over the years, before industrialization changed their natural habitat, the mutant black moths fell prey to the birds more easily than did the normal white moths because they could be more clearly seen on the white trees. Natural selection militated against the black moths. The mutant gene, which conferred blackness upon them, was passed on to succeeding generations with low frequency. Once the trees had been blackened, however, it was the black peppered moth that survived more successfully. Rare as it was to begin with, the black peppered moth now was surviving with ease and multiplying, whereas its white counterpart was becoming extinct. With fantastic speed, essentially the entire population of white peppered moths in the vicinity of Birmingham was replaced by a population of black ones.

We conceive of an almost infinite number of changes in environmental conditions occurring throughout evolution, each giving an edge to one mutant organism over others. Just as with the peppered moths, when a mutation is beneficial to an organism, the mutant gene tends to persist in the population because it gives an organism a better chance of surviving and procreating. Since the transfer of genetic information from one generation to the next is precisely controlled, the mutant gene is passed on intact, just as all the normal genes are. The story of the peppered moths illustrates how efficient the combined processes of mutation and natural selection can be.

If Darwinian evolution is to operate as described above, then a number of ingredients are essential to the evolving cells. Such cells must possess organized genetic material and a mechanism for the equitable distribution of this material between daughter cells. If mutations are to have any meaning functionally, they must produce structural or functional changes—that is, they must be translated into alterations in the structures of proteins. Thus, we must add a mechanism for protein synthesis to our list of equipment necessary for the evolving cell. It is also clear that the organisms undergoing this type of evolutionary process must be separated from other organisms by a limiting membrane. Add to all these universals a system for generating high-energy chemical compounds, which would be required for all the biosynthetic work of the organism, and one ends up with a fairly complete description of what was referred to in Chapter 1 as the minimal cell. Thus, from genetic considerations we arrive at the same conclusion we reached previously on the basis of the fact of biochemical universals—namely, that the earliest cell on which Darwinian evolution could operate already had within it most of the universal biochemical systems.

Let us designate this cell, which led to the contemporary cells in the species, as the "precursor cell." The evolutionary process in the Darwinian sense came *after* the time that the universals had been developed in the precursor cell. We must distinguish between this phase of evolution, which did not involve intrinsic change in the universals, and the process by which the precursor cell arose. The popular conception of primitive cells as the starting point for the origin of the species is really erroneous. There was nothing functionally primitive about such cells. They contained basically the same biochemical equipment as do their modern counterparts.

How, then, did the precursor cell arise? The only unequivocal rejoinder to this question is that we do not know. Undoubtedly, selection played a role in the process, although the efficiency was probably not as great as in Darwinian evolution. Speculations on the origin of the precursor cell concern such matters as the spontaneous formation of the organic molecules used later in living systems, the primitive forms of energy production which may have preceded glycolysis and oxidative phosphorylation, the mechanism by which polypeptides may have arisen by polymerization of several amino acids without benefit of any organic template, and the nature of the earliest forms of nucleic acid, which may have contained less than four different nucleotides.

Fig. 16.1. *Biton betularia,* the peppered moth. Both the white and the black forms are shown at rest. A: on a lichen-covered tree trunk in the unpolluted countryside; and B: on a soot-covered tree trunk near Birmingham, England. Courtesy of Dr. H. B. D. Kettlewell, Genetics Laboratory, Department of Zoology, Oxford.

In Figure 16.2 an evolutionary scheme is shown. It is a very general scheme, intended to show merely the increasing organizational complexity that the evolutionary process produced. Although seven steps are shown, leading from atoms to ecosystems, there is one step that far outweighs the others in enormity: the step from macromolecules to cells. All the other steps can be accounted for on theoretical grounds—if not correctly, at least elegantly. However, the macromolecule-to-cell transition is a jump

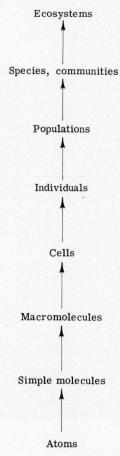

Ecosystems

Species, communities

Populations

Individuals

Cells

Macromolecules

Simple molecules

Atoms

Fig. 16.2 An evolutionary scheme, emphasizing increasing orders of complexity.

of fantastic dimensions, which lies beyond the range of testable hypothesis. In this area all is conjecture. The available facts do not provide a basis for postulating that cells arose on this planet.* This is not to say that some paraphysical forces were at work. We simply wish to point out the fact that there is no scientific evidence. The physicist has learned to avoid trying to specify when time began and when matter was created, except within the framework of frank speculation. The origin of the precursor cell appears to fall into the same category of unknowables. It is an area with fascinating conceptual challenges, but at the present time, and perhaps forever, the facts cannot be known.

Suggested Reading

Books

Anfinsen, C. B., "The Molecular Basis of Evolution," John Wiley and Sons, New York, 1959.

Calvin, M., "Chemical Evolution," University of Oregon Press, Eugene, Oregon, 1961.

Commemoration of the centennial of the publication of "The Origin of the Species" by Charles Darwin. *Proc. Am. Phil. Soc.* **103** (1959).

Dobzhansky, T., "Genetics and the Origin of Species," Columbia University Press, New York, 1951.

Dobzhansky, T., "Evolution, Genetics, and Man," John Wiley and Sons, New York, 1955.

Florkin, M., ed., "Some Aspects of the Origin of Life," Pergamon Press, London, 1961.

Haldane, J. B. S., *in* "The Inequality of Man," Penguin Books, 1937: on the origins of life.

Keosian, J., "The Origin of Life," Reinhold Publishing Corp., New York, 1964.

Oparin, A. (ed.), "The Origin of Life on the Earth," Reports on the International Symposium, The Publishing House of the Academy of Sciences of the U.S.S.R., 1957.

Savage, J. M., "Evolution," Modern Biology Series, Holt, Rinehart and Winston, New York, 1963.

Sinnott, E. W., Dunn, L. C., and Dobzhansky, T., "Principles of Genetics," McGraw-Hill Book Co., New York, 1958.

Smith, H., "Kamongo," The Viking Press, New York, 1956.

---

* To postulate that life arose elsewhere in the universe and was then brought to earth in some manner would be merely begging the question; we should then ask how life arose wherever it may have done so originally.

Special Articles

Abelson, P. H., and Cloud, P. E., Jr., *Proc. Natl. Acad. Sci. U.S.* 47, 1705 (1961): on major biologic innovations and the geologic record.

Calvin, M., *Am. Scientist* 44, 248 (1956): on chemical evolution and the origin of life.

Calvin, M., and Calvin, G. J., *Am. Scientist,* 52, 163–186 (1964): on atom to Adam.

Hanson, E. D., *Quart. Rev. Biol.* 41, 1 (1966): on the evolutionary step from macromolecules to cells.

Horowitz, N. H., *Proc. Natl. Acad. Sci. U.S.* 31, 153 (1945): on the evolution of biosynthetic pathways.

Kettlewell, H. B. D., *Science* 148, 1290 (1965): on insect survival and selection for pattern.

Wald, G., *in* "The Scientific Endeavor," The Rockefeller Institute Press, New York, 1965: on the origins of life.

CHAPTER 17

Some Aspects of the Strategy of Biochemical Research

An intrinsic part of an understanding of biochemistry is some appreciation of the modalities and tactics of biochemical research. As a preliminary to this discussion a brief account of the history of biochemistry will be given, followed by a discussion of several key problems that loom in the future. With this background of information, some of the strategic aspects of biochemical research can be discussed more incisively.

Three Phases of Biochemical Research

The early pioneers in biochemistry had no choice but to occupy themselves with the isolation, chemical description, and characterization of the constituents of living systems, and with methods for the recognition and estimation of these constituents. During this phase, which began in earnest in the second half of the nineteenth century, the foundations of biochemistry were laid, on which the subsequent developments were built. The chemical composition of compounds such as proteins, lipids, and carbohydrates had to be ascertained with precision before more esoteric areas of biochemistry could be penetrated. The analytical chemist played a major role in this early phase. The great figures of biochemistry in the late nineteenth and early twentieth centuries were those who developed new techniques of isolation and analysis and those who applied these techniques to the components of living organisms. Organic chemists found in natural products a rich and inexhaustible area for study. The tools of organic chemistry were applied to the determination of the structure of amino acids, lipids, carbohydrates, sterols, purines, pyrimidines, etc. By about 1925 the chemical foundations of biochemistry had been laid.* The broad categories of the chemical constituents of the cell had been defined, and the structures of most of the essential building blocks had been worked out.

In the 1930's the second phase of biochemical research was inaugurated—the enzymological and metabolic phase. The various categories of enzymes and the metabolic role of organized systems of enzymes were charted. The systematic isolation and description of each of the hundreds of enzymes of living systems reached its high point during the 1950's. This second phase of biochemical research was so intense that in a span of 25 years the basic documentation was virtually completed; few major metabolic systems remained to be defined by the beginning of the 1960's. Of great assistance in this accomplishment were newly available and relatively inexpensive instruments, such as the visible and ultraviolet spectrophotometer, the ultracentrifuge, the glass electrode, and the new and powerful analytical techniques such as paper and column chromatography and radioactive labeling. The introduction of enzymes as reagents in analytical and degradative procedures was an extremely important addition to the techniques for determining the structures of biological catalysts and other macromolecules.

The third phase of biochemical research made its debut during the 1950's, while the second phase was at its height. In this phase biochemists have been concerned with life processes at the molecular level, especially with the coordinated reactions implemented by organized systems. We may call this phase the *systems and molecular phase*. The emphasis shifted from individual molecules and processes to organized systems, and from a description of the gross chemical properties of macromolecules to a characterization of the fine molecular details. Biochemistry became both more biological, with the increasing emphasis on the organized systems, and more chemical, with the application of precise physical and chemical methodology.

* The important role of the pioneer nutritionist and the microbiologist in helping to set the scene during this phase should not be underestimated.

All phases of biochemical research are still represented on the contemporary scene. Only the emphasis and the relative intensity of the effort have changed. Each of the different approaches in biochemical research has played a decisive role in producing the flourishing science that biochemistry is today. The intent of this brief historical survey is not to downgrade any of the different approaches to biochemistry. Without new methods and instrumentation the tools would be lacking to study more complex problems. Without a truly biological orientation the science would lose its relevance to life processes. For biochemistry to be a vigorous science, a balance must be achieved between those who are concerned primarily with methodology, instrumentation, and structural analysis, and those who use these tools, and the information derived from their use, for the study of biological problems. The history of biochemistry has shown that an ingenious new method, such as paper chromatography, or a unique instrument, such as the ultracentrifuge, can accelerate progress to an enormous degree.

On the Future Problems of Biochemistry

As we stated above, the broad problems of biochemistry are narrowing to those which can be fitted into either of two categories: (1) biologically important molecules and macromolecules; and (2) biological systems. In the first category are problems which lend themselves to a chemical and physical approach: the molecules and macromolecules of living systems are isolated and then studied with all the rigor that presently can be applied to *well-defined chemical entities*. In the second category are problems which lend themselves to a more biological approach; complex cellular processes are studied, either in living cells or in isolated cell fractions *as whole systems*. The distinctions between the problems of the two categories are not hard and fast. In fact, the chemically and physically oriented experimentalists may sometimes find their niche in systems research, and the biologically oriented may sometimes gravitate to the physicochemical study of biologically important molecules. Moreover, the findings of biochemists studying problems of the first category often can be explained only in terms of bio-

logical systems, whereas the findings of biochemists studying problems of the second category often can be explained only in terms
of the structure and function of the individual parts of biological
systems.

Research at the Molecular Level

The chemical and physical description of the properties of molecules of biological importance, particularly of the macromolecules,
constitutes the subject matter of the first major category of biochemical research. This domain is, in a sense, a branch of physics
and chemistry; the same standards of rigor can be, and have been,
applied to research in this field as to research in the physical
sciences. If there is a difference, it is in emphasis. The interest of
the biochemist is focused on those properties of molecules which
are relevant to their biological roles. The interest of the pure
chemist or physicist may not be so narrowly focused.

The richest and most productive area of molecular research centers around the properties of macromolecules—carbohydrates, proteins, and nucleic acids. The three-dimensional structures of proteins, and how these structures are predetermined by specific amino
acid sequences, are among the most exciting problems of molecular
research today. The nature of the interaction between a protein and
its prosthetic group (in conjugated proteins), and the way in which
the properties of each are modified by its attachment to the other,
is another of the key problems. Perhaps most illustrative of the
general nature of molecular research in biochemistry are the studies
of the relation between structure and function at the molecular
level. Biochemistry has finally reached the stage at which suitable
and sufficient tools are at hand to tackle the fine details of the
problem of how biological macromolecules work. Among the macromolecules of greatest interest are the enzymes, the proteins which
serve as instruments of energy transduction, and the nucleic acids.

In order to understand the function of a macromolecule (such
as an enzyme) in terms of its structure, one must know the full details of its three-dimensional structure and the properties of the
array of functional groups in proximity to the catalytic site. These
objectives are at present exceedingly difficult to attain. In only a

very few instances has a macromolecule been described in sufficient detail for the catalytic process to be formulated with a high degree of confidence and precision. However, the tempo of progress in this area is increasing, and it is only a question of time before the tactics for the final assault will have been perfected.

Each type of biological macromolecule poses its own special problem of mechanism. The problem of how actomyosin undergoes reversible conformational changes has entirely different facets from the problem of how hemoglobin transports oxygen, and from that of how double-stranded nucleic acid dissociates reversibly into single strands. There is a prodigious number of fascinating, as well as formidable, problems at the macromolecular level, and these will undoubtedly challenge biochemists for generations to come.

The molecular structure of membranes was, until recently, unexplored territory. This problem has now been defined with sufficient clarity to attract the attention it deserves of molecular biochemists. The modalities of lipid-protein packing, and of the nesting of protein repeating units to form a membranous continuum, are clearly susceptible to incisive analysis. When the properties of membranes at the molecular level become better defined, the task of elucidating the mode of action of hormones and drugs which modify and regulate the properties of the membrane will be enormously simplified.

Systems Research

It appears that the predominant emphasis of the biochemistry of the future will be on integrated systems. The problems encompassed by *systems research* (or *programmed research*) may be divided into a number of categories. Metabolic systems—that is, systems which carry out an integrated, multienzymic sequence such as glycolysis, citric cycle oxidations, and fatty acid oxidation—have been the classical subject matter of system research. These are neatly packaged problems of reasonable dimensions, ideally suited for systems research. Usually, the objective has been to chart the individual steps in the sequence, establish the nature of the intermediates, and specify the component enzymes. In general, this facet of such problems is nearly complete at the present time. What remains to be done is to specify precisely the localization of these metabolic systems within the membrane systems of the cell, and to explore the provisions for their control.

Physiological functions—such as blood clotting, antibody production, oxidative phosphorylation, electron transfer, ion translocation, active transport, tubular secretion, and contractile activity—are all integrations of multiple facets. They constitute a second category of problems in systems research. None is a self-contained problem; each is only a part of a much larger problem. It is not surprising, therefore, that they have yet to be brought to the same degree of definition as have the metabolic systems. The individual organelles of the cell and the isolatable membranes are subject matter ideally suited for systems research. Here the complexity of the problems, and not the difficulty of defining the problems, has been the principal road block to progress.

Protein biosynthesis is an example of a subject for systems research that cuts across categories. This subject involves a membrane system (endoplasmic reticulum or plasma membrane), a system of subcellular organelles (the ribosomes), and at least two metabolic systems (one for the formation of acyl amino acids linked to t-RNA, and the other for amino acid polymerization on the m-RNA template). The dimensions of the problem exceed, by far, the capacity of any single group of investigators. However, it is occasionally possible to parcel out from a large problem a sector that is self-contained and uniquely suited for exploitation by systems research. The elucidation of the genetic code is a good example of this tactic. A cell-free protein-synthesizing system is provided with a synthetic "messenger-RNA." From the identity of the amino acids present in the protein, the synthesis of which was induced by the synthetic RNA, the code has been deciphered. The ingredients of this sector of the problem of protein biosynthesis are: (1) the system for synthesis of protein *in vitro;* and (2) the synthesis of RNA molecules of known composition. Although the problem of deciphering the genetic code is only one ingredient of the larger problem of protein synthesis, its elucidation has been a mammoth achievement and has opened new avenues for the study of the larger problem.

The problem of how entire organs function will, in time, provide a very great challenge for systems research. Into this category fall problems relating to the structure and function of cardiac muscle, kidney tubules, and the peripheral and central nervous systems. An equally complex set of problems, dealing with the function of the organ systems of plants, awaits solution. Problems of organ function are of such great complexity that many of the less complex component problems will have to be solved before any of these can be attacked as a whole.

There is an even more complex category of systems research that concerns events in the whole organism. The development of the embryo from the fertilized egg, the nature of mind and memory, and the problem of complex diseases are among the problems which involve the whole organism rather than specific organs or cells. Such problems are completely outside the realm of the individual investigator. Indeed, only systems research of a highly sophisticated order can begin to make a dent in problems of such magnitude.

Although most of the key problems of biochemistry center about organized systems, it is very rare that the requirements and special needs of systems research are discussed. The first and crucial aspect of systems research is the sheer magnitude of any one problem— far beyond the scope and capability of a single investigator, however gifted and industrious. We shall consider as one illustration of this point one of the classical areas of systems research, the mitochondrion. This subcellular organelle has an elaborate ultrastructure, consisting of two separable (inner and outer) membranes with an elaborate system of compartmentalization built into the membrane systems. It contains at least one hundred different species of protein, bonded together in a multiplicity of subunits. The repeating units of the inner membrane carry out electron transfer, coupled phosphorylation, and ion translocation. The repeating units of the outer membrane carry out the citric cycle, fatty acid oxidation, and fatty acid elongation, as well as other ancillary reactions. There are more than twenty different catalytic species of relatively low molecular weight in each mitochondrion. The mitochondrion is profoundly influenced by the nature of its medium; it may swell or shrink as the medium changes. The mechanistic principles which underlie electron transfer, coupled phosphorylation, and ion translocation have yet to be fully worked out. The problem of the comparative aspects of mitochondria from different sources has enormous dimensions. The origin of the mitochondrion is still an enigma. Given a problem of such dimensions, how does one go about solving it? Clearly, it cannot be conceived of in the classical terms of one investigator working on a circumscribed problem. The mitochondrion poses not one problem but hundreds of problems, each of considerable magnitude. One could say it is foolhardy to attack problems of this magnitude, that hundreds of different investigators, each working in his own laboratory over a period of many years, will eventually make all the discoveries essential to the complete understanding of the mitochondrion. This is an unrealistic view. It seems that when a problem exceeds a certain critical size, the earliest solution can be obtained by the single massive effort of a coordinated group rather than by the efforts of many individual isolated biochemists.

Advances in systems research are most often made by groups explicitly dedicated to, and programed for, the solution of a particular systems problem. The remarkable success of Jacob and Monod and their collaborators at the Pasteur Institute in probing the question of regulation in protein biosynthesis provides an excellent example. It appears that a commitment by a group of investigators for directing their research exclusively toward one single major objective increases the chances of making a major contribution to the problem as a whole. The sheer magnitude of a systems research problem makes it more likely to yield to a multipronged attack by a group of associated investigators. In such a group all the relevant facets should, if possible, be studied simultaneously, and close communication among the associated investigators should be fostered. In this way, each individual in the group may benefit from the findings of the others, and various parts of the total problem may be fitted together most expeditiously. Meticulous planning and vision are required in directing the activities of the group. However, realistic planning must allow for surprises. Nature does not always conform to plans, and rigid planning is destined to be shipwrecked on the shoals of the unexpected. The dilemma that will face biochemistry is how to reconcile the imperatives of systems research with the principle of the individual investigator. There are too few organized groups of investigators in institutes, or in departments of large universities, to cover the needs of systems research. The means required to bring the individual investigator into systems research will have to be explored.

Balance in Biochemical Research

A vigorous science calls for a balance between programmed and unprogrammed research. The wellspring of discoveries will always be provided by unprogrammed research. This is the area in which the lone investigator may make a crucial contribution. No one can predict where and how discoveries will be made; consequently, a major segment of the scientific effort has to be reserved for unprogrammed research. However, no matter how productive the unprogrammed sector of science, the solution of problems involving integrated systems will be immensely accelerated by programmed research. The needs and goals of the two sectors of research are not completely independent. Systems research will, of course, draw heavily from the discoveries and innovations made by the individual biochemists, and, conversely, the findings elaborated by systems research will open new doors to unprogrammed research.

Modes and Styles of Biochemical Research

Just as there are many styles in painting and in composing music, each with its own validity, so there are many styles of doing research. The range of variation is far more extensive than the classical separation of investigators into the experimentalists and the theoreticians. In each of these two broad categories there are many subdivisions—the generalizers and the particularizers; those with a passion for high precision and those who are content to deal with orders of magnitude; the lone wolves and the gregarious who thrive on collaboration; the methodologist and the problem-oriented. Many biochemists alternate between categories and fluctuate in their preference depending on their mood. It is not our purpose to analyze these different styles or to evaluate their merits. The important point is that no one style is superior to any other. Each investigator must find the style that best suits his temperament and circumstances. Each style can be carried off superbly or poorly. Thus, it is not the style, but the standards of the style, that are the measure of the investigator. The exponent of precision can make the most noteworthy of measurements, or exact measurements that lack significance. The "order-of-magnitude" experimentalist can leave a trail of error behind him or make one important discovery after another. The lesson to be learned from the many different ways in which successful biochemical research is pursued is the need for a tolerant attitude towards the various styles. The classical animosity between experimentalist and theoretician provides an endless reservoir of humorous stories, but this is not the only form of intolerance that plagues the sciences. The style of group enterprises in high-energy physics was deplored for a long time, but now the efficacy of this style is undisputed. The rapid tempo of the molecular biologist, and the large component of theory in his work, have been resented by the classical biochemist, but the power and vigor of molecular biology which derive from this tempo and style are unquestioned facts. The mathematical biologist took more than his fair share of criticism from his experimentalist colleagues, but his respectability in the scientific community is now well established. As science progresses new styles, adapted to the new problems, are inevitable, and it is towards these new developments that a tolerant and receptive attitude most becomes the thoughtful scientist.

Some Concluding Remarks

In the first chapter we stated that the credo of the biochemist is that all aspects of the life process can be expressed in terms of the known (or at least the knowable) principles of physics and chemistry. To what extent is this credo justified? Certainly, no phenomenon has yet been encountered in living systems that has engendered serious doubt as to the validity of the hypothesis. However, this idea must not be extended too far. The most detailed understanding of the molecular basis of living systems does not suffice as a final description of these systems. The biochemical level of understanding is one of many levels. Biochemistry can never *replace* other biological disciplines; it simply adds a new dimension. It would be just as naive to expect complete understanding of the human eye, for example, from a knowledge of the biochemistry of vision as to expect such understanding from a knowledge of the anatomy of the eye. The idea that life processes can be expressed in terms of physical and chemical principles does not mean that such an expression can, *by itself*, yield a complete understanding of those processes.

The highest aim of science is to see, amid the mass of bewildering facts, the few concepts which are basic, and those from which predictions can be made. In the physical sciences this aim has been achieved with considerable success. Biochemistry is only now approaching the stage at which this aim can be approximated. The theme of this book is that the most complex phenomena of living systems are reducible to a relatively small set of basic principles and that the proper approach to an understanding of such systems is to seek out these principles. Accordingly, the emphasis has been placed not on a systematic exploration of all the known facts of biochemistry but on the essential ideas which can integrate these facts into a meaningful structure. The history of science teaches us that it would be unwise not to expect that many so-called facts are in error; that many of the concepts are, at best, crude approximations to the truth. The basic principles which have been discussed in this book can serve as the temporary scaffolding for an edifice of understanding yet to be built. New observations compel reinterpretation of older data and revision of current concepts, but the conviction that essences can be found, and that these essences are the keys to a full understanding, is the first step in the growth of a sound point of view.

Suggested Reading

Books

Arber, A., "The Mind and the Eye," Cambridge University Press, London and New York, 1954.

Beveridge, W. I. B., "The Art of Scientific Investigation," 2nd ed., Heinmann, Melbourne, 1953.

Bonner, J., and Galston, A. W., "Principles of Plant Physiology," W. H. Freeman and Co., San Francisco, 1952.

Brown, G. L., "Chance and Design in Physiological Research," H. K. Lewis, London, 1951.

Ray, P. R., "The Living Plant," Modern Biology Series, Holt, Rinehart and Winston, New York, 1963.

Selye, H., "From Dream to Discovery," McGraw-Hill, New York, 1964.

Wiener, P. P. (ed.), "Readings in Philosophy of Science," Charles Scribner's Sons, New York, 1953.